# The UK Mathematics Trust

# Yearbook

# 2009 – 2010

This book contains an account of UKMT activities from 1st September 2009 to 31st August 2010. It contains all question papers, solutions and results as well as a variety of other information.

Published by the United Kingdom Mathematics Trust.
School of Mathematics, The University of Leeds, Leeds LS2 9JT
Telephone: 0113 343 2339
Website: http://www.ukmt.org.uk

Cover design: – The backdrop is a Penrose tiling whose complexity
reflects the activities of the UKMT.


The photographs are


Front Cover:
Certificate winners from Oakmeeds Community College
(Burgess Hill, West Sussex);


Back Cover:
UKMT National Mathematical Summer School;
Best in School at Manchester Islamic High School for Girls.

ISBN 978-1-906001-13-1

Printed and bound in Great Britain by
H. Charlesworth & Co. Ltd, Wakefield

# Contents

# Foreword

I am very pleased to have the opportunity for the first time to introduce this yearbook, after taking over the chair of the UK Mathematics Trust from Bernard Silverman in April. I would like to start by thanking Bernard himself, the Director, Mary Wimbury, and all the staff and volunteers at UKMT for their warm welcome to me and their help and advice.

I first found out about the excellent work which UKMT does to stimulate and encourage children's interests in mathematics a decade ago, not as a professional mathematician but as a parent; my three children (now all past school) very much enjoyed taking part in UKMT Challenges, as do very many thousands of others each year.

Entry numbers for the Senior Challenge remained broadly the same this year at 91,982. Numbers for the Intermediate and Junior Challenges were down slightly at 254,720 and 288,640 respectively, but that can be accounted for by changes in the cohort. The percentage of the population taking part remains the same at 11.5% and 19.9%. This difference in take up reflects the fact that the entry figure for the Junior Challenge is larger even though it is aimed at two school years rather than the Intermediate's three. This is presumably because schools want to reduce the burden on students in their exam years, but it seems a shame that they cannot combine the broader education offered by the challenges with preparation for GCSEs.

Team Challenge entries were slightly down at 1448 this year, compared with 1500 last year. The new regulations on covering for teachers taking pupils out of the classroom seem to have had an effect, which is sad. On the other hand the Senior Team Challenge, our collaboration with the Further Maths Support Programme, continues to grow with 900 schools taking part, an increase on the previous year's 853.

Congratulations are due to the UK International Mathematical Olympiad team who achieved one gold, one silver and two bronze medals and two honourable mentions in Kazakhstan in July. I would also like to congratulate the UK team who participated in the Chinese Girls Mathematical Olympiad in August and were awarded two silver medals and a bronze, as well as a first prize for the dance aerobics competition!

Finally I must reiterate my thanks to the UKMT staff and all the UKMT volunteers who devote so much time and effort to all the Trust's activities: in particular to the invention of stimulating and inspiring questions, as well as to marking Olympiad papers and running the team challenges, mentoring schemes, summer schools and other camps, not to mention supporting UK teams in faraway places like Kazakhstan and China. And of course special thanks must go to Bill Richardson for his work, not only on the challenges, but also in compiling yearbooks which record the Trust's activities each year.

Professor Frances Kirwan FRS
Balliol College, Oxford

# Introduction

## Foundation of the Trust

National mathematics competitions have existed in the UK for several decades. Up until 1987 the total annual participation was something like 8,000. Then there was an enormous growth, from 24,000 in 1988 to around a quarter of a million in 1995 – without doubt due to the drive, energy and leadership of Dr Tony Gardiner. By the end of this period there were some nine or ten competitions for United Kingdom schools and their students organised by three different bodies: the British Mathematical Olympiad Committee, the National Committee for Mathematical Contests and the UK Mathematics Foundation. During 1995 discussions took place between interested parties which led to agreement to seek a way of setting up a single body to continue and develop these competitions and related activities. This led to the formation of the United Kingdom Mathematics Trust, which was incorporated as a company limited by guarantee in October 1996 and registered with the Charity Commission.

In just over ten years of its existence, the UKMT has continued to nurture and expand the number of competitions. As a result, over six hundred thousand students throughout the UK now participate in the challenges alone, and their teachers (as well as others) not only provide much valued help and encouragement, but also take advantage of the support offered to them by the Trust.

The Royal Institution of Great Britain is the Trust's Patron, and it and the Mathematical Association are Participating Bodies. The Association of Teachers of Mathematics, the Edinburgh Mathematical Society, the Institute of Mathematics and Its Applications, the London Mathematical Society and the Royal Society are all Supporting Bodies.

## Aims and Activities of the Trust

According to its constitution, the Trust has a very wide brief, namely "to advance the education of children and young people in mathematics". To attain this, it is empowered to engage in activities ranging from teaching to publishing and lobbying. But its focal point is the organisation of mathematical competitions, from popular mass "challenges" to the selection and training of the British team for the annual International Mathematical Olympiad (IMO).

There are three main challenges, the UK Junior, Intermediate and Senior Mathematical Challenges. The number of challenge entries in 2009-2010 totalled 635,300, a decrease of 1% over the previous year. The challenges were organised by the Challenges Subtrust (CS). The Challenges are open to all pupils of the appropriate age. Certificates are awarded for the best performances and the most successful participants are encouraged to enter follow-up competitions.

At the junior and intermediate levels, a total of around 8000 pupils enter the follow-up competitions. These consist of the Junior Mathematical Olympiad and a suite of papers forming the Intermediate Mathematical Olympiad and Kangaroo under the auspices of the Challenges Subtrust.

The British Mathematical Olympiad Committee Subtrust (BMOS) organises two rounds of the British Mathematical Olympiad. Usually about 800 students who have distinguished themselves in the Senior Mathematical Challenge are invited to enter Round 1, leading to about 100 in Round 2. From the latter, around twenty are invited to a training weekend at Trinity College, Cambridge. Additionally, an elite squad, identified largely by performances in the UKMT competitions, is trained at camps and correspondence courses throughout the year. The UK team is then selected for the annual International Mathematical Olympiad (IMO) which usually takes place in July. The IMO was held in the USA in 2001, the UK in 2002, Japan in 2003, Athens in 2004, Mexico in 2005, Slovenia in 2006, Vietnam in 2007, Madrid in 2008, Bremen in 2009 and Kazakhstan in 2010. The BMOS also runs a mentoring scheme for high achievers at senior, intermediate and junior levels.

## Structure and Membership of the Trust

The governing body of the Trust is its Council. The events have been organised by three Subtrusts who report directly to the Council. The work of the Trust in setting question papers, marking scripts, monitoring competitions, mentoring students and helping in many other ways depends critically on a host of volunteers. A complete list of members of the Trust, its Subtrusts and other volunteers appears at the end of this publication.

## Challenges Office Staff

Mary Wimbury continues in her role as Director. Rachel Greenhalgh returned from maternity leave and has been ably supported by the office staff of Heather Macklin, Nicky Bray, Janet Clark and Jo Williams. Beverley Detoeuf left in January (but is to rejoin soon). Thanks are also due to the packing office staff of Mary Roberts, David Coxon, John Dales, Claire Hall, Gwyneth Hartley, Rachael Raby-Cox and Stewart Ramsay. Together, these two groups form a great team.

# An outline of the events

A brief description of the challenges, their follow-up competitions and other activities is given here with much fuller information later in the book.

## Junior competitions

The UK Junior Mathematical Challenge, typically held on the last Thursday in April, is a one hour, 25 question, multiple choice paper for pupils up to and including:

> Y8 in England and Wales;
> S2 in Scotland, and
> Y9 in Northern Ireland.

Pupils enter their personal details and answers on a special answer sheet for machine reading. The questions are set so that the first 15 should be accessible to all participants whereas the remaining 10 are more testing.

Five marks are awarded for each correct answer to the first 15 questions and six marks are awarded for each correct answer to the rest. Each incorrect answer to questions 16–20 loses 1 mark and each incorrect answer to questions 21–25 loses 2 marks. Penalty marking is used to discourage guessing.

Certificates are awarded on a proportional basis:– Gold about 6%, Silver about 14% and Bronze about 20% of all entrants. Each centre also receives one 'Best in School Certificate'.

The Junior Mathematical Olympiad is the follow-up competition to the JMC. It is normally held six weeks after the JMC and between 1000 and 1200 high scorers in the JMC are invited to take part. It is a two-hour paper which has two sections. Section A contains ten questions and pupils are required to give the answer only. Section B contains six questions for which full written answers are required. It is made clear to candidates that they are not expected to complete all of Section B and that little credit will be given to fragmentary answers. Gold, silver and bronze medals are awarded to very good candidates. In 2010 a total of 231 medals was awarded. All candidates who sat the paper received a certificate; the top 25% got Certificates of Distinction and the others Certificates of Participation. In addition, the top 50 students were given book prizes.

## Intermediate competitions

The UK Intermediate Mathematical Challenge is organised in a very similar way to the Junior Challenge. One difference is that the age range goes up to Y11 in England and Wales, to S4 in Scotland and Y12 in Northern Ireland. The other difference is the timing; the IMC is held on the first Thursday in February. All other arrangements are as in the JMC.

There are five follow-up competitions under the overall title 'Intermediate Mathematical Olympiad and Kangaroo' (IMOK). Between 400 and 550 in each of Years 9, 10 and 11 (English style) sit an Olympiad paper (Cayley, Hamilton and Maclaurin respectively). In 2010, each of these was a two-hour paper and contained six questions all requiring full written solutions. A total of around 5000 pupils from the three year groups took part in a Kangaroo paper. In the European Kangaroo papers, which last an hour, there are 25 multiple-choice questions. The last ten questions are more testing than the first fifteen and correct answers gain six marks as opposed to five. (Penalty marking is not applied.) The same Kangaroo paper (designated 'Pink') was taken by pupils in Years 10 and 11 and a different one, 'Grey', by pupils in Year 9. In 2010, all five papers were sat on the same day – Thursday 18th March. All pupils received one of three types of certificate: Participation, Merit or Distinction (the last being available only to those who sat an Olympiad paper) and a specially designed UKMT key fob. In addition, the top 50 students in each year group were given a book. Performance in the Olympiad papers and the IMC was a major factor in determining pupils to be invited to one of a pair of five-day summer schools early in July.

## Senior competitions

In 2009, the UK Senior Mathematical Challenge was held on Thursday 5th November. Like the other Challenges, it is a 25 question, multiple choice paper marked in the same way as the Junior and Intermediate Challenges. However, it lasts 1½ hours. Certificates (including Best in School) are awarded as with the other Challenges. The follow-up competitions are organised by the British Mathematical Olympiad Subtrust.

The first is BMO1, which was held on Thursday 3rd December 2009. About 800 are usually invited to take part. The paper lasted 3½ hours and contained six questions to which full written solutions are required.

About 100 high scorers are then invited to sit BMO2, which was held on Thursday 28th January 2010. It also lasted 3½ hours but contained four, very demanding, questions.

The results of BMO2 are used to select a group of students to attend a

Training Session at Trinity College, Cambridge at Easter. As well as being taught more mathematics and trying numerous challenging problems, this group sits a 4½ hour 'mock' Olympiad paper. On the basis of this and all other relevant information, a group of about eight is selected to take part in correspondence courses and assignments which eventually produce the UK Olympiad Team of six to go forward to the International Mathematical Olympiad in July.

## The growth of the Challenges

In the 2005 UKMT Yearbook, we showed the growth of the Challenges since UKMT was established and this has now been updated. The graphs below show two easily identifiable quantities, the number of schools and the number of entries. In each case, the lines, from top to bottom, represent the Junior, Intermediate and Senior Challenges. As those involved in the UKMT firmly believe that the Challenges are a very worthwhile endeavour, we hope that the upward trends are resumed.

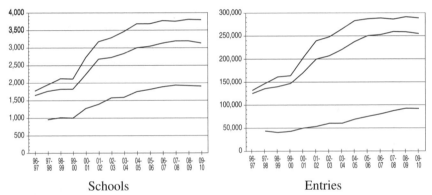

Schools                         Entries

## Team Maths Challenge

This event is the successor of the Enterprising Mathematics UK which was run in conjunction with the IMO in 2002. A team consists of four pupils who are in Year 9 (English style) or below with at most two members being in Year 9. Almost 1350 schools took part in Regional Finals and 79 teams competed in the National Final held in the grand surroundings of the Lawrence Hall, one of the prestigious Royal Horticultural Halls in Westminster, London on Monday 21st June.

In addition almost 900 schools took part in the Senior Team Maths Challenge which is aimed at pupils studying maths beyond GCSE. The final, which involved 58 teams, was held in the Camden Centre on Wednesday 3rd February.

## Report from the Director

The year 2009-2010 was one of consolidation for UKMT. Despite changing economic circumstances and a falling cohort, challenge entries continued to hold up. And it is always heartening to hear feedback from teachers about how much their pupils enjoyed and were inspired by the challenge. I know that there are pupils who we have inspired to take their mathematics further. Of course, we could not do so without our wonderful volunteers. To those who continue to write questions and put together inspiring papers, I say, we absolutely could not do it without you. But we are always looking for recruits to our question setting teams: so if you are reading this and thinking "hmmmm..... maybe I could do that" please do get in touch. Old hands are available to provide ideas about how to polish questions into something with a bit more pizzazz.

We also frequently get feedback from parents whose children have attended our camps telling us how stimulating they found them, how they never knew maths could be so interesting, and how much they appreciated meeting other children with similar interests. Again these camps could not be run without our volunteers who take on both pastoral and academic roles.

Our team challenge competitions continue to be a success. Our newest event the Senior Team Challenge, run jointly with the Further Maths Support Programme, who have done so much to increase uptake of Further Maths, increased its entries in its second full year. The National Final of our Team Challenge, for younger pupils, had finally outgrown the much-loved Camden Centre as its venue for the national final and this year we moved to Royal Horticultural Halls. A beautiful venue with plenty of room to accommodate as many teams as we can contemplate for the foreseeable future! Again these competitions could not run without our volunteers who make regional finals happen up and down the country.

I should also thank our staff who work diligently and effectively to ensure queries are answered, results are dispatched and much more besides.

Mary Wimbury

# The Actuarial Profession

## Profile

The Institute of Actuaries in England and Wales and the Faculty of Actuaries in Scotland are the two professional bodies for UK actuaries, working together across the UK as 'The Actuarial Profession'.

## What is an actuary?

Actuaries apply their statistical and mathematical expertise and knowledge to the financial world. They look at what has happened in the past and use it to make predictions about the future, developing strategies that are appropriate given the risks involved and the probability levels required.

Actuaries work in many areas that directly benefit the public through their work in life and non-life insurance, advising pension funds, savings, capital projects, investments, healthcare and risk management. Such work offers management opportunities, with actuaries having a commercial as well as a technical role.

## Training and development

To qualify as an actuary you'll need to complete the profession's exams. Most actuarial trainees take the exams whilst working for actuarial employers. Exemptions from some of the exams may be awarded to students who have studied to an appropriate standard in a relevant degree, or have studied actuarial science at postgraduate level. Qualification typically takes 3-6 years. Newly qualified actuaries can earn from £53,000 and over £100,000 as you gain more experience.

## International outlook

The UK qualification is already highly valued throughout the world, with 28 per cent of members based overseas. Mutual recognition agreements with other overseas actuarial bodies facilitate the ability of actuaries to move and work in other parts of the world and create a truly global profession.

For more information on qualifications and careers visit our website at

www.actuaries.org.uk

# Winton Capital Management

Winton Capital Management Limited is currently the second largest CTA in the world with assets under management of $12 billion. David Harding founded Winton in 1997 with a commitment to statistical research into financial markets. Research remains the very core of the company which now employs over 90 researchers with PhDs and Masters Degrees at specialist campuses in Oxford, Cambridge, West London and Hong Kong.

We employ more than 70 researchers holding postgraduate and doctorate degrees covering a wide range of fields, including mathematical statistics, astrophysics, electronic engineering and economics. Our offices are at the Oxford Science Park, Cambridge and in Kensington and Hammersmith (London).

Winton's success as a company is founded upon the mathematical skills of our employees but we also know the value of maths based skills in other areas of life.

Doctors need to be able to understand and present meaningful probabilities to patients to allow them to make informed decisions about their treatment. If a test for a disease is 99% accurate and your result comes back positive, it doesn't mean it's a 99% certainty you've got it!

Governments need to make use of sophisticated statistical analysis to ensure that they can effectively monitor the results of their policies.

Everyone needs to be able to understand the workings and risks of credit cards and mortgages to ensure their own welfare and the health of the wider economy.

The next generation of children in Britain will require more than ever before the proper mathematical skills as they negotiate a modern world racing forward on a wave of engineering, computer science and public statistics. We are therefore proud to support the UK Mathematics Trust whose work is significant in the promotion of mathematics in schools.

If you would like to know more about Winton Capital please contact Emma Watkins at e.watkins@wintoncapital.com.

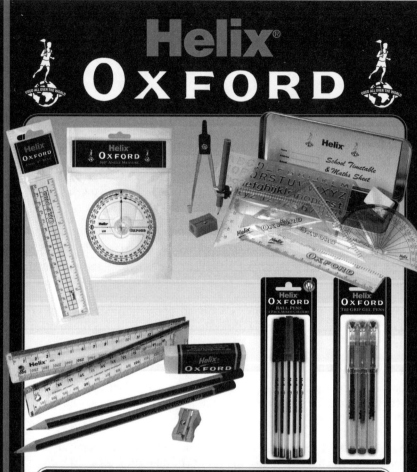

# The Junior Mathematical Challenge and Olympiad

The Junior Mathematical Challenge was held on Thursday 29th April 2010 and almost 239,000 pupils took part. Approximately 1200 pupils were invited to take part in the Junior Mathematical Olympiad which was held on Tuesday 15th June. In the following pages, we shall show the question paper and solutions leaflet for both the JMC and JMO.

We start with the JMC paper, the front of which is shown below in a slightly reduced format.

## UK JUNIOR MATHEMATICAL CHALLENGE

THURSDAY 29th APRIL 2010

Organised by the **United Kingdom Mathematics Trust**
**from the School of Mathematics, University of Leeds**

**The Actuarial Profession**
making financial sense of the future

**RULES AND GUIDELINES** (to be read before starting)

1. Do not open the paper until the Invigilator tells you to do so.

2. Time allowed: **1 hour**.
   No answers, or personal details, may be entered after the allowed hour is over.

3. The use of rough paper is allowed; **calculators** and measuring instruments are **forbidden**.

4. Candidates in England and Wales must be in School Year 8 or below.
   Candidates in Scotland must be in S2 or below.
   Candidates in Northern Ireland must be in School Year 9 or below.

5. **Use B or HB pencil only.** Mark *at most one* of the options A, B, C, D, E on the Answer Sheet for each question. Do not mark more than one option.

6. *Do not expect to finish the whole paper in 1 hour.* Concentrate first on Questions 1-15. When you have checked your answers to these, have a go at some of the later questions.

7. Five marks are awarded for each correct answer to Questions 1-15.
   Six marks are awarded for each correct answer to Questions 16-25.
   **Each incorrect answer to Questions 16-20 loses 1 mark.**
   **Each incorrect answer to Questions 21-25 loses 2 marks.**

8. Your Answer Sheet will be read only by a *dumb machine*. **Do not write or doodle on the sheet except to mark your chosen options**. The machine 'sees' all black pencil markings even if they are in the wrong places. If you mark the sheet in the wrong place, or leave bits of rubber stuck to the page, the machine will 'see' a mark and interpret this mark in its own way.

9. The questions on this paper challenge you to **think**, not to guess. You get more marks, and more satisfaction, by doing one question carefully than by guessing lots of answers.
   The UK JMC is about solving interesting problems, not about lucky guessing.

**The UKMT is a registered charity**
*http://www.ukmt.org.uk*

12

1. What is 2010 + (+2010) + (−2010) − (+2010) − (−2010) ?

   A  0          B  2010        C  4020        D  6030          E  8040

2. Each letter in the abbreviation shown is rotated through 90° clockwise.   **U K M T**
   Which of the following could be the result?

3. Which of the following could have a length of 2010 mm?

   A  a table     B  an oil tanker   C  a teaspoon    D  a school hall    E  a hen's egg

4. If the net shown is folded to make a cube, which
   letter is opposite X ?

   A        B        C        D        E

   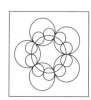

5. The diagram shows a pattern of 16 circles inside a square.
   The central circle passes through the points where the other
   circles touch.
   The circles divide the square into regions. How many regions
   are there?

   A  17    B  26    C  30    D  32    E  38

6. Which of the following has the largest value?

   A  $6 \div \dfrac{1}{2}$     B  $5 \div \dfrac{1}{3}$     C  $4 \div \dfrac{1}{4}$     D  $3 \div \dfrac{1}{5}$     E  $2 \div \dfrac{1}{6}$

7. Mr Owens wants to keep the students quiet during a Mathematics lesson. He asks them to
   multiply all the numbers from 1 to 99 together and then tell him the last-but-one digit of the
   result. What is the correct answer?

   A  0          B  1          C  2          D  8          E  9

8. In a triangle with angles $x°$, $y°$, $z°$ the mean of $y$ and $z$ is
   $x$.
   What is the value of $x$?

   A  90    B  80    C  70    D  60    E  50

   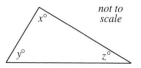

9. Which of the following is the longest period of time?

   A  3002 hours    B  125 days    C  $17\frac{1}{2}$ weeks    D  4 months    E  $\frac{1}{3}$ of a year

10. At the Marldon Apple-Pie-Fayre bake-off, prize money is awarded for 1st, 2nd and 3rd places
    in the ratio 3 : 2 : 1. Last year Mrs Keat and Mr Jewell shared third prize equally. What
    fraction of the total prize money did Mrs Keat receive?

    A  $\dfrac{1}{4}$       B  $\dfrac{1}{5}$       C  $\dfrac{1}{6}$       D  $\dfrac{1}{10}$       E  $\dfrac{1}{12}$

11. In the diagram shown, all the angles are right angles and all the sides are of length 1 unit, 2 units or 3 units.
    What, in square units, is the area of the shaded region?

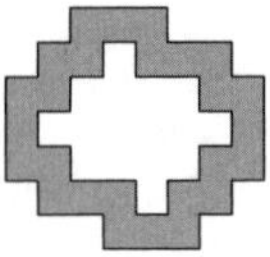

    A 22    B 24    C 26    D 28    E 30

12. Sir Lance has a lot of tables and chairs in his house. Each rectangular table seats eight people and each round table seats five people. What is the smallest number of tables he will need to use to seat 35 guests and himself, without any of the seating around these tables remaining unoccupied?

    A 4        B 5        C 6        D 7        E 8

13. The diagram shows a Lusona, a sand picture of the Tshokwe people from the West Central Bantu area of Africa. To draw a Lusona the artist uses a stick to draw a single line in the sand, starting and ending in the same place without lifting the stick in between. At which point could this Lusona have started?

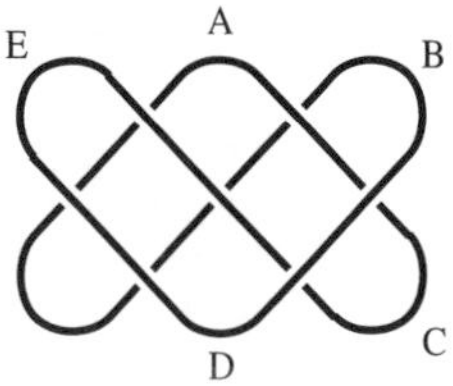

    A        B        C        D        E

14. The Severn Bridge has carried just over 300 million vehicles since it was opened in 1966. On average, roughly how many vehicles is this per day?

    A 600        B 2 000        C 6 000        D 20 000        E 60 000

15. A 6 by 8 and a 7 by 9 rectangle overlap with one corner coinciding as shown.
    What is the area (in square units) of the region *outside* the overlap?

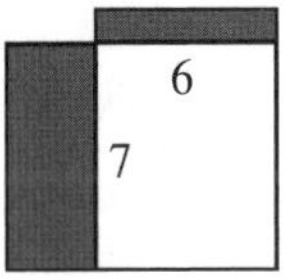

    A 6        B 21        C 27        D 42        E 69

16. One of the examination papers for Amy's Advanced Arithmetic Award was worth 18% of the final total. The maximum possible mark on this paper was 108 marks. How many marks were available overall?

    A 420        B 480        C 540        D 560        E 600

17. The lengths, in cm, of the sides of the equilateral triangle $PQR$ are as shown.
    Which of the following could *not* be the values of $x$ and $y$?

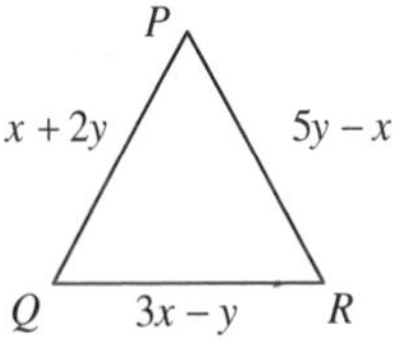

    A (18, 12)  B (15, 10)  C (12, 8)  D (10, 6)  E (3, 2)

18. Sam's 101st birthday is tomorrow. So Sam's age in years changes from a square number (100) to a prime number (101). How many times has this happened before in Sam's lifetime?

    A 1        B 2        C 3        D 4        E 5

14

19. Pat needs to travel down every one of the roads shown at least once, starting and finishing at home. What is the smallest number of the five villages that Pat will have to visit more than once?

A 1    B 2    C 3    D 4    E 5

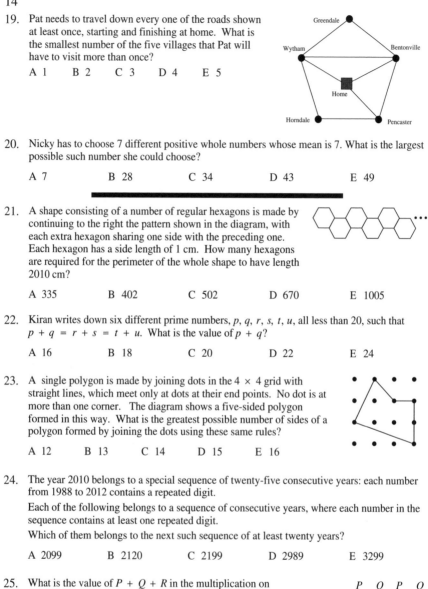

20. Nicky has to choose 7 different positive whole numbers whose mean is 7. What is the largest possible such number she could choose?

A 7          B 28          C 34          D 43          E 49

21. A shape consisting of a number of regular hexagons is made by continuing to the right the pattern shown in the diagram, with each extra hexagon sharing one side with the preceding one. Each hexagon has a side length of 1 cm. How many hexagons are required for the perimeter of the whole shape to have length 2010 cm?

A 335          B 402          C 502          D 670          E 1005

22. Kiran writes down six different prime numbers, $p, q, r, s, t, u$, all less than 20, such that $p + q = r + s = t + u$. What is the value of $p + q$?

A 16          B 18          C 20          D 22          E 24

23. A single polygon is made by joining dots in the 4 × 4 grid with straight lines, which meet only at dots at their end points. No dot is at more than one corner. The diagram shows a five-sided polygon formed in this way. What is the greatest possible number of sides of a polygon formed by joining the dots using these same rules?

A 12    B 13    C 14    D 15    E 16

24. The year 2010 belongs to a special sequence of twenty-five consecutive years: each number from 1988 to 2012 contains a repeated digit.

Each of the following belongs to a sequence of consecutive years, where each number in the sequence contains at least one repeated digit.

Which of them belongs to the next such sequence of at least twenty years?

A 2099          B 2120          C 2199          D 2989          E 3299

25. What is the value of $P + Q + R$ in the multiplication on the right?

A 13    B 12    C 11    D 10    E 9

| | | | $P$ | $Q$ | $P$ | $Q$ |
|---|---|---|---|---|---|---|
| × | | | | $R$ | $R$ | $R$ |
| 6 | 3 | 9 | 0 | 2 | 7 |

# The JMC solutions
The usual solutions leaflet was issued.

UK Junior Mathematical Challenge

THURSDAY 29th APRIL 2010

Organised by the **United Kingdom Mathematics Trust**
**from the School of Mathematics, University of Leeds**

*http://www.ukmt.org.uk*

**The Actuarial Profession**
making financial sense of the future

## SOLUTIONS LEAFLET

This solutions leaflet for the JMC is sent in the hope that it might provide all concerned with some alternative solutions to the ones they have obtained. It is not intended to be definitive. The organisers would be very pleased to receive alternatives created by candidates.

1.  **B**  The expression = $2010 + 2010 - 2010 - 2010 + 2010$
    $= (2010 - 2010) + (2010 - 2010) + 2010 = 2010.$

2.  **E**  In A, the letter T is incorrect; in B it is U which is incorrect; in C and D the incorrect letters are M and K respectively.

3.  **A**  2010 mm = 2.01 m so, of the alternatives given, only a table could be expected to have a length of 2010 mm.

4.  **D**  Let X be on the top face of the cube. If the base is placed on a horizontal surface, then A, B, C, E will all be on vertical faces of the cube and D will be on the base, opposite X.

5.  **D**  Each of the five outer circles is divided into six regions, giving 30 regions in total. In addition, there is one region in the centre of the diagram and one region between the circles and the sides of the square. So, in all, there are 32 regions.

6.  **C**  The values of the expressions are A 12; B 15; C 16; D 15 and E 12.

7.  **A**  As 2, 5 and 10 are all factors of the correct product, this product is a multiple of 100. So the last digit and the last-but-one digit are both zero.

8.  **D**  If the mean of $y$ and $z$ is $x$, then $y + z = 2x$. So the sum of the interior angles of the triangle is $(x + y + z)° = 3x°$. So $3x = 180$, that is $x = 60$.

9.  **A**  One year is, at most, 366 days, so one-third of a year is less than 125 days. No month is longer than 31 days, so 4 months is also less than 125 days, as is 17.5 weeks which equals 122.5 days. However 3002 hours equals 125 days 2 hours, so this is the longest of the five periods of time.

10. **E**  Third prize is worth one-sixth of the total prize money, so Mrs Keat received half of that amount, that is one-twelfth of the total.

11. **C**  Divide the whole figure into horizontal strips of height 1 unit: its area is $(3 + 6 + 8 + 8 + 8 + 6 + 3)$ units$^2$ = 42 units$^2$. Similarly, the unshaded area is $(1 + 4 + 6 + 4 + 1)$ units$^2$ = 16 units$^2$. So the shaded area is 26 units$^2$. *Alternative solution: notice that if the inner polygon is moved a little, the answer remains the same – because it is just the difference between the areas of the two polygons. So, although we are not told it, we may assume that the inner one is so positioned that the outer shaded area can be split neatly into 1 by 1 squares – and there are 26 of these.*

**12.** **C** There are 36 people to be seated so at least five tables will be required. The number of circular tables must be even. However, five rectangular tables will seat 40 people and three rectangular and two circular will seat 34. So at least six tables are needed. Two rectangular and four circular tables do seat 36 people: so six is the minimum number of tables.

**13.** **B** It is necessary to find a route for which the line is broken the first time it passes through any intersection and solid when it passes through that intersection for the second time. Only the route which starts at B and heads away from D satisfies this condition.

**14.** **D** The average number of vehicles per day $\approx \dfrac{300\,000\,000}{44 \times 365} \approx \dfrac{300\,000\,000}{40 \times 400}$
$= \dfrac{300\,000\,000}{16\,000} \approx \dfrac{300\,000\,000}{15\,000} = 20\,000.$

**15.** **C** The two shaded regions measure 3 by 7 and 1 by 6, so the total area outside the overlap is 27 units$^2$.

**16.** **E** As 108 marks represented 18% of the final total, 6 marks represented 1% of the final total. So this total was 600.

**17.** **D** As triangle $PQR$ is equilateral, $x + 2y = 3x - y = 5y - x$. Equating any two of these expressions gives $2x = 3y$.
The only pair of given values which does not satisfy this equation is $x = 10, y = 6$.

**18.** **D** The other times that this has happened previously are when Sam's age in years went from 1 to 2; from 4 to 5; from 16 to 17 and from 36 to 37.
*Note that since primes other than 2 are odd, the only squares which need to be checked, other than 1, are of even numbers.*

**19.** **C** Villages which have more than two roads leading to them (or from them) must all be visited more than once as a single visit will involve at most two roads. So Bentonville, Pencaster and Wytham must all be visited more than once. The route Home, Bentonville, Greendale, Wytham, Bentonville, Pencaster, Home, Wytham, Horndale, Pencaster, Home starts and finishes at Home and visits both Greendale and Horndale exactly once so the minimum number of villages is three.

**20.** **B** The seven numbers must total 49 if their mean is to be 7. The largest possible number will occur when the other six numbers are as small as possible, that is 1, 2, 3, 4, 5, 6. So the required number is $49 - 21 = 28$.

**21.**  **C**  The first and last hexagons both contribute 5 cm to the perimeter of the pattern. Every other hexagon in the pattern contributes 4 cm to the perimeter. The first and last thus contribute 10 cm, so we need another 2000 ÷ 4 = 500 hexagons. Therefore the total number of hexagons required is 502.

**22.**  **E**  The prime numbers less than 20 are 2, 3, 5, 7, 11, 13, 17, 19. It is not possible for 2 to be one of the six numbers Kiran wrote down, since that would give one of the pairs an odd sum, whereas both of the other pairs would add up to an even number. The sum of the remaining 7 primes is 75 which is a multiple of 3. The sum of the six primes making up the three pairs must also be a multiple of 3 since each pair has the same total. So the odd prime not used in the six pairs must be a multiple of 3 too. Therefore 3 is the odd prime not used. So each pair totals 72 ÷ 3, that is 24, and the pairs are 5 + 19, 7 + 17, 11 + 13.

**23.**  **E**  The number of sides of the polygon is equal to the number of corners it has. As no dot is at more than one corner, the maximum number of corners is 16. So the maximum possible number of sides is 16, provided that a 16-sided figure may be drawn. The figure on the right shows one of several ways in which this can be achieved.

**24.**  **B**  In the 21st Century, to obtain a sequence of two years or more then either a 2 or a 0 must be repeated in each year, or the sequence include years such as 2011, 2033, 2044 etc. So the only sequence after that mentioned in the question will be from 2020 to 2030, but this is too short.
In the 22nd Century, either a 2 or a 1 must be repeated. The first such sequence is 2110 to 2129 which does include 20 years, one of which is 2120.

**25.**  **A**  The three-digit number $RRR$ is equal to 111 multiplied by the single digit $R$. So $PQPQ \times R = 639027 \div 111 = 5757$. Now $PQPQ$ equals the two-digit number $PQ$ multiplied by 101. So $PQ \times R = 5757 \div 101 = 57$. The only ways in which 57 may be expressed as the product of a two-digit number and a single digit are $57 \times 1$ and $19 \times 3$. So $P = 5, Q = 7, R = 1$ or $P = 1$, $Q = 9, R = 3$. In both cases, $P + Q + R = 13$.

## The JMC answers

The table below shows the proportion of pupils' choices. The correct answer is shown in bold. [The percentages are rounded to the nearest whole number.]

| Qn | A | B | C | D | E | Blank |
|----|----|----|----|----|----|-------|
| 1 | 10 | **74** | 7 | 6 | 1 | 2 |
| 2 | 2 | 3 | 2 | 2 | **90** | 1 |
| 3 | **68** | 10 | 11 | 6 | 4 | 1 |
| 4 | 3 | 5 | 2 | **88** | 1 | 1 |
| 5 | 12 | 10 | 16 | **55** | 3 | 4 |
| 6 | 44 | 8 | **33** | 4 | 7 | 3 |
| 7 | **16** | 12 | 13 | 24 | 25 | 9 |
| 8 | 32 | 12 | 10 | **35** | 6 | 6 |
| 9 | **34** | 27 | 25 | 5 | 6 | 2 |
| 10 | 14 | 9 | 29 | 7 | **37** | 4 |
| 11 | 5 | 8 | **59** | 12 | 11 | 4 |
| 12 | 4 | 20 | **46** | 25 | 2 | 2 |
| 13 | 15 | **31** | 11 | 14 | 24 | 4 |
| 14 | 9 | 18 | 22 | **31** | 14 | 6 |
| 15 | 6 | 15 | **38** | 27 | 7 | 7 |
| 16 | 5 | 9 | 13 | 12 | **23** | 37 |
| 17 | 9 | 7 | 6 | **23** | 10 | 45 |
| 18 | 4 | 7 | 19 | **25** | 15 | 29 |
| 19 | 15 | 31 | **19** | 4 | 4 | 26 |
| 20 | 4 | **11** | 6 | 7 | 24 | 47 |
| 21 | 9 | 12 | **18** | 5 | 8 | 47 |
| 22 | 9 | 12 | 8 | 5 | **9** | 56 |
| 23 | 11 | 8 | 10 | 7 | **8** | 55 |
| 24 | 8 | **16** | 9 | 6 | 2 | 59 |
| 25 | **7** | 6 | 6 | 5 | 7 | 68 |

**JMC 2010: Some comments on the pupils' choices of answers as expressed in the feedback letter to schools**

We hope that teachers will have had the time to go over at least some of the questions with their students. A lot may be learned by comparing the national distribution of the answers with those given by your students. The national information is included with your results.

The mean score in 2010 was just below that of 2009. The table showing the national distribution of answers suggests that the judgement of the Problems Setting Group as to which were the easier and which were the harder questions was generally good. It was pleasing to see that questions 2, 3 and 4 were all answered correctly by well over half the pupils. In contrast the poor result on question 5 is disappointing, as it involves nothing more than arithmetic with fractions. If your pupils were unsuccessful in answering this question, please reflect on what this signifies. Although there may be a temptation to think that facility with arithmetic is not that important now that electronic calculators are commonplace, in fact, arithmetic facility underlies algebraic facility and, without algebra, advancement in mathematics is difficult.

Question 7 defeated most students, with the correct answer being less popular than two of the wrong answers. The solution explains how it is easy to see that the product $1 \times 2 \times 3 \times \ldots \times 99$ (which can be written as 99!) is divisible by 100. So, when written in standard decimal notation, it ends with two 0s. Hence, the last-but-one digit is 0. In fact, the number 99! ends with quite a large number of 0s. It would be a good classroom investigation, to try and work out exactly how many of them there are, and then to generalize this to deal with $n!$ .

As usual, the later questions are intended to be hard, and many pupils choose wisely not to attempt them. The proportion of answers to questions 16 to 25 that were correct varied between 45% for question 17, which is encouraging, and only 8% for question 23, which is worse than random guessing! This is rather surprising as question 23 does not depend on any mathematical technique, and again, would form the basis for an interesting investigation.

The profile of marks obtained is shown below.

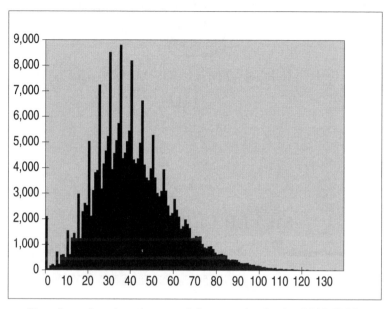

Bar chart showing the actual frequencies in the 2010 JMC

On the basis of the standard proportions used by the UKMT, the cut-off marks were set at

GOLD – 73 or over     SILVER – 56 to 72     BRONZE – 44 to 55

A sample of one of the certificates is shown on the next page.

The Junior Mathematical Olympiad is the follow-up competition to the Challenge. It was decided that candidates who obtained a JMC score of 102 or over were eligible to take part in the JMO. This resulted in 1190 candidates being invited.

22

# UK JUNIOR MATHEMATICAL CHALLENGE
# 2010

of

received a

## SILVER CERTIFICATE

The Actuarial Profession
making financial sense of the future

Chairman, United Kingdom Mathematics Trust

---

## THE UNITED KINGDOM JUNIOR MATHEMATICAL CHALLENGE

The Junior Mathematical Challenge (JMC) is run by the UK Mathematics Trust. The JMC encourages mathematical reasoning, precision of thought, and fluency in using basic mathematical techniques to solve interesting problems. It is aimed at the top third of pupils in years 7 and 8 in England and Wales, S1 and S2 in Scotland and years 8 and 9 in Northern Ireland. The problems on the JMC are designed to make students think. Most are accessible, yet challenge those with more experience; they are also meant to be memorable and enjoyable.

Mathematics controls more aspects of the modern world than most people realise – from iPods, cash machines, telecommunications and airline booking systems to production processes in engineering, efficient distribution and stock-holding, investment strategies and 'whispering' jet engines. The scientific and industrial revolutions flowed from the realisation that mathematics was both the language of nature, and also a way of analysing – and hence controlling – our environment. In the last fifty years, old and new applications of mathematical ideas have transformed the way we live.

All of these developments depend on mathematical thinking – a mode of thought whose essential style is far more permanent than the wave of technological change which it has made possible. The problems on the JMC reflect this style, which pervades all mathematics, by encouraging students to think clearly about challenging problems.

The UK JMC has grown out of a national challenge first run in 1988. In recent years over 250,000 pupils have taken part from around 3,700 schools. Certificates are awarded to the highest scoring 40% of candidates (6% Gold, 13% Silver, 21% Bronze).

There is an Intermediate and Senior version for older pupils. All three events are organised by the United Kingdom Mathematics Trust and are administered from the School of Mathematics at the University of Leeds.

Further information on the UK Mathematics Trust can be found at www.ukmt.org.uk

# The Junior Mathematical Olympiad

## UK Junior Mathematical Olympiad 2010

Organised by The United Kingdom Mathematics Trust

Tuesday 15th June 2010

### RULES AND GUIDELINES :
### READ THESE INSTRUCTIONS CAREFULLY BEFORE STARTING

1. Time allowed: 2 hours.

2. **The use of calculators, measuring instruments and squared paper is forbidden.**

3. All candidates must be in *School Year 8 or below* (England and Wales), *S2 or below* (Scotland), *School Year 9 or below* (Northern Ireland).

4. For questions in Section A *only the answer is required.* Enter each answer neatly in the relevant box on the Front Sheet. Do not hand in rough work. Write in blue or black pen or pencil.

   For questions in Section B you must give *full written solutions*, including clear mathematical explanations as to why your method is correct.

   Solutions must be written neatly on A4 paper. Sheets must be STAPLED together in the top left corner with the Front Sheet on top.

   *Do not hand in rough work.*

5. Questions A1-A10 are relatively short questions. Try to complete Section A within the first 45 minutes so as to allow well over an hour for Section B.

6. Questions B1-B6 are longer questions requiring *full written solutions*.
   This means that each answer must be accompanied by clear explanations and proofs.
   Work in rough first, then set out your final solution with clear explanations of each step.

7. These problems are meant to be challenging! Do not hurry. Try the earlier questions in each section first (they tend to be easier). Try to finish whole questions even if you are not able to do many. A good candidate will have done most of Section A and given solutions to at least two questions in Section B.

8. Answers must be FULLY SIMPLIFIED, and EXACT using symbols such as $\pi$, fractions, or square roots if appropriate, but NOT decimal approximations.

**DO NOT OPEN THE PAPER UNTIL INSTRUCTED BY THE INVIGILATOR TO DO SO!**

The United Kingdom Mathematics Trust is a Registered Charity.

24

# Section A

**A1**   What is the value of $\dfrac{1}{\frac{1}{1}} + \dfrac{2}{\frac{1}{2}} + \dfrac{3}{\frac{1}{3}} + \dfrac{4}{\frac{1}{4}} + \dfrac{5}{\frac{1}{5}}$ ?

**A2**   Given that $x : y = 1 : 2$ and $y : z = 3 : 4$, what is $x : z$ ?

**A3**   Tom correctly works out $20^{10}$ and writes down his answer in full.
How many digits does he write down in his full answer?

**A4**   Three monkeys Barry, Harry and Larry met for tea in their favourite café, taking off their hats
as they arrived. When they left, they each put on one of the hats at random. What is the
probability that none of them left wearing the same hat as when they arrived?

**A5**   The sum of two positive integers is 97 and their difference is 37. What is their product?

**A6**   In the diagram, the equilateral triangle is divided into two identical
equilateral triangles S and T, and two parallelograms Q and R which are
mirror images of each other.

What is the ratio of area R : area T ?

**A7**   What is the largest possible angle in an isosceles triangle, in which the difference between the
largest and smallest angles is 6°?

**A8**   The four square tiles having the designs as shown can be arranged to
create a closed loop.
How many distinct closed loops, including the one shown here, can be
made from the tiles?
(The tiles may be rotated, but a rotation of a loop is not considered
distinct. A loop need not use all four tiles and may not use more than
one of each type).

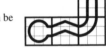

**A9**   Abbie, Betty and Clara write names on bookmarks sold for charity.

Abbie writes 7 names in 6 minutes, Betty writes 18 names in 10 minutes and Clara writes
23 names in 15 minutes.

If all of the girls work together at these rates, how long will it take them to write 540 names?

**A10**   In the diagram, $JK$ and $ML$ are parallel,
$JK = KO = OJ = OM$ and
$LM = LO = LK$.
Find the size of angle $JMO$.

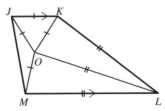

# Section B

Your solutions to Section B will have a major effect on your JMO results. Concentrate on one or two questions first and then **write out full solutions** (not just brief 'answers').

**B1** In a sequence of six numbers, every term after the second term is the sum of the previous two terms. Also, the last term is four times the first term, and the sum of all six terms is 13.

What is the first term?

**B2** The eight-digit number "*ppppqqqq*", where $p$ and $q$ are digits, is a multiple of 45.

What are the possible values of $p$?

**B3** Jack and Jill went up a hill. They started at the same time, but Jack arrived at the top one-and-a-half hours before Jill. On the way down, Jill calculated that, if she had walked 50% faster and Jack had walked 50% slower, then they would have arrived at the top of the hill at the same time.

How long did Jill actually take to walk up to the top of the hill?

**B4** The solution to each clue of this crossnumber is a two-digit number, not beginning with zero.

In how many different ways can the crossnumber be completed correctly?

Clues
Across
1. A triangular number
3. A triangular number

Down
1. A square number
2. A multiple of 5

**B5** The diagram shows part of a regular 20-sided polygon (an icosagon) $ABCDEF...$, a square $BCYZ$ and a regular pentagon $DEVWX$.

Show that the vertex $X$ lies on the line $DY$.

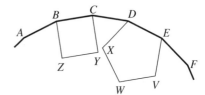

**B6** Sam has put sweets in five jars in such a way that no jar is empty and no two jars contain the same number of sweets. Also, any three jars contain more sweets in total than the total of the remaining two jars.

What is the smallest possible number of sweets altogether in the five jars?

# UK Junior Mathematical Olympiad 2010 Solutions

**A1**  **55**  $\dfrac{1}{1} + \dfrac{2}{\frac{1}{2}} + \dfrac{3}{\frac{1}{3}} + \dfrac{4}{\frac{1}{4}} + \dfrac{5}{\frac{1}{5}} = 1 + 2 \times 2 + 3 \times 3 + 4 \times 4 + 5 \times 5 = 1 + 4 + 9 + 16 + 25 = 55.$

**A2**  **3 : 8**  Since $y$ is common to both ratios, we change the ratios so that $x : y = 1 : 2 = 3 : 6$ and $y : z = 3 : 4 = 6 : 8$. Then we have $x : z = 3 : 8$.

**A3**  **14**  We can note that $20^{10} = (2 \times 10)^{10} = 2^{10} \times 10^{10}$. Since $2^{10} = 1024$ has 4 digits, and multiplying by $10^{10}$ adds 10 zeros to the end, Tom writes down 14 digits.

**A4**  $\dfrac{1}{3}$  The table shows the ways in which the monkeys (B, H and L) can select the hats. Let the hats of B, H and L be $b$, $h$ and $l$ respectively.

None of the monkeys have the same hat as when they arrived in only two of the six ways (*), hence the required probability is

$$\frac{2}{6} = \frac{1}{3}.$$

| Monkeys | | | |
|---|---|---|---|
| B | H | L | |
| $b$ | $h$ | $l$ | |
| $b$ | $l$ | $h$ | |
| $h$ | $b$ | $l$ | |
| $h$ | $l$ | $b$ | * |
| $l$ | $h$ | $b$ | |
| $l$ | $b$ | $h$ | * |

[*Alternatively*: There are $3 \times 2 \times 1 = 6$ possible ways to choose the three hats. There are two hats that B could choose. If B chose $h$, then L would have to choose $b$ and H would have to choose $l$. If B chose $l$, then H would have to choose $b$ and L would have to choose $h$. So once B has chosen his hat the other two are fixed. So there are just the two possible alternatives out of the six ways. So the probability is $\dfrac{2}{6} = \dfrac{1}{3}$.]

**A5**  **2010**  Let the two numbers be $a$ and $b$, where $a > b$. Then we have $a + b = 97$ and $a - b = 37$. Hence $2a = 134$ and therefore $a = 67$ and $b = 30$. The product of 67 and 30 is 2010.

**A6**  **1 : 1**  Let us call the large triangle P. Since triangles T and S are congruent, they have the same height, which is half the height of P. Thus the area of each of T and S is a quarter of the area of P. Therefore parallelograms Q and R together form the other half and thus each occupies a quarter of P. So R and T are equal in area.

**A7**  **64°**  Let the largest angle be $a°$, whence the smallest angle is $(a-6)°$. There are two possibilities, shown in the diagrams below.

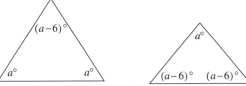

In the first we have $3a - 6 = 180$, so $a = 62$.
In the second we have $3a - 12 = 180$, so $a = 64$.
Thus the largest possible angle in such a triangle is $64°$.

**A8**  **13**  To create a closed loop, one must use ⊂ at one end and ⊃ at the other.

Let us assume that the loop starts with ⊂ (turned this way) and ends with the ⊃, in some orientation (⊃, Ս or Ռ).

There is just 1 loop that uses only these tiles. If one tile is put between them, there are two ways in which each of the other two tiles can connect them (⌒ or ⌄ and ⟍ or ⟋). So there are 4 loops with three tiles.

Using all four tiles, there are two orders in which ⌒ and ⟍ can be placed, and, there are two possible orientations for each of these tiles, making $2 \times 2 \times 2 = 8$ ways in all. Hence there are $1 + 4 + 8 = 13$ possible loops altogether.

**A9 2 hours**  Since the lowest common multiple of 6, 10 and 15 is 30, we can say that in 30 minutes Abbie writes $7 \times \dfrac{30}{6} = 35$ cards, Betty writes $18 \times \dfrac{30}{10} = 54$ cards, and Clara writes $23 \times \dfrac{30}{15} = 46$ cards. So together they write $35 + 54 + 46 = 135$ cards in half an hour. Thus the time taken to write 540 cards is $\dfrac{540}{135} = 4$ half-hours $= 2$ hours.

**A10**  **20°**  Since triangle $JKO$ is equilateral, $\angle JOK = \angle KJO = \angle JKO = 60°$.
Let $\angle JMO = m°$. Then, since $JMO$ is an isosceles triangle, $\angle MJO = m°$ and $\angle JOM = (180 - 2m)°$.
Let $\angle OKL = k°$ and so, since $KLO$ is an isosceles triangle, $\angle LOK = k°$.
Triangles $KLO$ and $OLM$ are congruent (SSS), and so $\angle MOL = \angle OML = k°$.

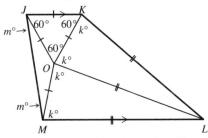

Now taking angles at point $O$, we have $180 - 2m + 60 + 2k = 360$, whence $k = m + 60$.
Since $JK$ is parallel to $ML$, $\angle KJM + \angle JML = 180°$ and so $(60 + m) + (m + k) = 180$.
Hence $180 = 60 + 2m + k = 60 + 2m + m + 60 = 3m + 120$, so $m = 20$, i.e. $\angle JMO = 20°$.

28

**B1** In a sequence of six numbers, every term after the second term is the sum of the previous two terms. Also, the last term is four times the first term, and the sum of all six terms is 13.

What is the first term?

*Solution*

Let the first and second terms be $a$ and $b$ respectively. Then we derive the sequence

$$a, \; b, \; a + b, \; a + 2b, \; 2a + 3b, \; 3a + 5b.$$

We know that the last term is four times the first term, so $3a + 5b = 4a$. Therefore $a = 5b$ and so the sequence is

$$5b, \; b, \; 6b, \; 7b, \; 13b, \; 20b.$$

The sum of these is 13, so $52b = 13$, $b = \dfrac{13}{52} = \dfrac{1}{4}$ and $a = 5 \times \dfrac{1}{4} = \dfrac{5}{4}$. Thus the first term is $1\frac{1}{4}$.

**B2** The eight-digit number "*ppppqqqq*", where $p$ and $q$ are digits, is a multiple of 45.

What are the possible values of $p$?

*Solution*

It might be argued that there is a trivial solution where $p = q = 0$. It is, however, usual to assume that numbers do not begin with zeros and so we shall proceed assuming that $p \neq 0$.

We first observe that every multiple of 45 is a multiple of both 5 and 9, and also that $p$ and $q$ are single-digit integers. Applying the usual rules of divisibility by 5 and 9 to the number *ppppqqqq* we deduce that $q = 0$ or $q = 5$ and that $4p + 4q$ is a multiple of 9.
In the case $q = 0$, $4p$ is a multiple of 9, hence $p = 9$.
In the case $q = 5$, $4p + 20 = 4(p + 5)$ is a multiple of 9. Therefore $p + 5$ is a multiple of 9. Hence $p = 4$.

(Thus there are two possible numbers: 99 990 000 and 44 445 555.)

**B3** Jack and Jill went up a hill. They started at the same time, but Jack arrived at the top one-and-a-half hours before Jill. On the way down, Jill calculated that, if she had walked 50% faster and Jack had walked 50% slower, then they would have arrived at the top of the hill at the same time.

How long did Jill actually take to walk up to the top of the hill?

*Solution*

Let $t$ be the number of hours that Jill took to the top of the hill.
So the time taken by Jack was $\left(t - 1\frac{1}{2}\right)$ hours.
If Jack had walked 50% more slowly, he would have taken twice as long, ie. $(2t - 3)$ hours.
If Jill had walked 50% faster, she would have taken $\frac{2}{3}$ of the time, ie. $\frac{2}{3}t$ hours.
So we know that $\frac{2}{3}t = 2t - 3$, whence $2t = 6t - 9$ and so $t = \frac{9}{4} = 2\frac{1}{4}$.
Hence Jill took $2\frac{1}{4}$ hours.

**B4** The solution to each clue of this crossnumber is a two-digit number, not beginning with zero.

In how many different ways can the crossnumber be completed correctly?

Clues
Across
1.  A triangular number
3.  A triangular number

Down
1.  A square number
2.  A multiple of 5

| 1 | 2 |
|---|---|
| 3 |   |

*Solution*

We start by listing the two-digit triangular numbers and two-digit square numbers:

triangular numbers:    10, 15, 21, 28, 36, 45, 55, 66, 78, 91
square numbers:        16, 25, 36, 49, 64, 81.

Since 2 Down is a multiple of 5, it ends in either 0 or 5.

Hence 3 Across ends in either 0 or 5 and there are four such triangular numbers: 10, 15, 45, and 55. In each case there is only one possible square number at 1 Down, as shown in the following figures:

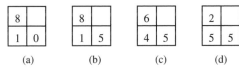

(a)          (b)          (c)          (d)

Now consider 1 Across, a triangular number. In (a) and (b), there is no two-digit triangular number whose first digit is 8, and hence we can rule out cases (a) and (b).

In (c), the only triangular number whose first digit is 6 is 66. In (d), there are two triangular numbers whose first digit is 2, namely 21 and 28.

Therefore there are three different ways in which the crossnumber can be completed:

| 6 | 6 |
|---|---|
| 4 | 5 |

| 2 | 1 |
|---|---|
| 5 | 5 |

| 2 | 8 |
|---|---|
| 5 | 5 |

30

**B5** The diagram shows part of a regular 20-sided polygon (an icosagon) $ABCDEF\ldots$, a square $BCYZ$ and a regular pentagon $DEVWX$.

Show that the vertex $X$ lies on the line $DY$.

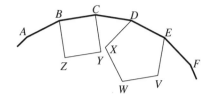

*Solution*

Considering the interior angles of the square, the regular pentagon, and the regular icosagon, $\angle BCY = 90°$, $\angle EDX = \left(180 - \frac{360}{5}\right)° = 108°$ and $\angle BCD = \left(180 - \frac{360}{20}\right)° = 162°$.

Now $\angle DCY = (162 - 90)° = 72°$ and also $\angle CDX = (162 - 108)° = 54°$.
Now consider triangle $CDY$.

Since the icosagon is regular, $BC = CD$ and, as $BCYZ$ is a square, $BC = CY$.

Therefore $CD = CY$ and $CDY$ is an isosceles triangle.

Hence $\angle CDY = \frac{1}{2}(180 - 72)° = 54°$.

However, as observed above, $\angle CDX = 54°$ and so $\angle CDX = \angle CDY$.

Thus we can conclude that point $X$ lies on the line $DY$.

**B6** Sam has put sweets in five jars in such a way that no jar is empty and no two jars contain the same number of sweets. Also, any three jars contain more sweets in total than the total of the remaining two jars.

What is the smallest possible number of sweets altogether in the five jars?

*Solution*

Let the number of sweets in the five jars be $a, b, c, d$ and $e$, where $a < b < c < d < e$. Since $d > c > b$, and $b, c$ and $d$ are integers, $d \geqslant b + 2$. Similarly $e \geqslant c + 2$.

Now, since any three jars contain more sweets in total than the total of the remaining two jars, in particular $a + b + c > d + e$, and so $a + b + c > b + 2 + c + 2$, hence $a > 4$.

Try $a = 5$. The smallest possible values of the other numbers are 6, 7, 8 and 9, which give a total of 35. Because 5, 6 and 7, the three smallest numbers, give a total of 18, which is over half of 35, any other selection of three of these numbers will have a total greater than that of the remaining two numbers.

Thus the smallest total is 35.

# The marking and results

The pupils' scripts began arriving very rapidly and the marking took place in Leeds the weekend following the paper, 19th and 20th June. The discussions as to how marks should be given and for what were ably led by Alex Voice who also directed the marking team of David Crawford, Mary-Teresa Fyfe, Tony Gardiner, Howard Groves, Rita Holland, Andrew Jobbings, Sylvia Neumann, Peter Neumann, Andy Parkinson, Stephen Power, Jenny Ramsden, Bill Richardson, Paul Russell, John Slater and David Webber.

As has been stated, the object of the JMO is for pupils to be *challenged*, possibly in ways they have not been before. Some participants may find all of Section B rather beyond them, but it is hoped that they achieve a degree of satisfaction from Section A. Satisfaction is an important aspect of this level of paper; nevertheless, those who do succeed in tackling Section B deserve credit for that and such credit is mainly dependent on getting solutions to questions in Section B which are 'perfect' or very nearly so. The awarding process is somewhat complicated, some might say bizarre. Firstly there are certificates which come in two versions, Participation and Distinction. All who took part are awarded a certificate with about a quarter obtaining a Certificate of Distinction. There were book prizes for the top fifty. The book prize for 2010 was *The Penguin Dictionary of Curious and Interesting Numbers* by David Wells. Finally, there were medals of the traditional Gold, Silver, Bronze varieties of design introduced in 2004.

The paper itself was found to be of a similar standard to the 2009 paper. The numbers of medals awarded were: 25 Gold, 71 Silver and 135 Bronze.

The list below includes all the medal winners in the 2010 JMO. Within each category, the names are in alphabetical order.

Special mention should be made of Wanfung Chui and Harry Metrebian who have two JMO Gold Medals; George Fortune who has three and Liam Hughes who has an astonishing four!

The results and all the extras (books, book plates, certificates and medals) were sent away with reasonable chance of reaching schools before pupils departed for their summer holidays.

# GOLD MEDALS

| | |
|---|---|
| Clement Chan | King Edward's School, Birmingham |
| Cyrus Cheng | West Island School (ESF) |
| Wanfung Chui | West Island School (ESF) |
| Samuel Coy | Forest School, London |
| Joe Davies | Lawrence Sheriff School, Rugby |
| George Fortune | Altrincham GS for Boys, Cheshire |
| Alex Gunasekera | Magdalen College School, Oxford |
| Alex Harris | Perse School, Cambridge |
| Elizabeth Hong | Stratford GS for Girls, Warwickshire |
| Daniel Hood | Heath Mount School, Hertfordshire |
| Liam Hughes | Welland Park CC, Market Harborough |
| Gareth Jones | Clifton College Prep School, Bristol |
| Stephen Jones | Magdalen College School, Oxford |
| Sampson Kwan | King George V School |
| Filipp Lavrentiev | Cherwell School, Oxford |
| Rowan Lee | Nottingham High School |
| Cong Lu | Robert Gordon's College, Aberdeen |
| Harry Metrebian | Beacon School, Amersham, Bucks |
| Hyeyoon Nah | Badminton School, Bristol |
| Adam Swinton | Altrincham GS for Boys, Cheshire |
| Callum Watson | Balfron High School, Glasgow |
| Alfred Wong | Reading School, Berkshire |
| Joanna Yass | North London Collegiate Sch., Middlesex |
| Owen She Yin | Brighton College Prep Sch., East Sussex |
| Ng Yuen | Rainham Mark GS, Gillingham, Kent |

# SILVER MEDALS

| | |
|---|---|
| Gaurav Agarwal | Langley Grammar School, Berkshire |
| Jowan Atkinson | Romsey School, Hampshire |
| Cassius Bandeen | Thomas's Battersea Preparatory S, London |
| Nodar Barbakadze | Durston House School, London |
| James Bell | King Edward VI Five Ways S, Birmingham |

| | |
|---|---|
| Joseph Boorman | Kings College School, Cambridge |
| Matthew Chaffe | Littleover Community School, Derby |
| Kieran Chan | Queen Elizabeth's School, Barnet, Herts |
| Daniel Chen | Queen Elizabeth's School, Barnet, Herts |
| Joanna Cheng | South Island School, Hong Kong |
| Kevin Choi | Sha Tin College, Hong Kong |
| Philip Christian | Gosforth Central Middle School |
| David Chu | Dulwich College Beijing |
| Horace Chu | German Swiss Int. Sch., Hong Kong |
| Peter Chua | Orley Farm School, Harrow, Middlesex |
| Daniel Clark | Woodhouse Grove School, Bradford |
| Dominic Clark | Abbeyfield School, Chippenham |
| Ale Cook | Adams Grammar School, Newport, Salop |
| Hoang Dang | British International School Vietnam |
| Henry Davidson | Highgate School, London |
| Dion Dong | Yew Chung International Sch. of Bejing |
| Laura Embrey | King's School, Macclesfield, Cheshire |
| Samuel England | King Edward VI Camp Hill BS, Birmingham |
| Victoria Farrant | Bishops Stortford College JS, Herts |
| Emily Flynn | Dr Challoner's High School, Bucks |
| James Fraser | Clifton College Prep School, Bristol |
| George Gao | St Olave's School, York |
| Harry Goodburn | Wilson's School, Wallington, Surrey |
| Joseph Hansard | Beechen Cliff School, Bath |
| Oliver Hanson | Queen Mary's Grammar School, Walsall |
| Priyanka Jha | Kendrick School, Reading |
| Samuel Johnson | Bishop of Hereford Bluecoat School |
| Heather Jolliff | The Priory Academy, Lincoln |
| Anthony Kattuman | Perse School, Cambridge |
| Andrew Kenyon-Roberts | Aberdeen Grammar School |
| Yoo Jin Lee | Overseas Family School, Singapore |
| Jackie Li | St Paul's Girls' School, London |
| Warren Li | Fulford School, York |

| | |
|---|---|
| Gemma Liu | Portsmouth Grammar School |
| Chen Lu | St John's Beaumont, Old Windsor, Berks |
| Beeshman Mahen | Merchant Taylors' School, Middlesex |
| Janahan Manivannan | Watford Grammar School for Boys, Herts |
| Robert Mateer | Somervale Comprehensive School, Bath |
| Callum McLean | International School of Aberdeen |
| Bhavik Mehta | Queen Elizabeth's School, Barnet, Herts |
| Itamar Morm | City of London School, London |
| Natalie Nguyen | Northampton High School |
| Alistair Parker | Northwood Prep School, Rickmansworth |
| Jonathan Patel | Colet Court School, London |
| James Pigden | Dame Alice Owen's School, Potters Bar |
| Marij Qureshi | Royal Grammar School, High Wycombe |
| Holly Richardson | Wolverhampton Girls' High School |
| Edward Rong | Westminster Under School, London |
| Daniel Saunders | Bradfield School, Sheffield |
| Michael Savery | St Bede's RC School, Bristol |
| Andrew Sellek | Torquay Boys' Grammar School |
| Naomi Solomons | Forest School, London |
| Jonathan Stark | George Watson's College, Edinburgh |
| Alan Sun | City of London School, London |
| Tobias Swann | Cowbridge CS, Vale of Glamorgan |
| Marguerite Tong | St Paul's Girls' School, London |
| Kavin Vijayakumar | Bancroft's Sch., Woodford Green, Essex |
| Theo Walton | Aysgarth School, Bedale, North Yorkshire |
| Isaac Webber | Solihull School, West Midlands |
| Santiago Weight | Milbourne Lodge School, Esher, Surrey |
| Dmitri Whitmore | King's School, Macclesfield, Cheshire |
| Matthew Wilson | St Edmund's College, Hertfordshire |
| Oliver Woollard | Robert May's School, Odiham, Hampshire |
| Yunzhou Xia | Canons High School, Edgware |
| Bohan Yu | Cherwell School, Oxford |
| Tianlin Zhang | Queen Elizabeth's School, Barnet, Herts |

# BRONZE MEDALS

| | |
|---|---|
| Olivia Aaronson | St Paul's Girls' School, London |
| Kavi Amin | Westminster Under School, London |
| Kensuke Ando | Sutton Grammar School for Boys, Surrey |
| Robyn Bailey | Wallington High School for Girls, Surrey |
| Joshua Banister | Liverpool Blue Coat School |
| Matthew Bannatyne | Westminster Under School, London |
| Mark Bobrovnikov | Whitgift School, Surrey |
| Max Bowling | Nottingham High School |
| Natalie Bowmaker | Seaham School, Co. Durham |
| Nishant Boyyamma | Homefield School, Surrey |
| Jamie Bragg | Alleyn's School, London |
| Hugh Brandreth | Homefield School, Surrey |
| Annie Calderba | Wycombe Abbey School, Bucks |
| Theo Caplan | Colet Court School, London |
| Felicia Chang | King Edward VI HS for Girls, Birmingham |
| Guy Cheng | German Swiss International Sch., Hong Kong |
| Jason Cheung | Renaissance College |
| Szeching Cheung | Queens Park Community School, London |
| Jiwon Chung | United World Coll. of SE Asia, Singapore |
| Tom Clarke | Dollar Academy, Clackmannanshire |
| Francis Clark Murray | Bancroft's School, Woodford Green |
| Thomas Compton | Beacon School, Amersham, Bucks |
| Mark Cooper | St Edward's Junior HS, Staffordshire |
| Jack Counsell | Judd School, Tonbridge, Kent |
| Rhys Counsell | Sullivan Upper Sch., Holywood, Co Down |
| Jonah Cowen | City of London School, London |
| Oliver Cripps | Parmiter's School, Hertfordshire |
| Sean Cuddihy | Royal Hospital School, Ipswich, Suffolk |
| Benjamin Darwent | Cotswold School, Cheltenham |
| Kier Davis | Lawrence Sheriff School, Rugby |
| Melissa Dicks | Swavesey Village College |
| Ankur Dodhia | Drayton Manor High School |
| Luke Elliott | Stewart's Melville College, Edinburgh |

| | |
|---|---|
| Annabel Estlin | St Leonards Mayfield, East Sussex |
| Claire Evans | St Bees School, Cumbria |
| Barnaby Fogg | Queen Elizabeth HS, Gainsborough |
| Chantell Foster | Aylesbury High School, Buckinghamshire |
| Roxanne Gardiner | John Port School, Derbyshire |
| Jason Gu | Perse School, Cambridge |
| Rohit Gupta | The Crossley Heath School, Halifax |
| Leo Haigh | King James's School, Huddersfield |
| James Hale | Sevenoaks School, Kent |
| Georgina Hansen | St Paul's Girls' School, London |
| Jack Hardcastle | St John's College, Southsea, Hampshire |
| Polly Harlow | Manchester High School for Girls |
| Timothy Havard | King Edward VI GS, Chelmsford, Essex |
| Masayuki Hirai | North London Int. Sch., London |
| Ivan Hitojo | Vienna International School |
| Jeremy Ho | King Edward's School, Birmingham |
| Shamel Hok | Roundhay School, Leeds, West Yorkshire |
| William Honeyman | Wilson's School, Wallington, Surrey |
| Katharine Hood | St Alban's HS for Girls, Hertfordshire |
| Charlie Hu | Hall Mead School, Upminster, Essex |
| Michael Hu | Clifton High School, Bristol |
| Elizabeth Huang | German Swiss International S., Hong Kong |
| Edward Huggins | Pate's Grammar School, Cheltenham |
| Andrew Hui | Queen Elizabeth's School, Barnet, Herts |
| David Hui | The King's School Worcester |
| Oliver Hulme | Beverley GS, East Yorkshire |
| Jared Jeyaretnam | The Academy Sch., Rosslyn Hill, London |
| Ying Jin | Boroughmuir High School, Edinburgh |
| Tomoka Kan | St Paul's Girls' School, London |
| Robert Keen | The Priory Academy, Lincoln |
| Daniel Kim | Westminster Under School, London |
| Heejung Kim | Emanuel School, London |
| Kijin Kim | Bromsgrove International School |
| Sungman Kim | Sutton Grammar School for Boys, Surrey |

| | |
|---|---|
| Woobin Kim | Aberdour School, Surrey |
| Koshiro Kiso | Westminster Under School, London |
| Balaji Krishna | Stanwell School, Penarth, Cardiff |
| Andrew Lawrence | Parmiter's School, Hertfordshire |
| Joanna Lee | Silcoates School, Wakefield |
| Nathan Lee | Sha Tin College, Hong Kong |
| Chris Liang | Royal Grammar School, High Wycombe |
| Hugh Lilburn | King Edward's School, Birmingham |
| David Liu | Dulwich College Beijing |
| Kevin Lo | Sha Tin College, Hong Kong |
| David Lunardi | Hutcheson's Grammar School, Glasgow |
| Robert Macfadyen | Torquay Boys' Grammar School |
| Norman Macgregor | Bell Baxter High School, Fife |
| Ben Mason | Roundwood Park Sch., Harpenden, Herts |
| George Metson | King Edward VI GS, Chelmsford, Essex |
| James Mitchell | Rosemary Musker High School, Thetford |
| Adam Mombru | Westminster Under School, London |
| Conor Murphy | Eltham College, London |
| Esther Na | Dulwich College Beijing |
| Nimrod Nehushtan | City of London School, London |
| William Nelson | King's College School, London |
| Hyungjoo Noh | Frankfurt International School, Germany |
| Nicholas Oon | Colet Court School, London |
| Ben Pace | Chetham's School of Music, Manchester |
| Felicity Parker | King Edward VI Five Ways Sch., Birmingham |
| Nathan Peters | King's School, Grantham, Lincolnshire |
| Philip Peters | Haberdashers' Aske's Sch. for Boys, Herts |
| Sajan Rajani | Haberdashers' Aske's Sch. for Boys, Herts |
| Mukunth Raveendran | Haberdashers' Aske's Sch. for Boys, Herts |
| Vidy Reddy | King Edward's School, Birmingham |
| Ethan Ren | Cardiff High School |
| Alex Rice | Judd School, Tonbridge, Kent |
| Marcus Roberts | The Grammar School at Leeds |
| George Robinson | Brooke Weston Academy, Corby |

| | |
|---|---|
| Jamie Robson | Harrogate Grammar School |
| Nicole Rosenfeld | North London Collegiate Sch., Middlesex |
| Alew Ruben | Bancroft's School, Woodford Green |
| Blaise Sadler | City of London Freemen's School, Surrey |
| Akash Sengupta | South Island School, Hong Kong |
| Jacob Shackleton | Forest School, London |
| Alex Shen | St George's School, Berks |
| James Shering | King's School, Macclesfield, Cheshire |
| Daniel Silber | St John the Baptist Sch., Woking, Surrey |
| Joshua Silverbeck | Haberdasher Aske's Junior School, Herts |
| Bradley Sims | Trinity School, Croydon, Surrey |
| Amritpal Singh | Myton School, Warwick |
| Antonia Siu | Tiffin Girls' School, Kingston-upon-Thames |
| Anna Skaria | Colchester County HS for Girls, Essex |
| Toby Squire | Colyton Grammar School, Devon |
| Adrian Tang | West Island School (ESF) |
| Donald Taylor | George Watson's College, Edinburgh |
| Akembom Titahmboh | King Edward VI Aston Sch., Birmingham |
| Natalie Underwood | Colyton Grammar School, Devon |
| Paul Vallis | Plymouth College |
| Jacob Warbrick | The Crossley Heath School, Halifax |
| Charlie Warburton | Stanah Primary School, Thornton, Lancs |
| Leah Ward | Kendrick School, Reading, Berkshire |
| Daniel Wilson | North Halifax Grammar School, Halifax |
| Ian Wilson | Reading School, Berkshire |
| Michael Woollard | King Edward VI Sch., Stratford-Upon-Avon |
| Andrew Wu | King Edward VI School, Southampton |
| Zack Xiang | Douglas Academy, Glasgow |
| David Yin | City of London School, London |
| Sophie Young | Dame Alice Owen's School, Potters Bar |
| Steph Yuen | United World Coll. of SE Asia, Singapore |
| Chen Zhang | Henrietta Barnett School, London |
| Michael Zhang | Colyton Grammar School, Devon |
| Roy Zhang | Reading School, Berkshire |

# The Intermediate Mathematical Challenge and its follow-up events

The Intermediate Mathematical Challenge was held on Thursday 4th February 2010. Entries numbered 254,720 and 202,163 pupils took part. There were several different IMOK follow-up competitions and pupils were invited to the one appropriate to their school year and mark in the IMC. Around 500 in each of Years 9, 10 and 11 sat the Olympiad papers (Cayley, Hamilton and Maclaurin respectively) and approximately 1700 more in each year group took a Kangaroo paper. We start with the IMC paper.

### UK INTERMEDIATE MATHEMATICAL CHALLENGE

THURSDAY 4TH FEBRUARY 2010

Organised by the **United Kingdom Mathematics Trust**
and supported by

**The Actuarial Profession**
making financial sense of the future

**RULES AND GUIDELINES** (to be read before starting)

1. Do not open the paper until the Invigilator tells you to do so.

2. Time allowed: **1 hour**.
   No answers, or personal details, may be entered after the allowed hour is over.

3. The use of rough paper is allowed; **calculators** and measuring instruments are **forbidden**.

4. Candidates in England and Wales must be in School Year 11 or below.
   Candidates in Scotland must be in S4 or below.
   Candidates in Northern Ireland must be in School Year 12 or below.

5. **Use B or HB pencil only**. Mark *at most one* of the options A, B, C, D, E on the Answer Sheet for each question. Do not mark more than one option.

6. *Do not expect to finish the whole paper in 1 hour.* Concentrate first on Questions 1-15.
   When you have checked your answers to these, have a go at some of the later questions.

7. Five marks are awarded for each correct answer to Questions 1-15.
   Six marks are awarded for each correct answer to Questions 16-25.
   **Each incorrect answer to Questions 16-20 loses 1 mark.**
   **Each incorrect answer to Questions 21-25 loses 2 marks.**

8. Your Answer Sheet will be read only by a *dumb machine*. **Do not write or doodle on the sheet except to mark your chosen options**. The machine 'sees' all black pencil markings even if they are in the wrong places. If you mark the sheet in the wrong place, or leave bits of rubber stuck to the page, the machine will 'see' a mark and interpret this mark in its own way.

9. The questions on this paper challenge you to **think**, not to guess. You get more marks, and more satisfaction, by doing one question carefully than by guessing lots of answers. The UK IMC is about solving interesting problems, not about lucky guessing.

**The UKMT is a registered charity**
*http://www.ukmt.org.uk*

1. What is the value of 10 + 10 × 10 × (10 + 10) ?

   A 21 000    B 20 100    C 2100    D 2010    E 210

2. Three of the interior angles of a given quadrilateral are each 80°. What is the fourth angle of this quadrilateral?

   A 120°    B 110°    C 100°    D 90°    E 80°

3. Exactly one of the following is a prime number. Which is it?

   A 2345    B 23 456    C 234 567    D 2 345 678    E 23 456 789

4. A radio advertisement claimed that using a particular brand of artificial sweetener every day would 'save 7 000 calories in a year'. Approximately how many calories is this per day?

   A 20    B 40    C 70    D 100    E 140

5. Which of the following has the greatest value?

   A one half of $\dfrac{1}{25}$    B one third of $\dfrac{1}{20}$    C one quarter of $\dfrac{1}{15}$

   D one fifth of $\dfrac{1}{10}$    E one sixth of $\dfrac{1}{5}$

6. In triangle $PQR$, $S$ is a point on $QR$ such that $QS = SP = PR$ and $\angle QPS = 20°$. What is the size of $\angle PRS$?

   A 20°    B 35°    C 40°    D 55°    E 60°

7. The Three Choirs Festival is held annually. Its venue rotates in a three-year cycle among Hereford, Gloucester and Worcester. In 2009, it was held in Hereford, in 2010 it will be held in Gloucester, next year it will be held in Worcester.

   Assuming that this three-year cycle continues, in which one of the following years will the Festival *not* be held in Worcester?

   A 2020    B 2032    C 2047    D 2054    E 2077

8. On my clock's display, the time has just changed to 02:31. How many minutes will it be until all the digits 0, 1, 2, 3 next appear together again?

   A 1    B 41    C 50    D 60    E 61

9. The perimeters of the three shapes shown are made up of straight lines and semi-circular arcs of diameter 2. They will fit snugly together as in a jigsaw.

   What is the difference between the total perimeter of the three separate pieces and the perimeter of the shape formed when the three pieces fit together?

   A 0    B 2 + 2π    C 8 + 4π    D 22 + 2π    E 30 + 6π

10. One year in the 1990s, January 1st fell on a Monday. Eleven years later, January 1st was also a Monday. How many times did February 29th occur during those eleven years?

   A 1          B 2          C 3          D 4          E 5

11. "You eat more than I do," said Tweedledee to Tweedledum.
   "That is not true," said Tweedledum to Tweedledee.
   "You are both wrong," said Alice, to them both.
   "You are right," said the White Rabbit to Alice.
   How many of the four statements were true?

   A 0          B 1          C 2          D 3          E 4

12. A cuboid is cut away from a cube of side 10 cm as shown. By what fraction does the total surface area of the solid decrease as a result?

   A $\frac{1}{4}$   B $\frac{1}{6}$   C $\frac{1}{10}$   D $\frac{1}{12}$   E $\frac{1}{18}$

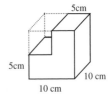

13. At Corbett's Ironmongery a fork handle and a candle cost a total of £6.10. The fork handle costs £4.60 more than the candle. What is the cost of two fork handles and four candles?

   A £14.45     B £13.70     C £12.95     D £12.20     E £8.35

14. Given that $4x - y = 5$, $4y - z = 7$ and $4z - x = 18$, what is the value of $x + y + z$?

   A 8          B 9          C 10          D 11          E 12

15. Bill is trying to sketch the graph of $y = 2x + 6$ but in drawing the axes he has placed the $x$-axis up the page and the $y$-axis across the page. Which of these five graphs is a correct sketch of $y = 2x + 6$ when the axes are placed in this way?

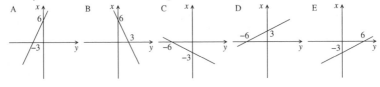

16. Albert Einstein is experimenting with two unusual clocks which both have 24-hour displays. One clock goes at twice the normal speed. The other clock goes backwards, but at the normal speed. Both clocks show the correct time at 13:00.
   What is the correct time when the displays on the clocks next agree?

   A 05:00     B 09:00     C 13:00     D 17:00     E 21:00

17. Last year Gill's cylindrical 21st birthday cake wasn't big enough to feed all her friends. This year she will double the radius and triple the height. What will be the ratio of the volume of this year's birthday cake to the volume of last year's cake?

   A 12:1     B 7:1     C 6:1     D 4:1     E 3:1

42

18. Supergran walks from her chalet to the top of the mountain. She knows that if she walks at a speed of 6 mph she will arrive at 1 pm, whereas if she leaves at the same time and walks at 10 mph, she will arrive at 11 am.
At what speed should she walk if she wants to arrive at 12 noon?

A 7.5 mph     B $7\frac{1}{7}$ mph     C 7.75 mph     D $\sqrt{60}$ mph     E 8 mph

19. A snail is at one corner of the top face of a cube with side length 1 m. The snail can crawl at a speed of 1 m per hour. What proportion of the cube's surface is made up of points which the snail could reach within one hour?

A $\frac{\pi}{16}$     B $\frac{\pi}{8}$     C $\frac{1}{4}$     D $\frac{1}{2}$     E $\frac{\sqrt{3}}{4}$

20. Shahbaz thinks of an integer, $n$, such that the difference between $\sqrt{n}$ and 7 is less than 1. How many different possibilities are there for $n$?

A 13     B 14     C 26     D 27     E 28

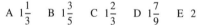

21. A square maze has 9 rooms with gaps in the walls between them. Once a person has travelled through a gap in the wall it then closes behind them. How many different ways can someone travel through the maze from X to Y?

A 8     B 10     C 12     D 14     E 16

22. Curly and Larry like to have their orange squash made to the same strength. Unfortunately, Moe has put 25 ml of squash with 175 ml of water in Curly's glass and 15 ml of squash with 185 ml of water in Larry's glass. How many millilitres of the mixture in Curly's glass must be put into Larry's glass so that they end up with drinks of the same strength?

A 5     B 7     C 10     D 12     E it is not possible

23. The diagram shows a pattern of eight equal shaded squares inside a circle of area $\pi$ square units. What is the area (in square units) of the shaded region?

A $1\frac{1}{3}$     B $1\frac{3}{5}$     C $1\frac{2}{3}$     D $1\frac{7}{9}$     E 2

24. A new taxi firm needs a memorable phone number. They want a number which has a maximum of two different digits. Their phone number must start with the digit 3 and be six digits long. How many such numbers are possible?

A 288     B 280     C 279     D 226     E 225

25. Two squares, each of side length $1 + \sqrt{2}$ units, overlap. The overlapping region is a regular octagon.
What is the area (in square units) of the octagon?

A $1 + \sqrt{2}$     B $1 + 2\sqrt{2}$     C $2 + \sqrt{2}$     D $2 + 2\sqrt{2}$     E $2 + 3\sqrt{2}$

# The IMC solutions

As with the Junior Challenge, a solutions leaflet was sent out.

## UK INTERMEDIATE MATHEMATICAL CHALLENGE

THURSDAY 4th FEBRUARY 2010

Organised by the **United Kingdom Mathematics Trust**
**from the School of Mathematics, University of Leeds**

*http://www.ukmt.org.uk*

**The Actuarial Profession**
making financial sense of the future

## SOLUTIONS LEAFLET

This solutions leaflet for the IMC is sent in the hope that it might provide all concerned with some alternative solutions to the ones they have obtained. It is not intended to be definitive. The organisers would be very pleased to receive alternatives created by candidates.

**The UKMT is a registered charity**

1. **D**  $10 + 10 \times 10 \times (10 + 10) = 10 + 10 \times 10 \times 20 = 10 + 2000 = 2010$.

2. **A**  The sum of the interior angles of a quadrilateral is 360°, so the fourth angle is $(360 - 3 \times 80)° = 120°$.

3. **E**  2345 has units digit 5 and so is a multiple of 5; 23 456 is even; the digit sum of 234 567 is 27 so it is a multiple of 9; 2 345 678 is even. So if exactly one of the numbers is prime then it must be 23 456 789.

4. **A**  The number of calories saved per day is $\dfrac{7000}{365} \approx \dfrac{7000}{350} = 20$.

5. **E**  The values are A $\dfrac{1}{50}$, B $\dfrac{1}{60}$, C $\dfrac{1}{60}$, D $\dfrac{1}{50}$, E $\dfrac{1}{30}$.

6. **C**  Triangle $PQS$ is isosceles with $PS = QS$ so $\angle PQS = \angle SPQ = 20°$. Therefore $\angle PSR = 20° + 20° = 40°$ (exterior angle theorem). Triangle $PSR$ is also isosceles, with $PS = PR$, so $\angle PRS = \angle PSR = 40°$.

7. **D**  The Festival will next be held in Worcester in 2011. As it follows a three-year cycle, the Festival is held in Worcester when the number of the year leaves a remainder of 1 when divided by 3. So it will be held in Worcester in 2020, 2032, 2047 and 2077, but not in 2054.

8. **B**  The next such display will be 03:12, that is in 41 minutes' time.

9. **C**  The difference in perimeters is the total length of the edges which are hidden when the pieces are fitted together. These are eight straight edges of length 1 and four semicircular arcs of radius 1.
So the required difference is $8 \times 1 + 4(\frac{1}{2} \times 2 \times \pi \times 1) = 8 + 4\pi$.

10. **C**  Every year, the day of the week on which a particular date falls is one day later than it fell the previous year unless February 29th has occurred in the meantime, in which case it falls two days later. As January 1st returned to a Monday after 11 years, it must have 'moved on' 14 days during that time, so February 29th occurred three times in those 11 years.

11. **B**  If the first statement is true, then the three other statements are all false. If the first statement is false, however, then the second statement is the only true statement. Either way, exactly one of the four statements is true.

12. **D**  When the cuboid is cut away, the surface area of the solid 'loses' two rectangles measuring 10 cm × 5 cm and two squares of side 5 cm. However, it also 'gains' two rectangles measuring 10 cm × 5 cm. So the surface area decreases by an area equal to one half of the area of one of the faces of the original cube, that is one twelfth of its original surface area.

13. **B**  Let the prices of a fork handle and a candle be £$x$ and £$y$ respectively.
Then $x + y = 6.1$ and $x - y = 4.6$. Adding these two equations gives $2x = 10.7$.
So a fork handle costs £5.35 and a candle costs £0.75.
Therefore the required total is £10.70 + £3.00 = £13.70.

**14. C**  Adding the three equations gives $3x + 3y + 3z = 30$, so $x + y + z = 10$. (*The equations may be solved to obtain $x = 2$, $y = 3$, $z = 5$. However, as the above method shows, this is not necessary in order to find the value of $x + y + z$.*)

**15. E**  The line $y = 2x + 6$ intersects the $y$-axis when $x = 0$ and $y = 6$. It intersects the $x$-axis when $x = -3$ and $y = 0$. So E is the correct line. (*Alternatively*: $y = 2x + 6$ may be rearranged to give $x = \frac{1}{2}y - 3$. So the required line looks the same as the line $y = \frac{1}{2}x - 3$ when the axes are drawn in the traditional way.)

**16. E**  After $x$ hours, the first clock will have gone forward $2x$ hours and the second clock will have gone back $x$ hours. So the next time they agree is when $2x + x = 24$, that is when $x = 8$. The correct time then is 21:00.

**17. A**  The volume of a cylinder of radius $r$ and height $h$ is $\pi r^2 h$. Replacing $r$ by $2r$ and $h$ by $3h$ multiplies this volume by 12.

**18. A**  Let the distance from the chalet to the top of the mountain be $x$ miles. Then, at 6 mph Supergran would take $\dfrac{x}{6}$ hours, whereas at 10 mph she would take $\dfrac{x}{10}$ hours. So $\dfrac{x}{6} - \dfrac{x}{10} = 2$, that is $5x - 3x = 60$, so $x = 30$. Hence Supergran's departure time is 8 am and to arrive at 12 noon she should walk at $\dfrac{30}{4}$ mph, that is $7\frac{1}{2}$ mph.

**19. B**  In one hour, the snail can reach points within 1 m of the corner at which it starts. So it can reach some of the points on the three faces which meet at that corner, but none of the points on the other three faces. On each of the three reachable faces, the points which the snail can reach form a quarter of a circle of radius 1 m.
So the required fraction is $\dfrac{3 \times \frac{1}{4}\pi \times 1 \times 1}{6 \times 1 \times 1} = \dfrac{\pi}{8}$.

**20. D**  If the difference between $\sqrt{n}$ and 7 is less than 1, then $6 < \sqrt{n} < 8$. Therefore $36 < n < 64$, so there are 27 possible values of $n$.

**21. E**  The rooms are labelled A, B, C, D, E, F, G, X, Y as shown. We look first at routes which visit no room more than once. We need consider only routes which go from X to A, since each of these routes has a corresponding route which goes from X to C. For example, the route X A D E Y corresponds to the route X C D G Y.
Routes which start X A then go to B or to D. There are three routes which start X A B, namely X A B E Y, X A B E D G Y and X A B E D C F G Y. There are also three routes which start X A D, namely X A D E Y, X A D G Y and X A D C F G Y.
The condition that a gap in a wall closes once a person has travelled through it means that it is not possible to visit a room more than once unless that room has at least four gaps leading into and out of it and the only such room is D. There

are two routes which start X A and visit D twice. These are X A D G F C D E Y and X A D C F G D E Y. So there are 8 routes which start X A and there are 8 corresponding routes which start X C so there are 16 routes in all.

**22. E**  Curly's drink has squash and water in the ratio 1: 7, whilst the corresponding ratio for Larry's drink is 3 : 37. This ratio is less than 1 : 7. When some of Curly's mixture is poured into Larry's, the strength will be between 1 : 7 and 3 : 37, but not equal to either.

**23. B**  Let the centre of the circle be $O$ and let $A$ and $B$ be corners of one of the shaded squares, as shown. As the circle has area $\pi$ units², its radius is 1 unit. So $OB$ is 1 unit long. Let the length of the side of each of the shaded squares be $x$ units.
By Pythagoras' Theorem: $OB^2 = OA^2 + AB^2$, that is $1^2 = (2x)^2 + x^2$. So $5x^2 = 1$. Now the total shaded area is $8x^2 = 8 \times \frac{1}{5} = 1\frac{3}{5}$ units².

**24. B**  There is the possibility of using only 3s giving one possible number 333333. Let's suppose a second digit is used, say $x$. After the initial digit 3, there are 5 positions into which we can put either 3 or $x$. So there are 2 choices in each of these 5 positions and so $2^5 = 32$ possible choices – except that one such choice would be five 3s. So we get 31 choices. There are 9 possible values for $x$, namely 0, 1, 2, 4, 5, 6, 7, 8, 9. So this gives $9 \times 31 = 279$ numbers. Together with 333333, this gives 280 numbers.

**25. D**  Let the length of the side of the regular octagon be $x$ units and let $A, B, C, D, E, F$ be the points shown. So $AC = CE = x$.
Now $\angle ACE = 135°$ (interior angle of regular octagon), so $\angle ACB = 45°$ and hence triangle $ABC$ is an isosceles right-angled triangle with $AB = BC$.
Also, by Pythagoras' Theorem: $AB^2 + BC^2 = AC^2 = x^2$ so $AB = BC = \frac{\sqrt{2}}{2}x$.
Similarly, $EF = \frac{\sqrt{2}}{2}x$.
Therefore $BF = \left(\frac{\sqrt{2}}{2}x + x + \frac{\sqrt{2}}{2}x\right)$ units $= x\left(1 + \sqrt{2}\right)$ units.
But we are given that $BF = \left(1 + \sqrt{2}\right)$ units so $x = 1$.
Now the area of the octagon formed by the overlap of the squares is equal to the area of one of these squares minus the sum of the area of four triangles, each of which is congruent to triangle $CDE$.
Thus, in square units, the required area is

$$\left(1 + \sqrt{2}\right)^2 - 4 \times \frac{1}{2} \times \frac{\sqrt{2}}{2} \times \frac{\sqrt{2}}{2} = 3 + 2\sqrt{2} - 1 = 2 + 2\sqrt{2}.$$

# The answers

The table below shows the proportion of pupils' choices.  The correct answer is shown in bold.  [The percentages are rounded to the nearest whole number.]

| Qn | A | B | C | D | E | Blank |
|---|---|---|---|---|---|---|
| 1 | 3 | 5 | 12 | **74** | 4 | 2 |
| 2 | **85** | 2 | 3 | 1 | 9 | 1 |
| 3 | 5 | 5 | 53 | 3 | **29** | 4 |
| 4 | **75** | 8 | 3 | 3 | 9 | 2 |
| 5 | 10 | 8 | 7 | 8 | **62** | 3 |
| 6 | 13 | 6 | **55** | 7 | 13 | 5 |
| 7 | 6 | 6 | 6 | **78** | 3 | 1 |
| 8 | 1 | **76** | 18 | 2 | 2 | 1 |
| 9 | 12 | 12 | **42** | 17 | 9 | 8 |
| 10 | 3 | 43 | **40** | 7 | 3 | 4 |
| 11 | 13 | **28** | 42 | 9 | 4 | 2 |
| 12 | 61 | 12 | 4 | **19** | 2 | 2 |
| 13 | 17 | **54** | 5 | 18 | 2 | 5 |
| 14 | 6 | 9 | **48** | 15 | 13 | 9 |
| 15 | 13 | 22 | 9 | 9 | **40** | 6 |
| 16 | 35 | 5 | 13 | 5 | **12** | 30 |
| 17 | **13** | 4 | 33 | 5 | 7 | 37 |
| 18 | **8** | 2 | 2 | 2 | 54 | 32 |
| 19 | 4 | **10** | 13 | 10 | 4 | 59 |
| 20 | 6 | 10 | 7 | **7** | 5 | 64 |
| 21 | 12 | 14 | 17 | 9 | **6** | 43 |
| 22 | 6 | 3 | 6 | 2 | **24** | 58 |
| 23 | 4 | **6** | 5 | 4 | 6 | 76 |
| 24 | 5 | **6** | 5 | 5 | 4 | 75 |
| 25 | 3 | 5 | 4 | **7** | 3 | 78 |

**IMC 2010: Some comments on the pupils' choice of answers as sent to schools in the letter with the results**

We are pleased that the mean score of 41.5 is significantly higher than in 2009. Most of the early questions were answered correctly by more than half the students. However, the greatest interest lies in the questions which proved unexpectedly difficult. We hope that you will find the comparison, given with your results, of the national distribution of answers with those of your pupils informative.

It is not easy to tell whether a large number is a prime without doing a lot of calculations. It is often easier to tell that a number is not a prime. So in Question 3 pupils were told that one of the given numbers is a prime, and they were expected to decide which it is by ruling out the other four numbers. It is easy to see that 2 345, 23 456 and 2 345 678 are not prime, so we can only assume that the 13% who selected one of these numbers either did not know what a prime number is, or were not taking the Challenge seriously. This leaves just 234 567 and 23 456 789 to choose between. It is a matter for concern that 53% of the pupils seemed to think that, of these two, it is 234 567 which is a prime number. If your pupils are typical of the majority, we hope you find the time to explain the answer. It is not difficult to check by a direct calculation that 234 567 is divisible by 3. It is even quicker to note that the sum of its digits is 27, which is a multiple of 9, and thus to deduce that 234 567 is divisible by 9. The digit sum test for divisibility by 9 and by 3 seems to be not as widely known as it should be. Apart from its usefulness in problems of this type, the explanation of why it works helps to reinforce place value, and is a good example of how it is possible to prove general facts about numbers.

It is important to read the questions carefully. In Question 16, 35% of the students chose the wrong option 05.00 and only 12% the correct answer 21.00. When the two clocks next agree, the time they both show is indeed 5.00, but the *correct* time at this moment is 21.00, and this is what the question asked for.

As expected, the later questions proved very challenging, and most students did not attempt them. Students with high scores can be rightly proud of their achievement.

The profile of marks obtained is shown below.

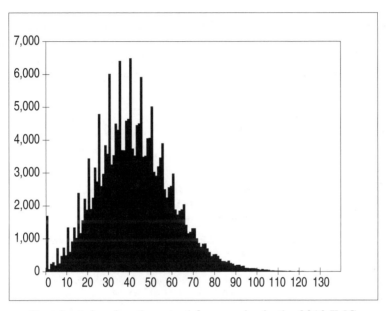

Bar chart showing the actual frequencies in the 2010 IMC

On the basis of the standard proportions used by the UKMT, the cut-off marks were set at

GOLD – 70 or over    SILVER – 56 to 69    BRONZE – 45 to 55

The certificates were virtually identical in design to those used for the JMC.

The cut-off scores for the follow-up competitions were

| Year (E&W) | Minimum mark | Event | Minimum mark | Event |
|---|---|---|---|---|
| 11 | 97 | Maclaurin | 80 | Kangaroo Pink |
| 10 | 91 | Hamilton | 80 | Kangaroo Pink |
| 9 | 83 | Cayley | 70 | Kangaroo Grey |

50

# The Intermediate Mathematical Olympiad and Kangaroo

## (a) *Kangaroo*

The 2010 European Kangaroo (a multiple choice paper with 25 questions) took place on Thursday 18th March. It was also held in many other countries across Europe and beyond with over three million candidates. As in previous years, the UKMT constructed two Kangaroo papers.

### EUROPEAN 'KANGAROO' MATHEMATICAL CHALLENGE
### 'GREY'
**Thursday 18th March 2010**

**Organised by the United Kingdom Mathematics Trust and the Association Kangourou Sans Frontières**

*Kangaroo papers are being taken by over 5.5 million students in 46 countries in Europe and beyond.*

RULES AND GUIDELINES (to be read before starting):

1. Do not open the paper until the Invigilator tells you to do so.

2. Time allowed: **1 hour**.
   No answers, or personal details, may be entered after the allowed hour is over.

3. The use of rough paper is allowed; **calculators** and measuring instruments are **forbidden**.

4. Candidates in England and Wales must be in School Year 9 or below.
   Candidates in Scotland must be in S2 or below.
   Candidates in Northern Ireland must be in School Year 10 or below.

5. **Use B or HB pencil only**. For each question mark *at most one* of the options A, B, C, D, E on the Answer Sheet. Do not mark more than one option.

6. Five marks will be awarded for each correct answer to Questions 1 - 15.
   Six marks will be awarded for each correct answer to Questions 16 - 25.

7. *Do not expect to finish the whole paper in 1 hour*. Concentrate first on Questions 1-15. When you have checked your answers to these, have a go at some of the later questions.

8. The questions on this paper challenge you **to think**, not to guess. Though you will not lose marks for getting answers wrong, you will undoubtedly get more marks, and more satisfaction, by doing a few questions carefully than by guessing lots of answers.

*Enquiries about the European Kangaroo should be sent to: Maths Challenges Office, School of Maths Satellite, University of Leeds, Leeds, LS2 9JT.*
*(Tel. 0113 343 2339)*
*http://www.ukmt.org.uk*

# 2010 European Grey Kangaroo

1. Toy kangaroos are packed in boxes. All the boxes used are cubes. One kangaroo is packed inside a small box. Exactly eight small boxes are packed snugly inside a larger box. How many kangaroos are on the bottom layer of a larger box?

   A 1       B 2       C 3       D 4       E 5

2. The diagram shows the plan of a room. Adjoining walls are perpendicular to each other and the lengths of some of the walls are shown. What is the length of the perimeter of the room?

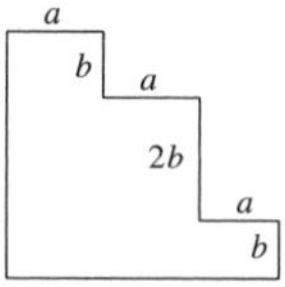

   A $3a + 4b$   B $3a + 8b$   C $6a + 4b$   D $6a + 6b$   E $6a + 8b$

3. Luis writes down seven consecutive positive integers. The sum of the three smallest numbers is 33. What is the sum of the three largest numbers?

   A 37       B 39       C 42       D 45       E 48

4. The diagram (which is not drawn to scale) shows a box measuring 5 cm by 5 cm. There are seven bars in the box, each measuring 1 cm by 3 cm. Kanga wants to slide the bars in the box so there is room for one more bar. What is the minimum number of bars that Kanga needs to move?

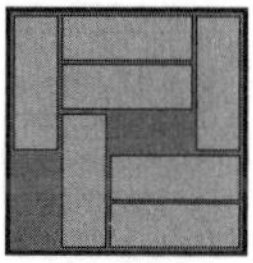

   A 2       B 3       C 4       D 5       E It is impossible

5. Grandma bakes a cake for her grandchildren who are going to visit her in the afternoon. She has forgotten whether 3, 5 or all 6 of her grandchildren will visit. She wants all the cake eaten and each grandchild to get the same amount of cake. To be prepared for all three possibilities, what is the smallest number of pieces into which she should cut the cake?

   A 12       B 15       C 18       D 24       E 30

6. A large square is divided into 4 equal-sized smaller squares. All the smaller squares are either shaded or unshaded. How many different ways are there to colour the large square? (Two colourings are considered to be the same if one can be rotated to look exactly like the other, as in the example shown.)

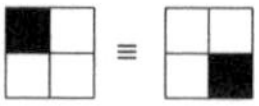

   A 5       B 6       C 7       D 8       E 9

7. Which of the following is the smallest two-digit number that cannot be written as the sum of three different one-digit numbers?

   A 10       B 15       C 23       D 25       E 28

8. A woodcutter chops logs in the forest. He chops one log at a time, splitting it into two smaller logs. Once the woodcutter has finished, he has made 53 chops and ended up with 72 logs. How many logs did he start with?

   A 17       B 18       C 19       D 20       E 21

9. The diagram shows a quadrilateral $ABCD$, in which $AD = BC$, $\angle CAD = 50°$, $\angle ACD = 65°$ and $\angle ACB = 70°$. What is the size of $\angle ABC$?

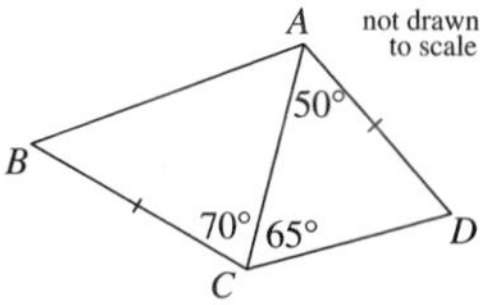

   A 50°   B 55°   C 60°   D 65°   E Impossible to determine

10. Cathy connects three short chains to make a long chain, but does not make them into a loop. It takes her 18 minutes. How long does it take her to make an even longer chain by connecting six short chains in the same way?

   A 27 minutes   B 30 minutes   C 36 minutes   D 45 minutes   E 60 minutes

52

11. What is the sum of the first hundred odd positive integers subtracted from the sum of the first hundred even positive integers?

   A  0　　　　　B  50　　　　　C  100　　　　　D  10100　　　　　E  15150

12. Andrea has wound some rope around a piece of wood, as shown in the diagram on the right. She rotates the wood 180° as shown by the arrow in the diagram. What does she see after the rotation?

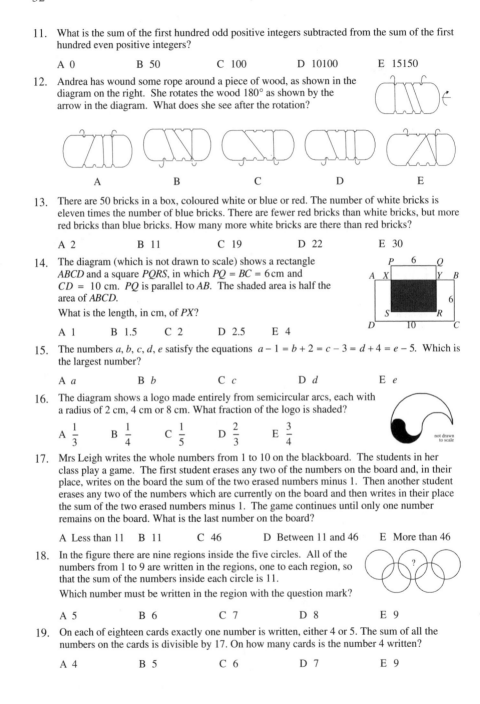

   A　　　　　B　　　　　C　　　　　D　　　　　E

13. There are 50 bricks in a box, coloured white or blue or red. The number of white bricks is eleven times the number of blue bricks. There are fewer red bricks than white bricks, but more red bricks than blue bricks. How many more white bricks are there than red bricks?

   A  2　　　　　B  11　　　　　C  19　　　　　D  22　　　　　E  30

14. The diagram (which is not drawn to scale) shows a rectangle $ABCD$ and a square $PQRS$, in which $PQ = BC = 6$ cm and $CD = 10$ cm. $PQ$ is parallel to $AB$. The shaded area is half the area of $ABCD$.
   What is the length, in cm, of $PX$?

   A  1　　B  1.5　　C  2　　D  2.5　　E  4

15. The numbers $a, b, c, d, e$ satisfy the equations $a - 1 = b + 2 = c - 3 = d + 4 = e - 5$. Which is the largest number?

   A  $a$　　　　　B  $b$　　　　　C  $c$　　　　　D  $d$　　　　　E  $e$

16. The diagram shows a logo made entirely from semicircular arcs, each with a radius of 2 cm, 4 cm or 8 cm. What fraction of the logo is shaded?

   A  $\dfrac{1}{3}$　　B  $\dfrac{1}{4}$　　C  $\dfrac{1}{5}$　　D  $\dfrac{2}{3}$　　E  $\dfrac{3}{4}$

17. Mrs Leigh writes the whole numbers from 1 to 10 on the blackboard. The students in her class play a game. The first student erases any two of the numbers on the board and, in their place, writes on the board the sum of the two erased numbers minus 1. Then another student erases any two of the numbers which are currently on the board and then writes in their place the sum of the two erased numbers minus 1. The game continues until only one number remains on the board. What is the last number on the board?

   A  Less than 11　　B  11　　　C  46　　　　D  Between 11 and 46　　　E  More than 46

18. In the figure there are nine regions inside the five circles. All of the numbers from 1 to 9 are written in the regions, one to each region, so that the sum of the numbers inside each circle is 11.
   Which number must be written in the region with the question mark?

   A  5　　　　　B  6　　　　　C  7　　　　　D  8　　　　　E  9

19. On each of eighteen cards exactly one number is written, either 4 or 5. The sum of all the numbers on the cards is divisible by 17. On how many cards is the number 4 written?

   A  4　　　　　B  5　　　　　C  6　　　　　D  7　　　　　E  9

20. Mr Gagač goes to a barter market where the items are exchanged according to the table on the right. Mr Gagač wants to take away 1 goose, 1 turkey and 1 duck. What is the minimum number of hens that he needs to bring to the barter market?

| Exchange Rates |
| --- |
| 1 turkey = 5 ducks |
| 1 goose + 2 hens = 3 ducks |
| 4 hens = 1 goose |

   A  14       B  15       C  16       D  17       E  18

21. A rectangular strip of paper is folded three times, with each fold line parallel to the short edges. It is then unfolded so that the seven folds up or down can all be seen. Which of the following strips, viewed from a long edge, could not be made in this way?

A

B

C

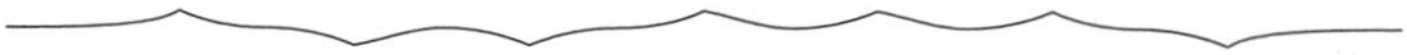

D

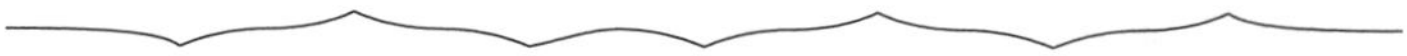

E

22. The town of Ginkrail is inhabited entirely by knights and liars. Every sentence spoken by a knight is true, and every sentence spoken by a liar is false. One day some inhabitants of Ginkrail were alone in a room and three of them spoke.

The first one said: "There are no more than three of us in the room. All of us are liars."
The second said: "There are no more than four of us in the room. Not all of us are liars."
The third said: "There are five of us in the room. Three of us are liars."

How many people were in the room and how many liars were among them?

A    3 people, 1 of whom is a liar       B    4 people, 1 of whom is a liar
C    4 people, 2 of whom are liars       D    5 people, 2 of whom are liars
E    5 people, 3 of whom are liars

23. Kanga has a large collection of small cubes measuring $1 \times 1 \times 1$. Each cube is a single colour. Kanga wants to use 27 small cubes to make a $3 \times 3 \times 3$ cube so that any two cubes with at least one common vertex are of different colours. What is the minimum number of colours that Kanga needs to use?

   A  6       B  8       C  9       D  12       E  27

24. The diagram shows a large equilateral triangle divided into 36 small equilateral triangles, each with area 1 cm$^2$. What is the area of the shaded triangle, in cm$^2$ ?

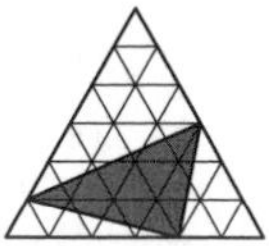

   A  11       B  12       C  13       D  14       E  15

25. The lowest common multiple of 24 and $x$ is less than the lowest common multiple of 24 and $y$. Which of the following can $\dfrac{y}{x}$ never equal?

   A  $\dfrac{6}{7}$       B  $\dfrac{7}{6}$       C  $\dfrac{2}{3}$       D  $\dfrac{7}{8}$       E  $\dfrac{8}{7}$

54

# Solutions to the 2010 European Grey Kangaroo

**1.  D**  Since eight small boxes are packed snugly inside a larger cube, they are packed two by two by two. So there are $2 \times 2 = 4$ boxes on the bottom layer.

**2.  E**  One long wall has length $b + 2b + b = 4b$ and the perpendicular long wall has length $a + a + a = 3a$. So the length of the perimeter is $6a + 8b$.

**3.  D**  Let $n, n + 1, n + 2, \ldots, n + 6$ be the seven consecutive integers. The sum of the smallest three numbers is $n + (n + 1) + (n + 2) = 33$. Solving this gives $n = 10$. The three largest numbers are therefore 14, 15 and 16 and their sum is 45.

*Alternatively*: Adding 4 to each of the smallest three numbers, we get the three largest numbers. Therefore the sum of the largest three is $33 + 3 \times 4 = 45$.

**4.  B**  Label three of the bars X, Y and Z as shown in the diagram. At the start Kanga can only move bar X down. Now Y and Z are the only bars that can be moved and Kanga must slide these bars to the left. Only now is there space for one more bar and Kanga has moved 3 bars.

**5.  E**  Grandma needs to cut the cake into a number of pieces which is divisible by 3, 5 and 6. For this to be the smallest number of pieces, it must be the lowest common multiple of 3, 5 and 6, namely 30.

**6.  B**

**7.  D**  The largest two-digit number that can be written as the sum of three different one-digit numbers is $7 + 8 + 9 = 24$. The smallest two-digit number is 10 and this can be written as $2 + 3 + 5$. By successively increasing the digit 5 up to 9, one unit at a time, and then the digit 3 up to 8 and finally the digit 2 up to 7, we can obtain every two-digit number between 10 and 24. Therefore the smallest two-digit number that cannot be written as the sum of three different one-digit numbers is 25.

**8.  C**  Each chop corresponds to an extra log being made. Since 53 chops have been made, the woodcutter started with $72 - 53 = 19$ logs.

**9.  B**  From the angle sum of a triangle, $\angle ADC = 65°$. Since $\angle ADC = \angle ACD$, triangle $ACD$ is isosceles and so $AC = AD = BC$. Triangle $ABC$ is therefore isosceles and from the angle sum of a triangle, $\angle BAC = \angle ABC = 55°$.

**10.  D**  To connect three short chains, Cathy needs to make two connections and each connection will take her $\frac{1}{2} \times 18$ minutes $= 9$ minutes. To connect six short chains, she needs to make five connections. This will take her $5 \times 9$ minutes $= 45$ minutes.

**11.  C**  The expression $(2 + 4 + \ldots + 200) - (1 + 3 + \ldots + 199)$ can be rewritten as $(2 - 1) + (4 - 3) + \ldots + (200 - 199)$. Each bracket is equal to 1 and there are 100 brackets. The value of the expression is therefore 100.

**12.  D**  When Andrea started, the rope passed through each notch at the top of the piece of wood. When the wood is rotated through 180°, the rope must now pass through each notch at the bottom of the piece of wood. This means, of the options available, she must see D.

However, there is an alternative view that she could see after the rotation. Consider the initial piece of wood and label the notches along the top 1, 2, 3, 4 and the notches along the bottom $P$, $Q$, $R$, $S$ as shown in the diagram. The reverse of the piece of wood could also show $P$ to 3, then $S$ to 2 and finally $R$ to 4.

$P$ $Q$ $R$ $S$

**13. C** Let $b$ be the number of blue bricks. Then the number of white bricks is $11b$ and the number of red bricks is $50 - b - 11b = 50 - 12b$. Thus we have $b < 50 - 12b < 11b$. Therefore $13b < 50 < 23b$, so that $b < 4$ and $b > 2$. Thus $b = 3$ and there are 33 white bricks and 14 red ones. Hence there are 19 more white bricks than red bricks.

**14. A** The area of rectangle $ABCD$ is $6 \times 10 = 60$ cm². The shaded area, $RSXY$, is half the area of $ABCD$ and is therefore 30 cm². So $XS$ is 5 cm. Since $PQRS$ is a square, $PS$ is 6 cm and therefore $PX$ is 1 cm.

**15. E** Since all the expressions are equal, the largest number is the one from which most is subtracted. This is $e$.

*Alternatively*: Add 5 to the set of equations to get $a + 4 = b + 7 = c + 2 = d + 9 = e$. Therefore $e$ is larger than each of $a$, $b$, $c$ and $d$.

**16. B** The shaded shape and the whole logo are in proportion and the ratio of corresponding lengths is 1 : 2. Therefore the ratio of their areas is 1 : 4 and the shaded area is $\frac{1}{4}$ of the logo.

*Alternatively:* The shaded area can be rearranged into a semicircle of radius 4 cm which has an area of $\frac{1}{2} \times \pi \times 4^2 = 8\pi$ cm². The total logo can be rearranged into a semicircle of radius 8 cm which has an area of $\frac{1}{2} \times \pi \times 8^2 = 32\pi$ cm². Therefore the shaded area is $\dfrac{8\pi}{32\pi} = \dfrac{1}{4}$ of the logo.

**17. C** Each time a student takes part in the game, there will be one fewer number written on the board. After nine students have taken part in the game, there will only be one number left on the board. This number will be 9 less than the sum of all the numbers from 1 to 10 since each student has subtracted 1. The number 46 is always left on the board.

**18. B** The sum of the digits from 1 to 9 is 45. There are 5 circles and the sum of the numbers in each circle is 11, which gives a total of $5 \times 11 = 55$. However, this counts the four numbers which are in more than one circle twice and the sum of these numbers is $55 - 45 = 10$. Therefore the 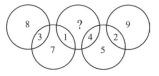 shared numbers are 1, 2, 3, 4 since this is the only combination of four different digits that add to 10. Now in order to give 11 as the total in each circle, 1 must go in a circle with two other digits and let $P$ be the other number in a circle with two other digits. Suppose that $P$ is replaced by the number 2. Then the region with the question mark must contain the number 8. But 3 and 8 must then be in one of the outer circles and this is not possible if we are to use each digit only once. Similarly, if $P$ is replaced by the number 3, then the region with the question mark must contain the number 7. But 4 and 7 must then be in one of the outer circles, and again, this isn't possible. Therefore $P$ must be replaced by the number 4. Hence 6 is in the region with the question mark and the diagram shows that there is an arrangement as desired.

56

**19. B** If all the cards had the number 4 written on them, the sum would be $18 \times 4 = 72$. If all the cards had the number 5 written on them, the total would be $18 \times 5 = 90$. The only number between 72 and 90 (inclusive) which is divisible by 17 is 85, obtained by a combination of five cards with the number 4 and thirteen cards with the number 5.

**20. C** For 1 turkey, Mr Gagač needs to exchange hens and geese for 5 ducks. This means he needs 2 geese and 4 hens. Since he only takes hens to the market, he needs to start by exchanging 8 hens for 2 geese. This is a total of 12 hens for 1 turkey and Mr Gagač will also be left with 1 duck from this exchange. To take 1 goose home, he will need to bring 4 more hens. Hence Mr Gagač needs to bring at least 16 hens to the barter market.

**21. D** Imagine refolding these strips once, as is shown in the diagram on the left. The peaks on one side of the fold must match with hollows on the other side (which they all do!). We obtain the half-size strips shown in the diagram on the right. Now imagine refolding these strips about their mid-points. We can see that, in D, there are troughs on both sides, so D is not possible; but all the others are possible.

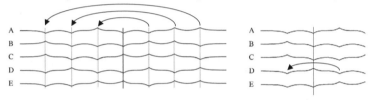

**22. C** Let the speakers be X, Y and Z respectively. Now X cannot be a knight since X's second sentence would then be false, a contradiction. So X is a liar and both X's sentences are false, that is, there are more than three of them in the room and not all of them are liars. This means that Y's second sentence is true, so that Y is a knight. Therefore Y's first sentence is also true so there are no more than four of them in the room. Hence there are exactly four of them in the room. So Z's first sentence is false, which means that Z is a liar and thus Z's second sentence is also false. So far, we have two liars (X, Z) and one knight (Y), and the only way that "Three of us are liars" can be false is for the fourth person to be a knight.

**23. B** Consider one small cube. Around a vertex, there are up to eight small cubes and they must all be different colours. Eight is therefore the minimum number of colours that can be used. With eight colours, labelled 1 to 8, the diagrams below show that this is possible.

| Bottom Layer | | |
|---|---|---|
| 1 | 2 | 1 |
| 3 | 4 | 3 |
| 1 | 2 | 1 |

| Middle Layer | | |
|---|---|---|
| 5 | 6 | 5 |
| 7 | 8 | 7 |
| 5 | 6 | 5 |

| Top Layer | | |
|---|---|---|
| 1 | 2 | 1 |
| 3 | 4 | 3 |
| 1 | 2 | 1 |

**24.** **A**  For each of the parallelograms *ABCO*, *CDEO*, *EFAO* in the diagram, half of its area is from the shaded triangle. Hence the triangle is half of the hexagon formed by the three parallelograms. Since the hexagon is made of 22 triangles, the shaded triangle must have area 11 cm$^2$.

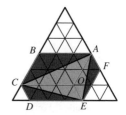

**25.** **A**  It is possible to find pairs $(x, y)$ satisfying the conditions of B, C, D and E. For example:

B (6, 7)        C (24, 16)        D (8, 7)        E (56, 64).

We will use the notation $[p, q]$ to stand for the lowest common multiple of $p$ and $q$.

It is not possible to find a solution for A. For suppose $\dfrac{y}{x} = \dfrac{6}{7}$, then $y = 6k$ and $x = 7k$ for some integer $k > 0$. Now $[24, x] = [24, 7k] = 7 \times [24, k]$ and $[24, y] = [24, 6k]$.

If $k$ is divisible by 3 but not by 8, then $[24, \ 6k] \ = \ 3 \times [24, k]$.
If $k$ is divisible by 8 but not by 3, then $[24, \ 6k] \ = \ 2 \times [24, k]$.
If $k$ is divisible by both 3 and 8, then $[24, \ 6k] \ = \ 6 \times [24, k]$.

In all three cases, $[24, \ 6k] \ < \ 7 \times [24, \ k]$ which contradicts the condition given in the question. In other words, $\dfrac{y}{x}$ cannot be $\dfrac{6}{7}$.

58

# 2010 European Pink Kangaroo

1. What is the result of dividing 20102010 by 2010?

   A  11          B  101          C  1001          D  10001          E  not an integer

2. Ivan, Tibor and Alex sat a test and achieved 85%, 90% and 100% respectively. Tibor scored just one more mark than Ivan. How many marks did Alex get?

   A  5          B  17          C  18          D  20          E  25

3. Four cubes, each with surface area 24 cm², are placed together to form a cuboid as shown. What is the surface area of this cuboid, in cm² ?

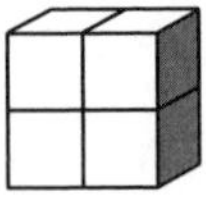

   A  24     B  32     C  64     D  92     E  96

4. A rectangular strip of paper is folded in half three times, with each fold line parallel to the short edges. It is then unfolded so that the seven folds up or down can all be seen. Which of the following strips, viewed from a long edge, could not be made in this way?

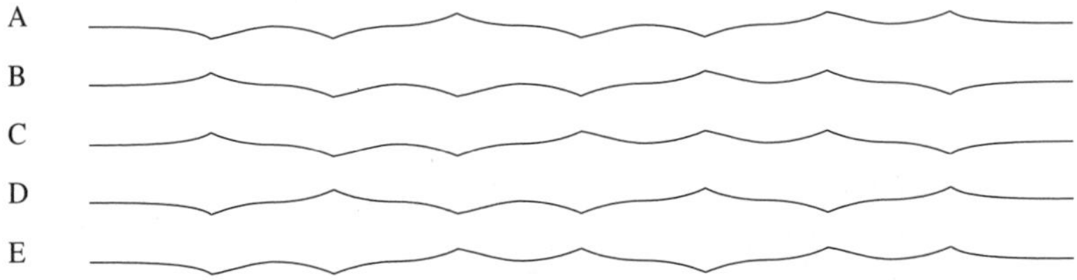

   A

   B

   C

   D

   E

5. Six points are marked on a sheet of squared paper as shown. Which of the following shapes **cannot** be made by connecting some of these points using straight lines?

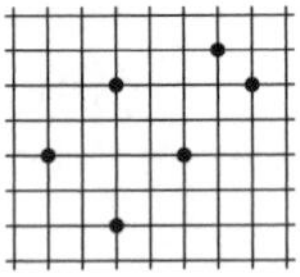

   A  parallelogram          B  trapezium     C  right-angled triangle
   D  obtuse-angled triangle     E  all the shapes A – D can be made

6. Brigitte plans to visit Verona. Starting and finishing at Verona train station, she wants to cross each of the five famous bridges across the river Adige at least once, without crossing any other bridge. Brigitte realises that there are only certain possibilities for the number of times she would cross the river. Which of the following is possible?

   A  4          B  5          C  6          D  7          E  9

7. The diagram shows a square $PQRS$ and two equilateral triangles $RSU$ and $PST$. $PQ$ has length 1. What is the length of $TU$?

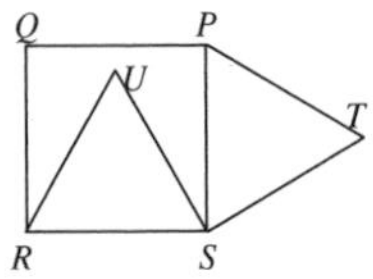

   A  $\sqrt{2}$     B  $\dfrac{\sqrt{3}}{2}$     C  $\sqrt{3}$     D  $\sqrt{5}-1$     E  $\sqrt{6}-1$

8. Today is my teacher's birthday. He says that the product of his age in years and his father's age in years is 2010. In which year was my teacher born?

   A  1943          B  1953          C  1980          D  1995          E  2005

9. In the diagram, angle $PQR$ is 20°, and the reflex angle at $P$ is 330°. The line segments $QT$ and $SU$ are perpendicular. What is the size of angle $RSP$?

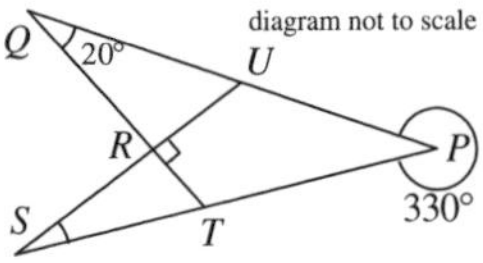

   A  10°     B  20°     C  30°     D  40°     E  50°

diagram not to scale

10. A positive integer is called 'jumpy' if the sum of its digits is 2010 and the product of its digits is 2. How many 'jumpy' integers are there?

    A 2010        B 2009        C 2008        D 1005        E 1004

11. Today's date is Thursday the 18th of March, which is an even day of the month. In a certain month, three Thursdays fell on even days. What day of the week was the 21st day of that month?

    A Monday      B Tuesday     C Wednesday   D Thursday    E Friday

12. A circle of radius 4 cm is divided into four congruent parts by arcs of radius 2 cm as shown. What is the length of the perimeter of one of the parts, in cm?

    A $2\pi$      B $4\pi$      C $6\pi$      D $8\pi$      E $12\pi$

13. The scatter graph shows the distance run and time taken by five students during a training session. Who ran with the fastest average speed?

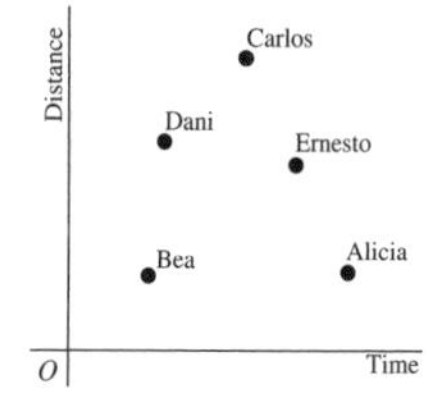

    A Alicia   B Bea   C Carlos   D Dani   E Ernesto

14. A triangular piece of paper is folded along the dotted line shown in the left-hand diagram to form the heptagon shown in the right-hand diagram. The total area of the shaded parts of the heptagon is 1 cm$^2$. The area of the original triangle is 1½ times the area of the heptagon. What is the area of the original triangle, in cm$^2$ ?

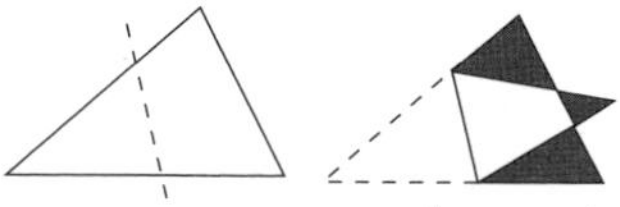

    diagram not to scale

    A 2        B 3        C 4        D 5        E more information needed

15. In a supermarket trolley park, there are two lines of tightly-packed trolleys. The first line has ten trolleys and is 2.9 m long. The second line has twenty trolleys and is 4.9 m long. What is the length of one trolley, in m?

    A 0.8      B 1        C 1.1      D 1.2      E 1.4

16. The diagram shows a large equilateral triangle divided into 36 small equilateral triangles, each with area 1 cm$^2$. What is the area of the shaded triangle, in cm$^2$ ?

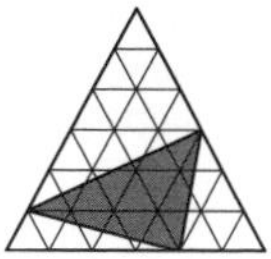

    A 11       B 12       C 13       D 14       E 15

17. The diagram shows a trapezium $FGHI$ with $FG$ parallel to $IH$. $GH$ and $FI$ both have length 2. The point $M$ is the midpoint of $FI$ and $\angle HMG = 90°$. What is the length of the perimeter of the trapezium?

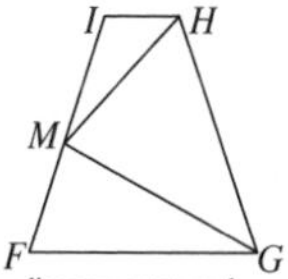

    A 5   B 6   C 7   D 8   E impossible to determine       diagram not to scale

18. How many integers $n$, between 1 and 100 inclusive, have the property that $n^n$ is a square number?

    A 99         B 55         C 50         D 10         E 5

60

19. The island of Nogardia is inhabited by dragons, each of which has either six, seven or eight legs. Dragons with seven legs always lie; dragons with an even number of legs always tell the truth. One day four dragons met.
The blue one said, "We have 28 legs altogether."
The green one said, "We have 27 legs altogether."
The yellow one said, "We have 26 legs altogether."
The red one said, "We have 25 legs altogether."
Which of the following statements is true?

A the red dragon definitely has 6 legs    B the red dragon definitely has 7 legs
C the red dragon definitely has 8 legs
D the red dragon has either 6 or 8 legs, but we can't be sure which
E the red dragon has 6, 7, or 8 legs, but we can't be sure which

20. The diagram shows a square with sides of length 2. Four semicircles are drawn whose centres are the four vertices of the square. These semicircles meet at the centre of the square, and adjacent semicircles meet at their ends. Four circles are drawn whose centres lie on the edges of the square and which each touch two semicircles. What is the total shaded area?

A $4\pi(3 - 2\sqrt{2})$    B $4\pi\sqrt{2}$    C $\frac{16}{9}\pi$    D $\pi$    E $\frac{4}{\sqrt{2}}\pi$

21. The first three terms of a sequence are 1, 2, 3. From the fourth term onwards, each term is calculated from the previous three terms using the rule "Add the first two and subtract the third." So the sequence begins 1, 2, 3, 0, 5, −2, 7, … . What is the 2010th term in the sequence?

A −2006    B −2004    C −2002    D −2000    E some other number

22. A single natural number is written on each edge of a pentagon so that adjacent numbers never have a common factor greater than 1 and non-adjacent numbers always have a common factor greater than 1. Which of the following could be one of the numbers?

A 1            B 8            C 9            D 10            E 11

23. How many 3-digit integers have the property that their middle digit is the mean of the other two digits?

A 9            B 12            C 16            D 25            E 45

24. An oval is constructed from four arcs of circles. Arc $PQ$ is the same as arc $RS$, and has radius 1 cm. Arc $QR$ is the same as arc $PS$. At the points $P$, $Q$, $R$, $S$ where the arcs touch, they have a common tangent. The oval touches the midpoints of the sides of a rectangle with dimensions 8 cm by 4 cm. What is the radius of the arc $PS$, in cm?

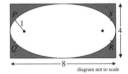
diagram not to scale

A 6            B 6.5            C 7            D 7.5            E 8

25. A bar code of the type shown is composed of alternate strips of black and white, always beginning and ending with a black strip. Each strip in the bar code has width either 1 or 2, and the total width of the bar code is 12. Two bar codes are different if they read differently from left to right. How many different bar codes of this type can be made?

A 24    B 132    C 66    D 116    E 144

# Solutions to the 2010 European Pink Kangaroo

1. **D**   $20102010 = 20100000 + 2010 = 2010 \times (10000 + 1) = 2010 \times 10001.$

2. **D**   Tibor scored 5% more than Ivan, which is one more mark. Since $100\% = 20 \times 5\%$, Alex scored 20 marks.

3. **C**   Each cube has six identical faces, so the area of each face is $24 \div 6 = 4$ cm$^2$. The cuboid has 16 such faces on its surface so has surface area $16 \times 4 = 64$ cm$^2$.

4. **D**   Imagine refolding these strips once, as is shown in the diagram on the left. The peaks on one side of the fold must match with hollows on the other side (which they all do!). We obtain the half-size strips shown in the diagram on the right. Now imagine refolding these strips about their mid-points. We can see that, in D, there are troughs on both sides, so D is not possible; but all the others are possible.

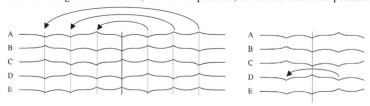

5. **E**   The shape $RSUV$ is a parallelogram; $RSTU$ is a trapezium; $RSU$ is a right-angled triangle; $RSV$ is an obtuse-angled triangle.
Therefore all the shapes can be made.

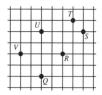

6. **C**   Brigitte must cross an even number of times so that she returns to the same side of the river as the train station. However, four crossings are not sufficient to cross all five bridges, so the only possibility from the options available is six crossings. Six crossings are possible because she can cross all five bridges, and then return over one of these to the station side.

7. **A**   The angles in equilateral triangles are all $60°$ so $\angle PSU = 90° - 60° = 30°$, $\angle TSU = 30° + 60° = 90°$ and $US = 1 = ST$. Using Pythagoras' theorem on the right-angled triangle $TSU$ we have $TU^2 = 1^2 + 1^2 = 2$ so $TU = \sqrt{2}$.

8. **C**   The prime factor decomposition of 2010 is $2 \times 3 \times 5 \times 67$ so the product pairs that make 2010 are $1 \times 2010, 2 \times 1005, 3 \times 670, 5 \times 402, 6 \times 335, 10 \times 201, 15 \times 134, 30 \times 67$. The only realistic ages for my teacher and his father would be 30 and 67, so my teacher was born 30 years ago, in 1980.

9. **D**   Angle $UPT$ is $360° - 330° = 30°$ and the reflex angle $QRS$ is $270°$. Since the angles in the quadrilateral $PQRS$ add to $360°$, we have
$\angle RSP = 360° - (270° + 30° + 20°) = 40°$.

10. **B**   Since the product of the digits is 2, there must be a digit 2 somewhere in a 'jumpy' integer, and all the other digits are 1. The digits add to 2010 so there must be exactly 2008 digits that are 1. The digit 2 can be placed before all the ones, after all the ones, or in any of the 2007 places between two ones. Hence there are 2009 'jumpy' integers.

62

**11. B** Successive Thursdays are seven days apart, so 'even' Thursdays must be 14 days apart. For there to be three even Thursdays, they must fall on the 2nd, 16th, and 30th days of the month. Hence the 21st day would be five days after a Thursday, which is a Tuesday.

**12. C** Each of the four congruent parts has three arcs on its perimeter: Two semicircles of radius 2 cm (which have total length $2 \times \pi \times 2 = 4\pi$ cm) and a quarter-arc of radius 4 cm (length $\frac{1}{4} \times 2 \times \pi \times 4 = 2\pi$ cm). Therefore the perimeter has length $6\pi$ cm.

**13. D** For each runner, the gradient of the line joining the origin to his or her plotted point is equal to the total distance divided by the time taken, which is also his or her average speed. Hence the fastest runner has the steepest line, so it is Dani.

**14. B** Let $U$ be the unshaded area of the heptagon. Then the area of the triangle is $2U + 1$, as shown in the diagram. This is $1\frac{1}{2}$ times the area of the heptagon, which is $U + 1$, so we can form the equation $2U + 1 = \frac{3}{2}(U + 1)$. So $4U + 2 = 3U + 3$, hence $U = 1$ and the area of the triangle is $2 \times 1 + 1 = 3$.

**15. C** There are 10 more trolleys in the second line, which adds 2 m to the length, so each trolley adds 0.2 m. If we subtract nine of these extra lengths from the first line, we will be left with the length of one trolley, namely 2.9 m $- 9 \times 0.2$ m $= 1.1$ m.

**16. A** For each of the parallelograms $ABCO$, $CDEO$, $EFAO$ in the diagram, half of its area is from the shaded triangle. Hence the triangle is half of the hexagon formed by the three parallelograms. Since the hexagon is made of 22 triangles, the shaded triangle must have area 11 cm².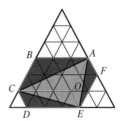

**17. B** In the diagram, $GF$ and $HM$ are extended to meet at $J$. Since $M$ is the midpoint of $IF$, we have $IM = MF$. Also $\angle HMI = \angle FMJ$ (vertically opposite) and $\angle HIM = \angle JFM$ (alternate angles because $IH$ and $JF$ are parallel). Therefore triangles $HMI$ and $FMJ$ are congruent by ASA and in particular $JF = IH$ and also $HM = MJ$.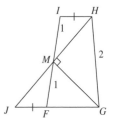

Also triangles $GMJ$ and $GMH$ are congruent by SAS since they share the side $GM$, $HM = MJ$, and $\angle GMJ = \angle GMH (= 90°)$. In particular we have $HG = GJ$ so $GJ = 2$. But $GJ = GF + FJ = GF + IH$ so $GF + IH = 2$. The perimeter of the trapezium is therefore $GH + IM + MF + GF + IH = 2 + 1 + 1 + 2 = 6$.

**18. B** If $n$ is even, say $n = 2m$, then $n^n = n^{2m} = (n^m)^2$ so $n^n$ is a square. There are 50 such $n$. If $n$ is odd, then $n^n$ cannot be an even power unless $n$ itself is an even power, that is $n$ must be a square. There are five odd squares between 1 and 100 (1, 9, 25, 49, 81). The total number of possibilities for $n$ is $50 + 5 = 55$.

**19. B** At most one of the statements given by the dragons can be true, so there are at least three liars among them. Since liars have seven legs, these three liars have 21 legs between them. If the fourth dragon is also a liar, they will have 28 legs altogether, meaning that the blue dragon is truthful, causing a contradiction. So the fourth dragon tells the truth, and must have 6 or 8 legs, giving a total number of 27 or 29 legs. The only dragon who could be truthful is the green one who says there are 27 legs. Hence the red dragon is a liar and definitely has 7 legs.

**20. A** The diagram shows one of the four shaded circles. The point $A$ is a vertex of the original square and $O$ is its centre. So $AY = YO = 1$, and $AX = AO = \sqrt{2}$ by Pythagoras. Also $XY = AX - AY = \sqrt{2} - 1$. So each shaded circle has radius $\sqrt{2} - 1$. Hence the area of the four shaded circles is $4 \times \pi(\sqrt{2} - 1)^2 = 4\pi(2 - 2\sqrt{2} + 1) = 4\pi(3 - 2\sqrt{2})$.

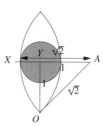

**21. A** The sequence continues $1, 2, 3, 0, 5, -2, 7, -4, 9, -6, 11$, and it can be seen that the terms with even positions are decreasing by 2 (starting with 2). The 2010th term is the 1005th even positioned term, so appears after 1004 decreases. Hence it is $2 - 2 \times 1004 = -2006$.

*Alternative*: We can show this more clearly by considering the terms in pairs. The $n$ th pair has terms $2n - 1$ and $4 - 2n$; this is certainly true for the first two pairs: $2 \times 1 - 1 = 1$ and $4 - 2 \times 1 = 2$ giving the first pair of terms $1, 2$, and $2 \times 2 - 1 = 3$ and $4 - 2 \times 2 = 0$, giving the second pair $3, 0$. Hence the $n$ th pair and $(n + 1)$ th pair will be $2n - 1, 4 - 2n, 2(n + 1) - 1, 4 - 2(n + 1)$ which simplify to $2n - 1, 4 - 2n, 2n + 1, 2 - 2n$. The rule for finding subsequent terms gives the next pair as $(4 - 2n) + (2n + 1) - (2 - 2n) = 2n + 3 = 2(n + 2) - 1$ and $(2n + 1) + (2 - 2n) - (2n + 3) = 4 - 2(n + 2)$. These have the same form as $2n - 1$ and $4n - 2$ but with $n$ replaced by $n + 2$. Hence the pattern will continue. The 2010th term is in the 1005th pair, so is $4 - 2 \times 1005 = -2006$.

**22. D** Let the five numbers be $R, S, T, U, V$ as shown. Then $R$ and $T$ share a common factor greater than 1; so they must also share a common prime factor $p$, say. Similarly $T$ and $V$ share a common prime factor $q$, say. But $R$ and $V$ are adjacent so do not share a factor other than 1, meaning that $p, q$ are distinct primes. Therefore $T$ has two distinct prime factors, $p$ and $q$. This is true for all the edge numbers, but the only option that has two distinct prime factors is

$10 = 2 \times 5$. One can check that the five numbers $10, 21, 22, 35, 33$ in order, are as required; so 10 is indeed possible.

**23. E** Let $A$ be the first digit and $B$ the last, then the middle digit is $\frac{1}{2}(A + B)$ which must be a whole number so $A + B$ is even. There are five odd possibilities for $A$ (1, 3, 5, 7, 9), each of which has five possible pairings for $B$ (1, 3, 5, 7, 9), giving 25 possible numbers. There are four even possibilities for $A$ (2, 4, 6, 8), each of which has five possible pairings for $B$ (0, 2, 4, 6, 8), giving 20 possible numbers. Altogether this is 45 possible numbers.

**24. A**    Let $C$ be the centre of the arc $PS$ with radius $r$, and let $T$ be the centre of the arc $PQ$. The tangent at $P$ is common to both arcs so the perpendicular at $P$ to this tangent passes through both centres $T$ and $C$. Let $M$ be the midpoint of the top of the rectangle. The rectangle is tangent to arc $PS$ so the perpendicular from $M$ also passes through $C$.

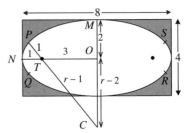

Let $O$ be the centre of the rectangle and $N$ the midpoint of the left-hand side. Then $TN = 1$ so $OT = 3$. Also, triangle $TCO$ is right-angled at $O$ with $OT = 3$, $OC = r - 2$ and $CT = r - 1$ so by Pythagoras' Theorem, $(r - 2)^2 + 3^2 = (r - 1)^2$. This gives $r^2 - 4r + 4 + 9 = r^2 - 2r + 1$ so $-4r + 13 = -2r + 1$, leading to $2r = 12, r = 6$.

**25. D**    The bar code consists of strips of length one and two, which we can call one-strips and two-strips respectively. Let $a$ be the number of two-strips and $b$ be the number of one-strips. The total length is 12 so $2a + b = 12$. Also, the first and last strips must be black so there is an odd number of alternating strips, meaning $a + b$ is odd.

We know that $a + b$ is odd and $2a + b = 12$ which is even. Therefore $a = (2a + b) - (a + b)$ is odd. Also $a$ is less than 6 since $2a + b = 12$. This gives us three cases:

(i) If $a = 5$, $b = 12 - 10 = 2$.

There are 7 strips altogether. If the first one-strip is the first strip of the bar code then there are 6 options for the position of the second one-strip.

If the first one-strip is the second strip then there are 5 options for the position of the second one-strip, etc. This gives the number of options as $6 + 5 + 4 + 3 + 2 + 1 = 21$.

(ii) If $a = 3$, $b = 12 - 6 = 6$.

If the first two-strip is the first strip, then there are 8 places where the second two-strip can appear, which would leave 7, 6, 5, 4, 3, 2, 1 places for the third two-strip respectively, totalling 28 options.

If the first two-strip is the second strip, then there are 7 places for the second two-strip and 6, 5, 4, 3, 2, 1 places for the third two-strip. Continuing in this way, we see that the total number of options is $28 + 21 + 15 + 10 + 6 + 3 + 1 = 84$.

(iii) If $a = 1$, then $b = 12 - 2 = 10$.

There are 11 strips so the two-strip can appear in 11 places.

In total the number of options is $21 + 84 + 11 = 116$.

*Alternatively*: the number of ways of choosing the position of 5 two-strips out of 7 is $^7C_2 = 21$ and the number of ways of choosing 3 two-strips out of 9 is $^9C_3 = 84$.

# (b) *The IMOK Olympiad*

 The United Kingdom Mathematics Trust

UKMT            UKMT

## Intermediate Mathematical Olympiad and Kangaroo (IMOK)

## Olympiad Cayley/Hamilton/Maclaurin Papers

Thursday 18th March 2010

### READ THESE INSTRUCTIONS CAREFULLY BEFORE STARTING

1.  Time allowed: 2 hours.

2.  **The use of calculators, protractors and squared paper is forbidden.**
    Rulers and compasses may be used.

3.  Solutions must be written neatly on A4 paper. Sheets must be STAPLED together in the top left corner with the Cover Sheet on top.

4.  Start each question on a fresh A4 sheet.
    You may wish to work in rough first, then set out your final solution with clear explanations and proofs.
    *Do not hand in rough work.*

5.  Answers must be FULLY SIMPLIFIED, and EXACT using symbols like $\pi$, fractions, or square roots if appropriate, but NOT decimal approximations.

6.  Give full written solutions, including mathematical reasons as to why your method is correct.
    Just stating an answer, even a correct one, will earn you very few marks; also, incomplete or poorly presented solutions will not receive full marks.

7.  **These problems are meant to be challenging!** The earlier questions tend to be easier; the last two questions are the most demanding.
    Do not hurry, but spend time working carefully on one question before attempting another. Try to finish whole questions even if you cannot do many: you will have done well if you hand in full solutions to two or more questions.

### DO NOT OPEN THE PAPER UNTIL INSTRUCTED BY THE INVIGILATOR TO DO SO!

The United Kingdom Mathematics Trust is a Registered Charity.

*Enquiries should be sent to: Maths Challenges Office,*

*School of Mathematics, University of Leeds, Leeds, LS2 9JT.*

*(Tel. 0113 343 2339)*

*http://www.ukmt.org.uk*

# 2010 Olympiad Cayley Paper

---

**All candidates must be in *School Year 9 or below* (England and Wales), *S2 or below* (Scotland), or *School Year 10 or below* (Northern Ireland).**

---

1. The sum of three positive integers is 11 and the sum of the cubes of these numbers is 251.

   Find all such triples of numbers.

2. The diagram shows a square $ABCD$ and an equilateral triangle $ABE$. The point $F$ lies on $BC$ so that $EC = EF$.

   Calculate the angle $BEF$.

   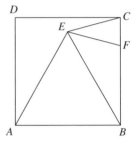

3. Find all possible solutions to the 'word sum' on the right.

   Each letter stands for one of the digits 0–9 and has the same meaning each time it occurs. Different letters stand for different digits. No number starts with a zero.

   $$\begin{array}{r} \text{O D D} \\ + \text{O D D} \\ \hline \text{E V E N} \end{array}$$

4. Walking at constant speeds, Eoin and his sister Angharad take 40 minutes and 60 minutes respectively to walk to the nearest town.

   Yesterday, Eoin left home 12 minutes after Angharad. How long was it before he caught up with her?

5. A square sheet of paper $ABCD$ is folded along $FG$, as shown, so that the corner $B$ is folded onto the midpoint $M$ of $CD$.

   Prove that the sides of triangle $GCM$ have lengths in the ratio $3 : 4 : 5$.

   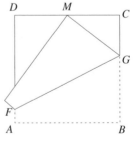

6. A 'qprime' number is a positive integer which is the product of exactly two different primes, that is, one of the form $q \times p$, where $q$ and $p$ are prime and $q \neq p$.

   What is the length of the longest possible sequence of *consecutive* integers all of which are qprime numbers?

# 2010 Olympiad Hamilton Paper

**All candidates must be in *School Year 10* (England and Wales), *S3* (Scotland), or *School Year 11* (Northern Ireland).**

1. The sum of three positive integers is 11 and the sum of the cubes of these numbers is 251.

   Find all such triples of numbers.

2. The diagram shows a triangle and two of its angle bisectors.
   What is the value of $x$?

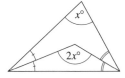

3. The first and second terms of a sequence are added to make the third term. Adjacent odd-numbered terms are added to make the next even-numbered term, for example,

   $$\text{first term} + \text{third term} = \text{fourth term}$$

   and    $$\text{third term} + \text{fifth term} = \text{sixth term}.$$

   Likewise, adjacent even-numbered terms are added to make the next odd-numbered term, for example,

   $$\text{second term} + \text{fourth term} = \text{fifth term}.$$

   Given that the seventh term equals the eighth term, what is the value of the sixth term?

4. The diagram shows a quarter-circle with centre $O$ and two semicircular arcs with diameters $OA$ and $OB$.

   Calculate the ratio of the area of the region shaded grey to the area of the region shaded black.

5. The diagram shows three touching circles, whose radii are $a$, $b$ and $c$, and whose centres are at the vertices $Q$, $R$ and $S$ of a rectangle $QRST$. The fourth vertex $T$ of the rectangle lies on the circle with centre $S$.
   Find the ratio $a : b : c$.

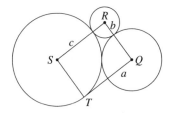

6. In the diagram, the number in each cell shows the number of shaded cells with which it shares an edge or a corner. The total of all the numbers for this shading pattern is 16. Any shading pattern obtained by rotating or reflecting this one also has a total of 16.

   Prove that there are exactly two shading patterns (not counting rotations or reflections) which have a total of 17.

| 2 | 1 | 2 |
|---|---|---|
| 3 | 2 | 2 |
| 1 | 2 | 1 |

68

# 2010 Olympiad Maclaurin Paper

**All candidates must be in *School Year 11* (England and Wales), *S4* (Scotland), or *School Year 12* (Northern Ireland).**

1. How many different ways are there to express $\frac{2}{15}$ in the form $\frac{1}{a} + \frac{1}{b}$, where $a$ and $b$ are positive integers with $a \leqslant b$?

2. The diagram shows a regular heptagon, a regular decagon and a regular 15-gon with an edge in common.

   Find the size of angle $XYZ$.

   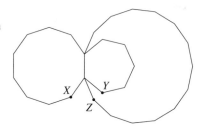

3. Solve the equations

   $$x + xy + x^2 = 9$$

   $$y + xy + y^2 = -3.$$

4. The diameter $AD$ of a circle has length 4. The points $B$ and $C$ lie on the circle, as shown, so that $AB = BC = 1$.

   Find the length of $CD$.

   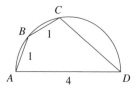

5. The diagram shows a rectangle divided into eight regions by four straight lines. Three of the regions have areas 1, 2 and 3, as shown.

   What is the area of the shaded quadrilateral?

   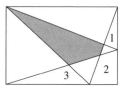

6. Every day for the next eleven days I shall eat exactly one sandwich for lunch, either a ham sandwich or a cheese sandwich. However, during that period I shall never eat a ham sandwich on two consecutive days.

   In how many ways can I plan my sandwiches for the next eleven days?

# Solutions to the 2009 Olympiad Cayley Paper

1  The sum of three positive integers is 11 and the sum of the cubes of these numbers is 251.
Find all such triples of numbers.

*Solution*

Let us calculate the first few cubes in order to see what the possibilities are:

$$1^3 = 1, \quad 2^3 = 8, \quad 3^3 = 27, \quad 4^3 = 64, \quad 5^3 = 125, \quad 6^3 = 216 \text{ and } 7^3 = 343. \quad (*)$$

The sum of the cubes of the positive integers is 251, which is less than 343, hence none of the integers is greater than 6.

Now $\frac{251}{3} = 83\frac{2}{3} > 64 = 4^3$, therefore at least one of the integers is 5 or more.

If one of the integers is 6, then the other two cubes add up to $251 - 6^3 = 251 - 216 = 35$. From (*) above, $3^3 + 2^3 = 27 + 8 = 35$ is the only possibility. Also, $6 + 3 + 2 = 11$ so that 6, 3 and 2 is a possible triple of numbers.

If one of the integers is 5, then the other two cubes add up to $251 - 5^3 = 251 - 125 = 126$. From (*) above $5^3 + 1^3 = 125 + 1 = 126$ is the only possibility. Also, $5 + 5 + 1 = 11$ so that 5, 5 and 1 is a possible triple of numbers.

Hence 2, 3, 6 and 1, 5, 5 are the triples of numbers satisfying the given conditions.

2  The diagram shows a square *ABCD* and an equilateral triangle *ABE*. The point *F* lies on *BC* so that $EC = EF$.
Calculate the angle *BEF*.

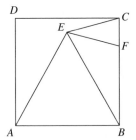

*Solution*

The diagram seems to include several isosceles triangles, and we solve the problem by proving this is the case. For example, since the square *ABCD* and the equilateral triangle *ABE* share the side *AB*, all their sides are the same length. That means the triangle *BCE* is isosceles.

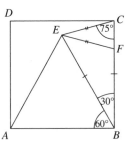

Now, angle *EBC* is $90° - 60° = 30°$ (since it is the difference between the interior angle of a square and the interior angle of an equilateral triangle). Hence angles *BCE* and *CEB* are each $\frac{1}{2}(180° - 30°) = 75°$, because they are the base angles of an isosceles triangle.

We are also given that triangle *CEF* is isosceles. Since we have worked out that angle *FCE* $= 75°$, we deduce that angle *CEF* $= 180° - (2 \times 75°) = 30°$.

Finally, we find that angle *BEF* $= \angle CEB - \angle CEF = 75° - 30° = 45°$.

3  Find all possible solutions to the 'word sum' on the right.
Each letter stands for one of the digits 0–9 and has the same
meaning each time it occurs. Different letters stand for different
digits. No number starts with a zero.

```
    O D D
  + O D D
  E V E N
```

*Solution*

Firstly, it is clear that the three-digit number 'ODD' lies between 100 and 999.
Therefore, since 'EVEN' = 2 × 'ODD', we have

$$200 < \text{'EVEN'} < 1998.$$

Hence the first digit E of 'EVEN' is 1 since it is a four-digit number.

We are left with the following problem:

```
    O D D
  + O D D
  1 V 1 N
```

Now the same numbers are added in the tens and units columns, but N ≠ 1, otherwise N
and E would be equal. The only way for different totals to occur in these columns is for
there to be a 'carry' to the tens column, and the greatest possible carry is 1, so that N = 0.

There are two possible digits D that give N = 0, namely 0 and 5. But 0 is already taken
as the value of N, so that D = 5. The problem is thus:

```
    O 5 5
  + O 5 5
  1 V 1 0
```

Now, the digit O has to be big enough to produce a carry, but cannot be 5, which is
already taken as the value of D. So the possibilities are

```
    6 5 5        7 5 5        8 5 5        9 5 5
  + 6 5 5      + 7 5 5      + 8 5 5      + 9 5 5
  1 3 1 0      1 5 1 0      1 7 1 0      1 9 1 0
```

but the second and fourth of these are not allowed since V repeats a digit used for
another letter. We are left with the two possibilities

```
    6 5 5        8 5 5
  + 6 5 5      + 8 5 5
  1 3 1 0      1 7 1 0
```

and it is clear that both of these work.

4  Walking at constant speeds, Eoin and his sister Angharad take 40 minutes and
60 minutes respectively to walk to the nearest town.
Yesterday, Eoin left home 12 minutes after Angharad. How long was it before he caught
up with her?

*Solution*

Let the distance from home to town be $D$ km. Now in every minute Eoin travels one-
fortieth of the way to town: that is, a distance of $\dfrac{D}{40}$ km. So after $t$ minutes, he has
travelled a distance

$$\frac{tD}{40} \text{ km}.$$

Similarly, in every minute Angharad travels one-sixtieth of the way to town: that is, a distance of $\frac{D}{60}$ km. But she has had 12 minutes extra walking time. So after Eoin has been walking for $t$ minutes, she has been walking for $t + 12$ minutes and so has travelled a distance

$$\frac{(t + 12)D}{60} \text{ km}.$$

We are asked how long Eoin has been walking when they meet. They meet when they have travelled equal distances, which is when

$$\frac{tD}{40} = \frac{(t + 12)D}{60}.$$

We cancel the $D$ from each side and multiply both sides by 120 to obtain

$$120 \times \frac{t}{40} = 120 \times \frac{t + 12}{60}.$$

Simplifying, we get

$$3t = 2(t + 12),$$

which we solve to give $t = 24$.

Thus Eoin catches up with Angharad after he has walked for 24 minutes.

5  A square sheet of paper $ABCD$ is folded along $FG$, as shown, so that the corner $B$ is folded onto the midpoint $M$ of $CD$.

Prove that the sides of triangle $GCM$ have lengths in the ratio $3 : 4 : 5$.

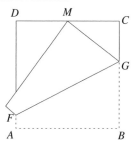

*Solution*

This problem does not give us units, and so we choose them so that the side length of the square is $2s$. Since $M$ is the midpoint of $CD$, we have $CM = s$. Then we define $x = CG$. Since $BC = 2s$, $GB = 2s - x$. But, as $GM$ is the image of $GB$ after folding, $GM = 2s - x$ too.

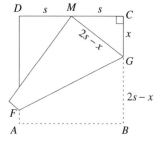

Now Pythagoras' theorem for triangle $MCG$ gives us

$$s^2 + x^2 = (2s - x)^2.$$

We multiply out to get

$$s^2 + x^2 = 4s^2 - 4sx + x^2.$$

Eliminating the $x^2$ terms and dividing by $s$ (which is not zero), we obtain

$$s = 4s - 4x,$$

which has the solution $x = \frac{3}{4}s$.

Thus the triangle $GCM$ has sides of length $x = \frac{3}{4}s$, $s$ and $2s - x = \frac{5}{4}s$. Multiplying all the sides by 4, we get $3s$, $4s$ and $5s$, so the side lengths are in the ratio $3 : 4 : 5$, as required.

6 A 'qprime' number is a positive integer which is the product of exactly two different primes, that is, one of the form $q \times p$, where $q$ and $p$ are prime and $q \neq p$.

What is the length of the longest possible sequence of *consecutive* integers all of which are qprime numbers?

*Solution*

To help to understand this problem, it is natural to test the first few numbers to see which small numbers are qprime, and which are not:

1 is not a qprime since it has no prime factors.

2 and 3 are not qprimes since they are prime.

4 is not qprime since it is $2 \times 2$.

5 is not qprime, since it is prime.

$6 = 2 \times 3$ is the first qprime number.

7 is not qprime.

8 is not qprime, since it is $2 \times 2 \times 2$.

9 is not, since it is $3 \times 3$.

$10 = 2 \times 5$ is another qprime.

11 is not.

12 is not, since it is $2 \times 2 \times 3$.

Of course, we cannot prove a general result just by continuing the list, but it can guide us to a proof, such as the one that follows.

We note that no multiple of 4 is ever qprime, since a multiple of 4 is a multiple of $2 \times 2$. This means that a string of consecutive qprime numbers can be of length at most three, because any sequence of four or more consecutive integers includes a multiple of 4.

We are therefore led to ask whether any strings of three consecutive qprime numbers exist. We have looked as far as 12 and not found any, but we will continue searching, using the fact that none of the numbers is a multiple of 4:

For $(13, 14, 15)$, the number 13 is prime and so not qprime.

For $(17, 18, 19)$, 17 is not qprime (nor are the others).

For $(21, 22, 23)$, 23 is not qprime.

For $(25, 26, 27)$, 25 is not qprime (nor is 27).

For $(29, 30, 31)$, 29 is not qprime (nor are the others).

For $(33, 34, 35)$, all three are qprime (being $3 \times 11$, $2 \times 17$ and $5 \times 7$).

So we have found a sequence of three consecutive qprimes, and have also proved that no sequence of four (or more) consecutive qprimes exists.

Thus the longest possible sequence of consecutive integers all of which are qprime numbers has length 3.

# Solutions to the 2010 Olympiad Hamilton Paper

1  The sum of three positive integers is 11 and the sum of the cubes of these numbers is 251.

   Find all such triples of numbers.

   *Solution*
   Let us calculate the first few cubes in order to see what the possibilities are:

   $$1^3 = 1, \quad 2^3 = 8, \quad 3^3 = 27, \quad 4^3 = 64, \quad 5^3 = 125, \quad 6^3 = 216 \text{ and } 7^3 = 343. \quad (*)$$

   The sum of the cubes of the positive integers is 251, which is less than 343, hence none of the integers is greater than 6.

   Now $\frac{251}{3} = 83\frac{2}{3} > 64 = 4^3$, therefore at least one of the integers is 5 or more.

   If one of the integers is 6, then the other two cubes add up to $251 - 6^3 = 251 - 216 = 35$. From (*) above, $3^3 + 2^3 = 27 + 8 = 35$ is the only possibility. Also, $6 + 3 + 2 = 11$ so that 6, 3 and 2 is a possible triple of numbers.

   If one of the integers is 5, then the other two cubes add up to $251 - 5^3 = 251 - 125 = 126$. From (*) above $5^3 + 1^3 = 125 + 1 = 126$ is the only possibility. Also, $5 + 5 + 1 = 11$ so that 5, 5 and 1 is a possible triple of numbers.

   Hence 2, 3, 6 and 1, 5, 5 are the triples of numbers satisfying the given conditions.

2  The diagram shows a triangle and two of its angle bisectors.
   What is the value of $x$?

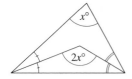

   *Solution*
   Let the sum of the two unlabelled angles in the smaller triangle be $y$. Then the sum of the two unlabelled angles in the whole triangle is equal to $2y$.

   The sum of the angles in a triangle is $180°$, hence in the small triangle

   $$2x + y = 180 \qquad (2.1)$$

   and in the whole triangle

   $$x + 2y = 180. \qquad (2.2)$$

   Doubling equation (2.1) and subtracting equation (2.2), we get $3x = 180$ and thus $x = 60$.

3  The first and second terms of a sequence are added to make the third term. Adjacent odd-numbered terms are added to make the next even-numbered term, for example,

first term + third term = fourth term

and    third term + fifth term = sixth term.

Likewise, adjacent even-numbered terms are added to make the next odd-numbered term, for example,

second term + fourth term = fifth term.

Given that the seventh term equals the eighth term, what is the value of the sixth term?

*Solution*

Let $a$ be the first term of the sequence and $b$ the second term. Thus the first eight terms of the sequence are:

$$a, b, a + b, 2a + b, 2a + 2b, 3a + 3b, 5a + 4b, 7a + 6b.$$

The seventh term equals the eighth term, hence $5a + 4b = 7a + 6b$. Therefore $2a + 2b = 0$ and so $a = -b$.

Hence the value of the sixth term is $3a + 3b = -3b + 3b = 0$.

4  The diagram shows a quarter-circle with centre $O$ and two semicircular arcs with diameters $OA$ and $OB$.

Calculate the ratio of the area of the region shaded grey to the area of the region shaded black.

*Solution*

Let $2r$ be the radius of the quarter-circle. Hence the radius of each semicircle is $r$. The diagram is divided into four regions; let their areas be $X$, $Y$, $Z$ and $T$, as shown below.

The area of the quarter-circle is $\frac{1}{4}\pi (2r)^2 = \pi r^2$. The area of each semicircle is $\frac{1}{2}\pi r^2$. Hence $X + Z = \frac{1}{2}\pi r^2$.

However, the area inside the quarter-circle but outside one semicircle is $\pi r^2 - \frac{1}{2}\pi r^2 = \frac{1}{2}\pi r^2$. This means that $X + T = \frac{1}{2}\pi r^2$.

Therefore $X + T = X + Z$. We conclude that $T = Z$, so that the areas of the shaded regions are equal.

Thus the ratio of the area of the region shaded grey to the area of the region shaded black is $1 : 1$.

5  The diagram shows three touching circles, whose radii are $a$, $b$ and $c$, and whose centres are at the vertices $Q$, $R$ and $S$ of a rectangle $QRST$. The fourth vertex $T$ of the rectangle lies on the circle with centre $S$.

Find the ratio $a : b : c$.

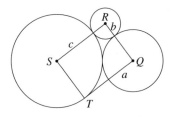

*Solution*

In the rectangle $QRST$, we have $QR = TS$ and hence

$$a + b = c. \tag{5.1}$$

In the right-angled triangle $QRS$, by Pythagoras' Theorem, $QS^2 = QR^2 + RS^2$. But $QS = a + c$, $QR = a + b$ and $RS = b + c$, therefore

$$(a + c)^2 = (a + b)^2 + (b + c)^2. \tag{5.2}$$

Substituting for $a$ from equation (5.1) into equation (5.2), we get

$$(2c - b)^2 = c^2 + (b + c)^2.$$

Thus

$$4c^2 - 4bc + b^2 = c^2 + b^2 + 2bc + c^2,$$

so that

$$2c^2 - 6bc = 0$$

and hence

$$c(c - 3b) = 0.$$

But $c \neq 0$, hence $c = 3b$. Again from equation (5.1), $a + b = 3b$ and thus $a = 2b$.

Therefore the ratio $a : b : c = 2 : 1 : 3$.

6  In the diagram, the number in each cell shows the number of shaded cells with which it shares an edge or a corner. The total of all the numbers for this shading pattern is 16. Any shading pattern obtained by rotating or reflecting this one also has a total of 16.

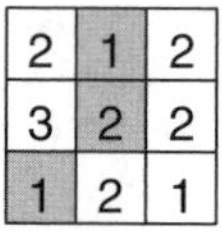

| 2 | 1 | 2 |
|---|---|---|
| 3 | 2 | 2 |
| 1 | 2 | 1 |

Prove that there are exactly two shading patterns (not counting rotations or reflections) which have a total of 17.

*Solution*

Whenever a cell is shaded, one is added to all the cells with which it shares an edge or corner. So consider an alternative numbering system: in each shaded cell write the number of cells with which it shares an edge or corner; leave each unshaded cell blank. For example, for the shading pattern given in the question we obtain:

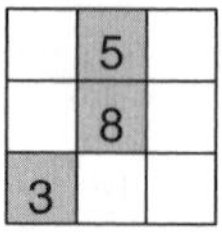

|   | 5 |   |
|---|---|---|
|   | 8 |   |
| 3 |   |   |

This is equivalent to the original numbering system; in particular, the total of all the numbers is the same.

Now a shaded corner cell has 3 adjacent cells; a shaded edge cell has 5 adjacent cells; the shaded central cell has 8 adjacent cells. Thus the total of all the numbers for a shading pattern is made up solely by adding multiples of 3, 5 and 8.

For a 3 × 3 diagram the available numbers are therefore: four 3s, four 5s and one 8.

If the 8 is used, a remaining total of $17 - 8 = 9$ is required. The only way to attain 9 is to use three 3s.

If the 8 is not used, since 17 is not a multiple of 3 at least one 5 is needed. Now $17 - 1 \times 5 = 12$, $17 - 2 \times 5 = 7$ and $17 - 3 \times 5 = 2$, but neither 7 nor 2 is a multiple of 3. So the only possibility is to use one 5 and then a remaining total of 12 is required. The only way to attain 12 is to use four 3s.

Thus the only possibilities are: 3, 3, 3, 3, 5 and 3, 3, 3, 8. Both of these are possible using the available numbers. What are the corresponding shading patterns?

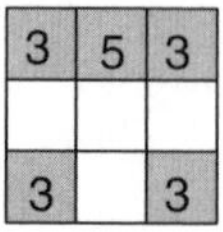

| 3 | 5 | 3 |
|---|---|---|
|   |   |   |
| 3 |   | 3 |

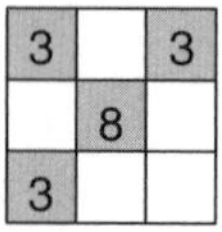

| 3 |   | 3 |
|---|---|---|
|   | 8 |   |
| 3 |   |   |

The diagrams above give examples of the only possible shading pattern for each set of numbers—all others are rotations of one of these. In the first case, the four corners are shaded to obtain four 3s, then there is only one way, up to rotation, to shade an edge cell to obtain the 5. In the second case, the centre is shaded to obtain the 8, then there is only one way, up to rotation, to shade three corner cells to obtain three 3s.

Therefore there are exactly two shading patterns with a total of 17.

# Solutions to the 2010 Olympiad Maclaurin Paper

1 How many different ways are there to express $\frac{2}{15}$ in the form $\frac{1}{a} + \frac{1}{b}$, where $a$ and $b$ are positive integers with $a \leqslant b$?

*Solution*

There are infinitely many integers and hence the number of potential values of $a$ and $b$ is infinite, so any satisfactory method first needs to reduce the problem to a finite number of cases. We demonstrate two methods of doing this.

*Method 1*

Since $0 < a \leqslant b$ we have $\frac{1}{b} \leqslant \frac{1}{a}$ and therefore $\frac{2}{15} = \frac{1}{a} + \frac{1}{b} \leqslant \frac{2}{a}$. Hence $a \leqslant 15$.

Also, since $b > 0$, we have $\frac{1}{b} > 0$ and so $\frac{2}{15} = \frac{1}{a} + \frac{1}{b} > \frac{1}{a}$. Hence $a > \frac{15}{2}$.

Therefore $8 \leqslant a \leqslant 15$ and the possible values of $a$ are 8, 9, ..., 15. In order to see which of these correspond to integer values of $b$, it is helpful to find $b$ in terms of $a$:

$$\frac{1}{b} = \frac{2}{15} - \frac{1}{a}$$
$$= \frac{2a - 15}{15a}$$

and so

$$b = \frac{15a}{2a - 15}.$$

We now see that we require $2a - 15$ to be a positive divisor of $15a$. So we can determine which values of $a$ will give integer values of $b$ from the table:

| $a$ | $2a - 15$ | $15a$ | Divisor? | $b$ |
|-----|-----------|-------|----------|-----|
| 8 | 1 | $15 \times 8$ | yes | 120 |
| 9 | 3 | $15 \times 9$ | yes | 45 |
| 10 | 5 | $15 \times 10$ | yes | 30 |
| 11 | 7 | $15 \times 11$ | no | – |
| 12 | 9 | $15 \times 12$ | yes | 20 |
| 13 | 11 | $15 \times 13$ | no | – |
| 14 | 13 | $15 \times 14$ | no | – |
| 15 | 15 | $15 \times 15$ | yes | 15 |

Hence there are five ways to express $\frac{2}{15}$ in the required form.

*Method 2*

We may multiply every term in the equation $\frac{2}{15} = \frac{1}{a} + \frac{1}{b}$ by $15ab$ in order to clear the fractions. We obtain $2ab = 15b + 15a$. We now rearrange this equation, first writing it in the form

$$4ab - 30a - 30b = 0,$$

then adding 225 to both sides to give

$$4ab - 30a - 30b + 225 = 225,$$

that is,

$$(2a - 15)(2b - 15) = 225.$$

Therefore $2a - 15$ is a divisor of $225 = 3^2 \times 5^2$, so that $2a - 15 = 1, 3, 5, 9, 15$. Larger values are not possible since $a \leqslant b$ and so $2a - 15 \leqslant 2b - 15$. Also, negative values are not possible since then $2a - 15$ would be at most $-15$, but $a > 0$ so that $2a - 15 > -15$.

Each of the corresponding values of $a$ and $b$ is an integer:
$$(a, b) = (8, \ 120), (9, \ 45), (10, \ 30), (12, \ 20) \text{ or } (15, \ 15).$$
Hence there are five ways to express $\frac{2}{15}$ in the required form.

2  The diagram shows a regular heptagon, a regular decagon and a regular 15-gon with an edge in common.

Find the size of angle $XYZ$.

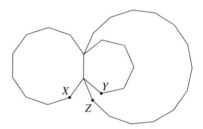

*Solution*
We shall give two methods, each of which involves finding the exterior angle of a regular polygon. If a regular polygon has $n$ sides, then each exterior angle is given by

$$\text{exterior angle} = \frac{360°}{n}. \qquad (2.1)$$

*Method 1*
Extend the common edge $PO$ to point $T$ as shown below. The angles labelled $x°$, $y°$ and $z°$ are exterior angles of the regular decagon, regular heptagon and regular 15-gon respectively.

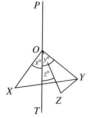

Hence, using the result (2.1),

$$x = \frac{360}{10} = 36,$$

$$y = \frac{360}{7} = 51\tfrac{3}{7}$$

$$\text{and} \quad z = \frac{360}{15} = 24.$$

It follows that $\angle XOY = x° + y° = 87\tfrac{3}{7}°$ and $\angle ZOY = y° - z° = 27\tfrac{3}{7}°$. Now the sides of the three polygons are all equal, so the triangles $XOY$ and $ZOY$ are isosceles. We can therefore find their base angles:

$$\angle XYO = \frac{180° - 87\tfrac{3}{7}°}{2} = 46\tfrac{2}{7}°$$

$$\text{and} \quad \angle ZYO = \frac{180° - 27\frac{3}{7}°}{2} = 76\frac{2}{7}°.$$

Thus $\angle XYZ = \angle ZYO - \angle XYO = 76\frac{2}{7}° - 46\frac{2}{7}° = 30°$.

*Method 2*

Let $PO$ be the common edge, as shown below. Since $OX = OY = OZ = OP$ the points $X$, $Y$, $Z$ and $P$ lie on a circle centre $O$.

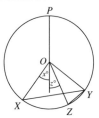

Now 'the angle at the circumference is half the angle at the centre', so

$$\angle XYZ = \tfrac{1}{2}\angle XOZ$$

$$= \frac{1}{2}(x + z)°.$$

But from (2.1)

$$x = \frac{360}{10} = 36$$

$$\text{and} \quad z = \frac{360}{15} = 24,$$

so that $\angle XYZ = \tfrac{1}{2}(36 + 24)° = 30°$.

3  Solve the equations

$$x + xy + x^2 = 9$$

$$y + xy + y^2 = -3.$$

*Solution*

'Substitution' is one of the standard methods of solving simultaneous equations: use one equation to find an expression for one unknown, then substitute this expression into the other equation, thereby forming a single equation in just one of the unknowns. Though it is possible to use a substitution method straight away here, the algebra is rather unpleasant, so we demonstrate two other approaches.

In passing, we note that the question places no restrictions on $x$ and $y$. In particular, we cannot assume that they are integers.

*Method* 1

Adding the two given equations, we get

$$x + y + x^2 + 2xy + y^2 = 6$$

so that

$$(x + y)^2 + (x + y) - 6 = 0,$$

which factorises to give

$$(x + y - 2)(x + y + 3) = 0.$$

Hence

$$x + y = 2 \quad \text{or} \quad x + y = -3. \tag{3.1}$$

Also, subtracting the two given equations, we get

$$x - y + x^2 - y^2 = 12$$

which factorises to give

$$(x - y) + (x - y)(x + y) = 12$$

so that

$$(x - y)(1 + x + y) = 12.$$

Hence, using (3.1),

$$x - y = 4 \quad \text{or} \quad x - y = -6, \tag{3.2}$$

which occur when $x + y = 2$ and $x + y = -3$ respectively.

We can now solve equations (3.1) and (3.2) by, for example, adding and subtracting, to obtain

$$(x, y) = (3, -1) \text{ or } \left(-\tfrac{9}{2}, \tfrac{3}{2}\right).$$

We now need to check whether these two pairs of values really do satisfy the equations given in the question. Each of them does, so the required solutions are $x = 3, y = -1$ and $x = -\tfrac{9}{2}, y = \tfrac{3}{2}$.

*Method* 2

Factorise each of the given equations to give

$$x(1 + y + x) = 9 \tag{3.3}$$

$$\text{and} \quad y(1 + x + y) = -3. \tag{3.4}$$

Since no side of either equation is zero, we may divide equation (3.3) by (3.4) to obtain $\frac{x}{y} = -3$, so that $x = -3y$. Now substitute this expression for $x$ into equation (3.4) to get

$$y(1 - 2y) = -3,$$

which may be rearranged to

$$2y^2 - y - 3 = 0,$$

or

$$(y + 1)(2y - 3) = 0.$$

Therefore $y = -1$ or $y = \frac{3}{2}$ and, since $x = -3y$, we have solutions

$$(x, y) = (3, -1) \text{ or } \left(-\frac{9}{2}, \frac{3}{2}\right).$$

We now need to check whether these two pairs of values really do satisfy the equations given in the question. Each of them does, so the required solutions are $x = 3, y = -1$ and $x = -\frac{9}{2}, y = \frac{3}{2}$.

4  The diameter $AD$ of a circle has length 4. The points $B$ and $C$ lie on the circle, as shown, so that $AB = BC = 1$.

Find the length of $CD$.

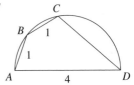

*Solution* 1

Let $O$ be the centre of the circle, so that $OA = OB = OC = 2$, and let chord $AC$ and radius $OB$ meet at $X$.

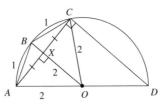

Triangle $OAC$ is isosceles and $OB$ bisects angle $AOC$ (because the chords $AB$ and $BC$ are equal and so subtend equal angles at the centre). Hence $OB$ is the perpendicular bisector of the base $AC$ of the isosceles triangle $AOC$. In other words, $AX = XC$ and $\angle AXO = 90°$, as shown in the diagram above.

Since angle $ACD$ is $90°$ (angle in a semicircle) triangle $ACD$ is a right-angled triangle with $CD$, whose length we have to find, as one side. We know $AD = 4$, so can find $CD$, using Pythagoras' theorem, from

$$CD^2 = AD^2 - AC^2, \tag{4.1}$$

provided we can find the length of $AC$. We shall do this by using areas, but there are other methods.

Now consider isosceles triangle $OAB$ and let $N$ be the midpoint of $AB$, so that triangle $ANO$ is right-angled.

Then, from Pythagoras' theorem, $NO^2 = 2^2 - (\frac{1}{2})^2 = \frac{15}{4}$, so that $NO = \frac{\sqrt{15}}{2}$. Hence the area of triangle $AOB$ is $\frac{1}{2} \times AB \times NO = \frac{\sqrt{15}}{4}$.

But the area of triangle $OAB$ is also $\frac{1}{2} \times OB \times AX$. Therefore $AX = \frac{\sqrt{15}}{4}$ and so $AC = 2AX = \frac{\sqrt{15}}{2}$. Using this value in equation (4.1). we get

$$CD^2 = AD^2 - AC^2 = 4^2 - \frac{15}{4} = \frac{49}{4}$$

and hence $CD = \frac{7}{2}$.

*Solution 2*

Let $O$ be the centre of the circle. Reflecting the sector $OBD$, shown shaded, about the diameter perpendicular to $BD$, so that $B$ and $D$ are interchanged, gives the right-hand diagram. If $C'$ is the reflection of $C$, then $BC' = CD$. Also, since reflection about a diameter reflects a circle to itself, we know that $C'$ lies on the circle.

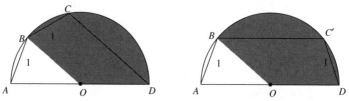

Now angles $AC'B$ and $C'AD$ are both angles at the circumference subtended by chords of length 1. These angles are therefore equal and so $BC'$ and $AD$ are parallel (alternate angles).

Draw perpendiculars from $B$ and $C'$ to $AD$ to create a rectangle $BXYC'$, as shown below, with $BC' = XY$.

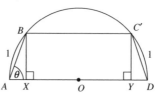

Then $AX = AB \cos\theta = \cos\theta$ and, by constructing the perpendicular bisector of $AB$ in isosceles triangle $OAB$, shown below, we see that $\cos\theta = \frac{1}{4}$. Therefore $AX = \frac{1}{4}$.

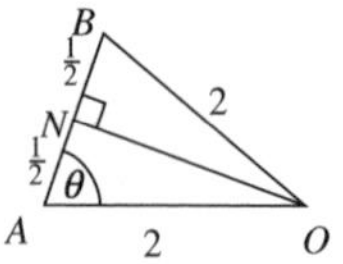

Similarly $DY = \frac{1}{4}$ and so $CD = BC' = XY = 4 - \frac{1}{4} - \frac{1}{4} = 3\frac{1}{2}$.

*Solution* 3

Let *P* be the intersection of *AB* produced and *DC* produced.

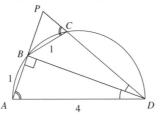

Now angles *ADB* and *BDC* are both angles at the circumference subtended by chords of length 1. These angles are therefore equal. Also, $\angle ABD$ = 90° (angle in a semicircle). Therefore triangles *ABD* and *PBD* are congruent (ASA). Hence BP = 1 and PD = 4.

Further, in triangles *BCP* and *DAP*, angle *P* is common and $\angle BCP$ = $\angle DAP$ (exterior angle of cyclic quadrilateral). These triangles are therefore similar and hence $PC : 1 = 2 : 4$. So $PC = \frac{1}{2}$ and $CD = PD - PC = 4 - \frac{1}{2} = 3\frac{1}{2}$.

5  The diagram shows a rectangle divided into eight regions by four straight lines. Three of the regions have areas 1, 2 and 3, as shown.

What is the area of the shaded quadrilateral?

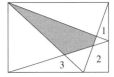

*Solution*

Notice that the shaded area is the intersection of the two triangles shown shaded in the following diagrams.

The area of each of these triangles is half the area of the rectangle, since each has the same base and height as the rectangle. Therefore the total unshaded area within the rectangle in the right-hand figure is also half the area of the rectangle. In other words, the shaded area in the left-hand figure is equal to the total unshaded area in the right-hand figure.

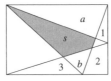

Using the notation indicated above, we therefore have
$a + s + b = a + 1 + 2 + b + 3$ and hence $s = 1 + 2 + 3 = 6$. So the area of the shaded quadrilateral is 6.

*Remark*

The result also applies if the rectangle is replaced by a parallelogram. Moreover, there is clearly nothing special about the values 1, 2 and 3.

6   Every day for the next eleven days I shall eat exactly one sandwich for lunch, either a ham sandwich or a cheese sandwich. However, during that period I shall never eat a ham sandwich on two consecutive days.

In how many ways can I plan my sandwiches for the next eleven days?

*Solution*

We shall use the notation $\binom{n}{r}$ for the number of ways of choosing $r$ objects from $n$. This is a binomial coefficient, sometimes written $^nC_r$. We have

$$\binom{n}{r} = \frac{n!}{r!\,(n-r)!} = \frac{n(n-1)\dots(n-r+1)}{1 \times 2 \times \dots \times r}.$$

We give three different methods, all of which create a plan for the next eleven days by constructing a line of Cs and Hs.

*Method* 1

Let $h(n)$ be the number of ways of creating a line of length $n$ starting with H, and $c(n)$ be the number starting with C.

For any line of length $n$ starting with C, we may construct a line of length $n + 1$ starting with H by adding H at the start. Also, for any line of length $n + 1$ starting with H, we may construct a line of length $n$ starting with C by deleting the initial H. Both of these statements depend on the rule that there are no consecutive Hs. Hence $h(n + 1) = c(n)$.

Similarly, adding C to the front of a line starting with H or one starting with C creates a longer line starting with C (and *vice versa*), so that $c(n + 1) = c(n) + h(n)$.

Therefore

$$h(n + 2) = c(n + 1)$$
$$= c(n) + h(n)$$
$$= h(n + 1) + h(n)$$

and

$$c(n + 2) = c(n + 1) + h(n + 1)$$
$$= c(n + 1) + c(n).$$

We thus have two sequences generated like the Fibonacci sequence: each term is the sum of the previous two terms. Moreover, letting $t(n)$ be the total number of ways to construct a line for $n$ days, then $t(n) = h(n) + c(n)$ and therefore $t(n + 2) = t(n + 1) + t(n)$. Hence $t(n)$ is also a Fibonacci-like sequence.

Now $t(1) = 2$, corresponding to the 'lines' C and H, and $t(2) = 3$, corresponding to the lines CC, CH and HC. So the first eleven terms of $t(n)$ are 2, 3, 5, 8, 13, 21, 34, 55, 89, 144 and 233. Hence the number required is 233.

*Method* 2

We create a plan for the next eleven days by constructing a line of Cs and Hs from two types of tile, $\boxed{C}$ or $\boxed{HC}$, which ensures that two Hs are never placed together. There are various possibilities, determined by the number of $\boxed{C}$ tiles which are used, which can be 11, 9, 7, 5, 3 or 1.

Eleven $\boxed{C}$ tiles can be placed in just one way, or $\binom{11}{0}$ ways.

Nine $\boxed{C}$ tiles and one $\boxed{HC}$ tile can be placed in $\binom{10}{1}$ ways, the number of ways of choosing the position of one $\boxed{HC}$ tile in a row of 10 tiles.

Seven $\boxed{C}$ tiles and two $\boxed{HC}$ tiles can be placed in $\binom{9}{2}$ ways, the number of ways of choosing the position of two $\boxed{HC}$ tiles in a row of 9 tiles.

Continuing in this way, we see that the total number of ways is

$$\binom{11}{0} + \binom{10}{1} + \binom{9}{2} + \binom{8}{3} + \binom{7}{4} + \binom{6}{5} = 1 + 10 + 36 + 56 + 35 + 6$$

$$= 144.$$

However, placing tiles in this way always ends the line with a C, so does not allow for the possibility of ending with an H. But if the line ends with an H, then the remainder of the line has ten letters and ends with a C. We may count the number of ways for this in a similar way to the above, but with a total of 10 letters instead of 11:

$$\binom{10}{0} + \binom{9}{1} + \binom{8}{2} + \binom{7}{3} + \binom{6}{4} + \binom{5}{5} = 1 + 9 + 28 + 35 + 15 + 1$$

$$= 89.$$

Therefore the total number of ways altogether is $144 + 89 = 233$.

*Method* 3

We create a plan for the next eleven days by starting with $k$ Cs in a line, where $k \leqslant 11$, and adding some Hs (possibly none) to construct a line of Cs and Hs. There are $k + 1$ slots into which a single H may be placed—at either end or between two Cs. We need to place $(11 - k)$ Hs so that each H is in a *different* slot, so we have to choose $11 - k$ of the $k + 1$ slots; there are $\binom{k + 1}{11 - k}$ ways in which this can be done.

Now we cannot add more Hs than the number of available slots, so $11 - k \leqslant k + 1$, that is, $k \geqslant 5$.

Therefore the total number of ways is the sum of $\binom{k + 1}{11 - k}$ for $5 \leqslant k \leqslant 11$, in other words

$$\binom{6}{6} + \binom{7}{5} + \binom{8}{4} + \binom{9}{3} + \binom{10}{2} + \binom{11}{1} + \binom{12}{0} = 1 + 21 + 70 + 84 + 45 + 11 + 1$$

$$= 233.$$

86

## Comments on the IMOK Olympiad Papers and Scripts

### General comments (Gerry Leversha)

Both candidates and their teachers will find it helpful to know something of the general principles involved in marking Olympiad-type papers. The preliminary paragraphs therefore serve as an exposition of the 'philosophy' which has guided both the setting and marking of all such papers at all age levels, both nationally and internationally.

What we are looking for, essentially, is solutions to *problems*. This approach is therefore rather different from what happens in public examinations such as GCSE, AS and A level, where credit is given for the ability to carry out individual techniques regardless of how these techniques fit into a protracted argument. Such marking is cumulative; a candidate may gain 60% of the available marks without necessarily having a clue about how to solve the final problem. Indeed, the questions are generally structured in such a way as to facilitate this approach, divided into many parts and not requiring an overall strategy for tackling a multi-stage argument.

In contrast to this, Olympiad-style problems are marked by looking at each question synoptically and deciding whether the candidate has some sort of overall strategy or not. An answer which is essentially a solution, but might contain either errors of calculation, flaws in logic, omission of cases or technical faults, will be marked on a '10 minus' basis. One question we often ask is: if we were to have the benefit of a two-minute interview with this candidate, could they correct the error or fill the gap? On the other hand, an answer which shows no sign of being a genuine solution is marked on a '0 plus' basis; up to 3 marks might be awarded for particular cases or insights. It is therefore important that candidates taking these papers realise the importance of the rubric about trying to finish whole questions rather than attempting lots of disconnected parts.

### Cayley (comments from James Cranch)

An Olympiad consists of mathematical *problems*: no question should be a matter of routine, and for all questions insight is required to make progress. Because of this, there are no easy marks. But it is always surprising to see what sophistication of thought is possible by students of this age, and this year as ever, many extremely high marks were awarded, including several perfect scores. Also because of this, we are not able to reward solutions in which the answer appears without any supporting evidence, or where the answer appears from a mass of unstructured calculation. We wish the student to have understood the structure of the problem, and the rubric demands that the student write up an account of this.

1. In Question 1, there are many ideas that can be used to get a handle on the problem. Most important is to realise that it is from the beginning a finite search: there are not many triples of positive integers which sum to 11. There are refinements, such as that no integer can be more than 6 since $7^3 > 251$.

   In order to enumerate the triple, it is necessary to have a system. The best is some variant of *lexicographic* order: sort them by increasing value of the smallest number, and within that by increasing value of the second smallest number. Taking into account the upper bound of 6, this list runs thus:

   (1, 4, 6), (1, 5, 5), (2, 3, 6), (2, 4, 5), (3, 3, 5), (3, 4, 4).

   The advantage of such a method is that is implicitly clear that all possible triples are being generated. This cannot be left to luck: writing them down until no more come to mind is not a systematic approach.

   Several candidates were punished for finding both solutions and then stopping. They earned few marks because finding solutions is relatively easy: what is difficult is to correctly exclude the possibility of further solutions. Some candidates claimed there was only one solution and then stopped; this is only a tiny bit worse.

   Several candidates lost marks for unexplained or spuriously justified restrictions to the search. Commonly this involved some claim such as that, once a solution with a 5 in has been found, there cannot be another: that there can be no solutions to $5^3 + a^3 + b^3 = 5^3 + c^3 + d^3 = 251$ for $a$ and $b$ different to $c$ and $d$. It is true that Ramanujan observed that the first number expressible as the sum of two cubes in two different ways is 1729 (which is in particular bigger than $126 = 251 - 5^3$). But this is far from obvious to most people, and certainly cannot be passed over without comment.

2. In Question 2, just a few incorrect approaches were seen time and again. Several candidates assumed that points $D$, $E$, $F$ are collinear. While true, this is not immediate and requires proof. A more glaring error was to try to work backwards: to guess the value of the angle by some process, and then to deduce other angles and decide that the resulting configuration is consistent. Unless the angle is fortuitously chosen to be 45°, the resulting configuration will of course in fact be inconsistent, but many candidates did not search hard enough to find the inevitable inconsistency. Moreover, it is not enough that the configuration be consistent with a certain angle: one must show that that angle is inevitable.

3. In Question 3, many candidates (and all of the markers) mused that the value of 'ODD' was in fact odd and that of 'EVEN' was in fact even.

Some assumed this (entirely unjustifiably) but doing so does not make the question vastly easier. The real difficulty with this question is to supply a correct account of the process of addition that is lucid enough to draw deductions from. Accordingly, the hallmark of almost all high-scoring scripts was the presence of words like *carry*, which demonstrate an insight into and familiarity with the process. This all needed to be embedded in a clear logical framework showing what has been deduced at all times.

4. There were many ways of doing Question 4. Some candidates explicitly used algebraic ideas. Others formed word equations, and kept the algebraic concepts implicit.

   One approach we had to reject was any kind of trial-and-error. It shows no insight into the problem to repeatedly test values until one works; there is in fact no guarantee that this approach should work.

   It was possible to do the question remarkably quickly with the proper insight. Killer observations included calculating that Angharad loses one minute's worth of her twelve-minute head start every two minutes, and thus is caught up after 24 minutes. This and similar approaches by proportionality revealed the answer with very little labour.

5. This was probably the hardest question on the paper, but nevertheless the markers were pleasantly surprised by the ingenuity shown. It had been expected that almost all successful attempts would proceed by choosing a variable as the length of some line segment, calculating the three sides of triangle *GCM* as linear forms in that variable, then using Pythagoras' theorem to produce a linear equation. Many solutions did in fact do this.

   Some also used coordinates, which is a rapid and concise approach. The standard failing was to get the logical order of the problem confused, and show instead the converse: that a 3 : 4 : 5 triangle does in fact give the configuration described in the problem. This is not difficult, but also not apparently useful. However, we were pleased to see one interesting perturbative approach which began with this verification. From there, it proceeded to observe, with a careful algebraic verification, that (fixing the side of the square to be of length 8 and thus fixing one side of *GCM* to be of length 4), if the other short side has length $s$ strictly less than 3 the hypotenuse would have length $h$ strictly more than 5, giving

   $$h^2 = s^2 + 4^2 < 3^2 + 4^2 = 5^2 < h^2,$$

   a contradiction; and similarly that if the short side had length $s$ strictly greater than 3 the hypotenuse would have length $h$ strictly less than 5 giving

   $$h^2 = s^2 + 4^2 > 3^2 + 4^2 = 5^2 > h^2,$$

   another contradiction.

6. This question falls into two parts: one is hard, one is easy, but both are necessary for a full solution. One is to prove that no run longer than three is possible. The other is to prove that a run of length three is indeed possible.

The first part requires an idea—that no multiple of 4 is a 'qprime'—and thus was responsible for the bulk of the marks. The second part is comparatively straightforward and can be found by steady searching. The first ten examples of such triples are:

(93, 94, 95),     (85, 86, 87),     (33, 34, 35),     (141, 142, 143),
(201, 202, 203),   (213, 214, 215),   (217, 218, 219),   (301, 302, 303),
(393, 394, 395),   (445, 446, 447).

Perhaps unsurprisingly, almost all successful candidates produced (33, 34, 35) as their example.


**Hamilton** (comments from Dean Bunnell)

We were extremely pleased with the efforts of the candidates. Trial and error would appear to be a thing of the past! Indications were that candidates engaged themselves fully in mathematical thought for the whole two hour period. I hope they enjoyed attempting to solve the questions as much as we did seeing their innovative approaches to many of the problems!

Question 1 was not as straightforward as it first appeared, but questions 2 and 3 were very popular, with candidates scoring highly here. Numbers 4, 5 and 6 then proved to be good discriminatory questions, culminating in a broad spread of final scores.

1. The most logical approach was made by only a few: Showing $6^3 < 251$, $7^3 > 251$ and $4^3 < \frac{251}{3}$ gave the highest cube as 5 or 6. From here the triples 2, 3, 6 and 1, 5, 5 were quickly found. This method doesn't depend on the sum of the triples being 11 but failure to check this lost a mark.

The most popular approach was to show $6^3$ was the highest cube then to list all the possible triples summing to 11:

(1, 4, 6),   (1, 5, 5),   (2, 3, 6),   (2, 4, 5),   (3, 3, 5),   (3, 4, 4).

The sum of the cubes of these triples were then found and the correct result obtained.

Finding triples without identifying the range of possible cubes was heavily penalised and 'correct answers only' scored a mark each.

2. This question proved to be straightforward for the majority of candidates. The two approaches used to show that $x = 60$ were to consider the two unlabelled angles either separately or as a sum. Either way the simultaneous equations formed from the two given triangles were usually solved correctly. The 'answer only' scored 1 mark. An answer of 60° was accepted.

   Reference to the fact that 'the sum of the angles in a triangle is 180°' was too frequently omitted and lost 1 mark.

3. Candidates scored well on this question, though a few thought that considering all eight terms to be zero meant that the sixth term was zero whatever the eight terms actually were. Algebra was essential in proving the sixth term to be zero in all such series.

   In most cases, two simultaneous equations had to be formed in order to move into the '10 minus' category.

4. It was pleasing to see so many candidates attempting a geometry question.

   This question was about black and grey regions but the candidates turned it into a question that became black or white! All who attempted the question defined a radius and found expressions for the area of the quarter-circle and the semicircles as multiples of $r^2$. They either stopped there (a '0 plus' solution) or progressed to a successful conclusion.

   Some clever approaches were made in identifying the coloured regions.

5. Many candidates correctly formed equations $QR = a + b$ and $SR = b + c$. Unfortunately, some then used $QT = 2a$ and not $QT = b + c$ when substituting into a quadratic. This kept us on our toes since using this value for $QT$ and Pythagoras' theorem gives an incorrect equation, $(c + a)^2 = (b + a)^2 + (2a)^2$, which actually leads to $a = 2b$, the correct answer! This incorrect method scored 1 or 2 marks only. The claim that $QT = 2a$ was probably made by looking at the figure.

   In order to progress to a '10 minus' solution a correct quadratic in two variables was required. A mark was deducted if the ratio wasn't simplified or reference to Pythagoras' theorem was omitted.

6. As is the case in all Olympiad papers, only 1 or 2 marks were given for 'correct answers only', in this case displaying one or two possible shading patterns. What is needed is a proof that there are *exactly* two.

   The essence of the question was to observe:

   (a) a shaded corner cell has 3 adjacent cells;

(b) a shaded edge cell has 5 adjacent cells;

(c) the shaded central cell has 8 adjacent cells.

The marking for this in the '0 plus' category was very straightforward: one mark for each of the above statements, these marks being additive. *Note that marks are not usually additive when marking Olympiad papers*, but it seemed appropriate in this case.

Showing clearly that $8 + 3 + 3 + 3 = 17$ and $5 + 3 + 3 + 3 + 3 = 17$ were the only possibilities, and that each corresponded to exactly one shading pattern, lead towards a complete solution.

## Maclaurin (comments from Gerry Leversha)

1. This question asks you find out how many pairs of positive integers satisfy a relationship. There are, of course, infinitely many pairs of positive integers, so the crux of this problem is to reduce it to an examination of finitely many cases. The smaller of $a$ and $b$ will produce the larger fraction, and this soon gives the condition that $a \leqslant 15$. From this point it is easy to look at all fifteen cases and see whether a suitable value of a exists. It is also possible to find a lower bound for $a$, namely $a \geqslant 8$, which reduces the search further. What was sometimes difficult to judge was whether candidates really understood why they could stop at 15. It is obvious that one solution to the problem is when are both 15, but you need to go a step further and explain why, when $a > 15$, it is also true that $a > b$, contrary to the information given in the question. An alternative, more sophisticated, approach is to realise that $2a - 15$ must be a factor of 225; this yields the solution very neatly, but very few candidates adopted it.

2. The key to solving this problem is to draw a clear diagram of the configuration containing $X$, $Y$ and $Z$ and see what calculations need to be done in order to find the required angle. This depends only on the external angles of the various polygons and is even more straightforward if you realise that $O$, as shown in the solutions, is the centre of the circumcircle of $\triangle XYZ$. In fact it turns out that the result is true even if the heptagon is any $n$-gon for $3 \leqslant n \leqslant 14$, since the angle of $51\frac{3}{7}°$ cancels in the subsequent calculation. Nevertheless, we deducted a mark from anyone who used decimals rather than exact fractions to describe it.

3. There are a number of good approaches to this algebra question. What we were looking for was the ability to manipulate the given equations so as to produce either a single equation in one variable or

simultaneous linear equations in two. Nearly all solutions required consideration of zero values, and it was deemed necessary to show that these are impossible (by reference to the original equations), if, at some point in the treatment, the candidate divides through by $x$ or $y$ or $1 + x + y$. It was disturbing to realise that there were candidates taking Maclaurin who did not recognise or know how to solve a quadratic equation. It was also necessary to pair the solutions $x$ and $y$; simply to say that $x = 3$ or $-\frac{9}{2}$ and $y = 1$ or $3$ allows the possibility of four solution pairs.

A further requirement (a commonplace for algebraic problems in Olympiads) is that the solution needs to be *checked*. In normal school algebra (quadratics, linear equations, and the like) one is using an implicit existence theorem: if the argument produces a 'solution', then the solution does indeed satisfy the equations. The argument has actually shown that, if certain equations are true, then the solution can only be a member of a particular set. This does not establish that every member of that set is a solution to the equations. Consider, for example, four linear equations in three variables: three of them might imply a unique solution, but this might not be a solution to the fourth. Similar considerations apply to equations of the type $\sqrt{\ldots} + \sqrt{\ldots} = \sqrt{\ldots}$ which involve square roots. The normal solving procedure involves squaring both sides, perhaps twice, but as a result solutions to other equations, such as $\sqrt{\ldots} + \sqrt{\ldots} = \sqrt{\ldots}$, are discovered, so it is essential to check that any solutions you have found apply to the equation you began with. Equivalently, it would be sufficient to check that the argument used in producing the solutions is reversible—but even if this is so, it is a good habit to carry out the check as a matter of course. Candidates for competitions such as Maclaurin should recognise the need for checking in any but the most straightforward cases.

4.  There were many successful approaches to this problem. Most looked for isosceles triangles and identified right-angles which would allow the use of Pythagoras. It was necessary to say why certain geometrical facts were true—for instance, the angle in the semicircle at $\angle ACD$ or the equality of $\angle BDA$ and $\angle CDA$ since they subtended equal chords. However, we did allow the candidate to cite properties of the kite $ABCO$. Those who adopted a purely trigonometrical proof were generally successful if they used a combination of the cosine rule and the double angle formula for cosine, but we did not permit an answer of the form $\cos\left(2\cos^{-1}a\right)$.

5. This was the least popular question, but ironically if you simply label a few areas and carry out some simple algebra it almost solves itself. Various dissections of the figure turned out to be useful, including calculating the total area in two different ways. It was also useful to know that the area of a triangle is half that of a parallelogram with the same base and height. Incidentally, this result is generalisable to any parallelogram and there is nothing special about the values 1, 2 and 3.

6. This was the most difficult problem to mark if only because a very large number of candidates achieved the correct answer of 233 but it was not clear whether they were just spotting patterns which they assumed continued. It was not necessary to be very sophisticated to gain full marks; in fact, a simple tree diagram which showed that C could be followed by C or H and H could only be followed by C was enough, so long as you drew the whole thing. This does, of course, lead to a recurrence relation and Fibonacci numbers, and there were some excellent three-line proofs using this fact which earned full credit. It was also possible to begin with a string of Cs and insert Hs as appropriate. An excellent idea, which few noticed, was to consider single C tiles and double HC tiles, and put them together to form a row of eleven places.

The most popular approach, however, was to divide the problem into cases according to the number of Hs. It turns out that the cases $H = 0$, 1 and 6 are easy, $H = 2$ is a bit more subtle, and the cases $H = 3, 4$ and 5 were critical. Attempts which simply supplied an algorithm (often involving telescoped sums of consecutive numbers) without explaining why it worked gained very few marks.

**Marking**

The marking was carried out on the weekend of 27th and 28th March in Leeds. There were three marking groups led by James Cranch, Dean Bunnell and Gerry Leversha. The other markers are listed later in this book.

94

## IMOK certificates

All participating students were awarded a certificate. Certificates came in three varieties: Participation, Merit and Distinction.

UKMT

*Intermediate Mathematical Olympiad and Kangaroo 2010*

of

received a

**CERTIFICATE of MERIT**

Bernard Silverman

Chairman, United Kingdom Mathematics Trust

## THE UKMT INTERMEDIATE MATHEMATICAL OLYMPIAD AND KANGAROO

In recognition of previous high performance in the UK Intermediate Mathematical Challenge, the top pupils in School Year 11 or below in England, S4 or below in Scotland and School Year 12 or below in Northern Ireland are invited to take part in one of the two strands of this follow-on competition.

The top-scoring pupils in each year are invited to sit the Olympiad, a two-hour examination which includes six demanding questions requiring full written solutions. The problems are designed to include interesting and attractive mathematics and may involve knowledge or understanding beyond the range of normal school work.

Other high-scoring pupils in each year-group are invited to enter the European Kangaroo. In 2010 the 'Kangourou sans Frontières' was taken by students in over forty countries in Europe and beyond. The multiple-choice questions involve amusing and thought-provoking situations which require the use of logic as well as mathematical understanding.

Further information on the UKMT and its activities can be found at www.ukmt.org.uk

## IMOK Olympiad awards

As in recent years, medals were awarded in the Intermediate Mathematical Olympiad. Names of medal winners are listed below. Book prizes were still awarded to the top 50 or so pupils in each year group. The Cayley book prizes were *Symmetry: The Ordering Principle* by David Wade and *The Golden Section* by Scott Olsen, the Hamilton book prize was *Professor Stewart's Cabinet of Mathematical Curiosities* by Ian Stewart and the Maclaurin book prize was *Mathematical Olympiad Primer* by Geoff Smith. In addition, key fobs with a related design as shown were awarded to all IMOK participants.

Find the area of the shaded rectangle,which touches equal circles whose centres form a 29,29, 40 triangle.

## IMOK medal winners

### Cayley

| | |
|---|---|
| Matthew Almond | Sheldon School, Chippenham, Wiltshire |
| James Astles | Salesian College, Farnborough, Hampshire |
| Hubert Au | Winchester College, Hampshire |
| Samuel Bodansky | The Grammar Sch. at Leeds, West Yorkshire |
| Joseph Boorman | Kings College School, Cambridge |
| Samuel Booth | Cardinal Wiseman HS, Greenford, Middlesex |
| Steve Brown | George Stephenson HS, Newcastle-upon-Tyne |
| Alastair Carr | King's Coll. Sch., Wimbledon Common, London |
| Darren Carver-Balsiger | Boston Spa School, West Yorkshire |
| Charlie Chen | King's Coll. Sch., Wimbledon Common, London |
| Max Cheun | King Edward VI Camp Hill Boys' S, Birmingham |
| Mijoo Choi | Luckley Oakfield School, Wokingham, Berks |
| Will Choi | Winchester College, Hampshire |
| Azmain Chowdhury | Westminster School, London |
| George Cole | Redhill School, Stourbridge, West Midlands |
| Eleanor Cook | Oundle School, Oundle |
| Michael Cui | Magdalen College School, Oxford |
| Hoagy Cunningham | Charter School, London |
| Aatreyee Das | Heckmondwike GS, West Yorkshire |
| Flora de Falbe | Twyford C of E High School, Acton, London |

| | |
|---|---|
| Stijn Degraaf | St Paul's School, London |
| Joshua Degromoboy | Bournemouth School |
| Rahul Dev | St Paul's School, London |
| Henry Dickie | Dulwich College, London |
| Madhi Elango | Queen Elizabeth's School, Barnet, Herts |
| Jon Arne Elke Toft | British Int. Sch. of Stavanger, Norway |
| Katharine Emden | North London Collegiate School, Edgware |
| Ece Eylul Eron | American Collegiate Institute, Izmir, Turkey |
| Helen Fishwick | St Paul's Girls' School, London |
| James Foord | Dragon School, Oxford |
| George Fortune | Altrincham GS for Boys, Cheshire |
| Gabriel Gendler | Queen Elizabeth's School, Barnet, Herts |
| Harry Goodburn | Wilson's School, Wallington, Surrey |
| Ben Grant | Tapton School, Sheffield |
| Edward Grogan | Magdalen College School, Oxford |
| Monica Gupta | Tiffin Girls' Sch., Kingston-upon-Thames, Surrey |
| Jae-Ho Han | British International School Vietnam |
| Greg Harker | Judd School, Tonbridge, Kent |
| Alex Harris | Perse School, Cambridge |
| Liam Hughes | Welland Park CC, Market Harborough |
| William Huntley | St Joseph's College, Stoke-on-Trent, Staffs |
| Freddie Illingworth | Magdalen College School, Oxford |
| Edward Ingram | St George's School, Harpenden, Hertfordshire |
| Ben Jang | Eton College, Berks |
| Akash Jayasekara | Westminster School, London |
| Alan Jiang | Eton College, Berks |
| Stephen Jones | Magdalen College School, Oxford |
| Gareth Jones | Clifton College Prep School, Bristol |
| Joo Han Ka | Frankfurt International School, Germany |
| Jung Min Kang | British International School Vietnam |
| Alexander Kendall | Marlborough College, Wiltshire |
| Andrew Kim | Overseas Family School, Singapore |
| Edward Kirkby | Amery Hill School, Alton, Hampshire |
| Philip Knott | Wilson's School, Wallington, Surrey |
| Jaeseung Ko | Tapton School, Sheffield |
| Seung Hun Koh | Frankfurt International School, Germany |
| Ryo Kojima | Haberdashers' Aske's Sch. for Boys, Elstree, Herts |

| | |
|---|---|
| Jae Ryoung Koo | United World College of SE Asia, Singapore |
| Kai Laddiman | Heathfield Community College, East Sussex |
| Rama Lakshman | Bottisham Village College, Cambridge |
| Ron Lam | Lancing College, West Sussex |
| Jae-Been Lee | Bristol Grammar School, Clifton, Bristol |
| Soo Hyun Lee | Bangkok Patana School, Bangkok |
| James Lee | British International School Vietnam |
| Elizabeth Lee | Loughborough High School, Leicestershire |
| Tim Lennox | King Edward VII School, Sheffield |
| Warren Li | Fulford School, York |
| Yuxin Liu | Royal School, Haslemere, Surrey |
| Akuan Liu | Cherwell School, Oxford |
| Lorcan McCullagh | Queen Mary's Grammar School, Walsall |
| Fangda Mei | St Christoper's School, Lincoln |
| Harry Metrebian | Beacon School, Amersham, Buckinghamshire |
| Alistair Miller | Hampton School, Middlesex |
| Anurag Modi | Queen Elizabeth's GS, Horncastle, Lincs |
| George Moore | Oathall Community College, Hayward Heath |
| Joshua Morey | Thomas Hardye School, Dorchester, Dorset |
| Eva Morton | King Edward VI Camp Hill Girls' S., Birmingham |
| Rachel Newhouse | Skipton Girls' High School, North Yorkshire |
| Bernard Ng | Abingdon School, Oxfordshire |
| Yuen Ng | Rainham Mark GS, Gillingham, Kent |
| Chee Won Oh | British International School Vietnam |
| Ossian O'Sullivan | St Paul's School, London |
| Oliver Philcox | Bishop's Stortford High School, Hertfordshire |
| Ramsay Pyper | Eton College, Berks |
| Edward Qin | Tapton School, Sheffield |
| Luke Ramsden | Cottenham Village College, Cambridge |
| Donsung Rhee | Ewell Castle School, Surrey |
| Mark Richards | Adams Grammar School, Newport, Salop |
| Katya Richards | School of St Helen and St Katharine, Abingdon |
| Jong Hoon Shin | South Island School, Hong Kong |
| Hyeonseop Shin | Gosforth High School, Newcastle-upon-Tyne |
| Alec Shute | Kingswood School, Bath, Somerset |
| Jeremy Soper | Taunton School, Somerset |
| Kaushik Sureshkumar | Trinity School, Croydon, Surrey |

| | |
|---|---|
| Timothy Thong | United World College of SE Asia, Singapore |
| Kavin Vijayakumar | Bancroft's School, Woodford Green, Essex |
| Jonathan Wall | King Edward VI GS, Chelmsford, Essex |
| Callum Watson | Balfron High School, Glasgow |
| Alistair Webb | Island School, Hong Kong |
| Adam Weller | Reading School, Berkshire |
| Sanjay Willder | St Paul's School, London |
| Alex Williams | Ranelagh School, Bracknell, Berkshire |
| Terence Wu | King Edward VI Camp Hill Boys' Sch., Birmingham |
| Hannah Wu | Harrow International School, Beijing |
| Bill Wu | Eton College, Berks |
| Donald Yau | Truro School, Cornwall |
| Gloria Yin | St Paul's Girls' School, London |
| Lian Zhu | King Edward VI Camp Hill Boys' Sch., Birmingham |

## Hamilton

| | |
|---|---|
| Chris Acheson | High School of Dundee |
| Keith Barker | Wilson's School, Wallington, Surrey |
| Charles Barton | Westminster School, London |
| Isar Bhattacharjee | St Paul's School, London |
| Jack Boericke | St Paul's School, London |
| Timothy Bond | Watford Grammar School for Boys, Herts |
| Anthony Boyle | Hampton School, Middlesex |
| Philip Boyle Smith | The Grammar School at Leeds |
| Sam Brennan | Northgate High School, Ipswich, Suffolk |
| Leonardo Buizza | St Paul's School, London |
| Alex Burgess | Hemel Hempstead School, Hertfordshire |
| Andrew Carlotti | Sir Roger Manwood's Sch., Sandwich, Kent |
| Toby Cathcart Burn | Clitheroe Royal GS, Lancashire |
| Justin Chan | Dulwich College, London |
| Aditya Chander | Westminster School, London |
| Pawit Chantaworakit | Bangkok Patana School, Bangkok |
| Samuel Cheshire | Clifton Comprehensive Sch., Rotherham |
| Jaehoon Cho | Mayflower CHS, Billericay, Essex |
| Soohyun Choi | Bromsgrove Int. Sch., Bangkok |
| Jake Cohen-Setton | St Paul's School, London |
| James Coxon | St Paul's School, London |
| Charles Cummins | St Paul's School, London |

| | |
|---|---|
| Oscar Darwin | Highgate School, London |
| Harry Dent | St Paul's School, London |
| Jin Ah Eum | Overseas Family School, Singapore |
| James Fage | Westminster School, London |
| Oliver Feng | Olchfa Comp. Sch., Sketty, Swansea |
| Alvina Fok | South Island School, Aberdeen, Hong Kong |
| James Fuller | King Edward VI School, Southampton |
| Humphrey Galbraith | Winchester College, Hampshire |
| David Gibson | High School of Glasgow, Glasgow |
| Sookwon Ha | Dulwich College Beijing, Beijing |
| Jon Hall | Charterhouse, Godalming, Surrey |
| Jennie Han | Redland High School, Bristol |
| Jack Harding | St Paul's School, London |
| Eleanor Holderness | Latymer Upper School, Hammersmith, London |
| Riki Houlden | Westminster School, London |
| Daniel Hu | City of London School, London |
| Yunli Huang | Overseas Family School, Singapore |
| Nicholas Huang | Taipei European School, Taipei |
| Yunha Hwang | Sevenoaks School, Kent |
| Riho Ikeuchi | Overseas Family School, Singapore |
| Matthew Jasper | St Crispin's School, Wokingham, Berks |
| Mark Jerjian | Westminster School, London |
| Ralph Jordan | Bishops Stortford College, Hertfordshire |
| James Jordon | Prudhoe Community HS, Northumberland |
| Hugh Judge | Merchant Taylors' School, Middlesex |
| Isaac Kang | Westminster School, London |
| Sahl Khan | St Paul's School, London |
| Danielle Kim | Cheltenham Ladies College, Gloucestershire |
| Yongwhi Kim | British International School Vietnam |
| Seungwoo Ko | Ewell Castle School, Surrey |
| Dabin Kwon | Badminton School, Bristol |
| Andrew Lee | Loughborough Grammar School, Leicestershire |
| Baichuan Li | Highgate School, London |
| Weiyao Li | Cherwell School, Oxford |
| Matei Mandache | Loughborough Grammar School, Leicestershire |
| Nathan Mattock | The Crossley Heath School, Halifax |
| Soo Young Moon | Dulwich College Beijing, Beijing |
| Jae Yoon Moon | Overseas Family School, Singapore |

| | |
|---|---|
| Benjamin Morley | Wells Cathedral School, Somerset |
| Marcus Nielsen | Aylesbury GS, Buckinghamshire |
| Neal Pabari | St Paul's School, London |
| Liyang Pan | Royal Grammar School, High Wycombe, Bucks |
| Junwoo Park | United World College of SE Asia, Singapore |
| Amit Patel | Dr Challoner's GS, Amersham, Bucks |
| Johnny Patterson | St Paul's School, London |
| James Perry | Charterhouse, Surrey |
| Kwesi Peterson | Westminster School, London |
| Jungwoo Rhee | Claremont Fan Court Sch., Esher, Surrey |
| Jack Robinson | Caistor Grammar School, Lincolnshire |
| Alex Ruff | Ashcroft Technology Academy, London |
| Sreya Saha | Altrincham Girls' GS, Cheshire |
| Saravanan Sathyanandha | Haberdashers' Aske's School for Boys, Herts |
| Jonathan Shen | Eton College, Berks |
| Sam Shepherd | Hayes School, Bromley, Kent |
| Asiya Siddiqua | King Edward VI HS for Girls, Birmingham |
| Dylon Sivam | Haberdashers' Aske's School for Boys, Herts |
| Josephine Solowiej-Wedderburn | |
| | Alleyn's School, Dulwich, London |
| Alastair Stanley | High School of Glasgow, Glasgow |
| Ratanon Suemanothom | British International School, Phuket |
| Chang Sun | Felsted School, Great Dunmow, Essex |
| Kim Sunghoon | Sutton Grammar School for Boys, Surrey |
| Barnum Swannell | Kingsley College, Redditch, Worcs |
| Thierry Tan | Alice Smith School, Malaysia |
| Joe Tomkinson | Harry Carlton Sch., East Leake, Loughborough |
| Fred Tomlinson | Westminster School, London |
| Vladimir Vankov | Royal Grammar School, Newcastle-upon-Tyne |
| Alfie Wallace | Eton College, Berks |
| Han-Xi Wang | Watford GS for Girls, Hertfordshire |
| Vincent Wang | West Island School (ESF), Hong Kong |
| Emily Warne | Sir William Borlase's GS, Marlow, Bucks |
| Philip Warren | Sutton Grammar School for Boys, Surrey |
| Ricky Won | Eton College, Berks |
| Susan Xue | Marymount International School, Surrey |
| Chuyi Yang | King Edward VI Camp Hill Girls' School |
| Tae Han Yoon | Dulwich College Beijing, Beijing |

| Paul Yoon | Cheltenham College, Gloucestershire |
| Calum You | Eton College, Berks |
| Linan Zhang | Millfield School, Street, Somerset |
| Zhengchi Zhang | Harrow International School, Beijing |
| Hokwan Zhang | Concord College, Shrewsbury, Shropshire |
| Feilong Zhao | United World College of SE Asia, Singapore |

## Maclaurin

| James Aaronson | St Paul's School, London |
| Ashwin Aggarwal | Royal Grammar School, High Wycombe |
| Ashwin Ahuja | St Paul's School, London |
| Nirmala Arulampalam | King Henry VIII School, Coventry |
| Ian Baldwin | Forest School, London |
| Alex Barron | St Paul's School, London |
| Max Baxter Allen | Millfield School, Street, Somerset |
| Natalie Behague | Dartford Girls' Grammar School, Kent |
| Duncan Bell | St Olave's GS, Orpington, Kent |
| Rory Bennett | Tudor Grange School, Solihull |
| Niloy Biswas | Denbigh High S, Luton, Bedfordshire |
| Adam Brown | Alcester Grammar School, Warwickshire |
| Callum Bungey | Westminster School, London |
| Sam Cappleman-Lynes | Shebbear College, Beaworthy, Devon |
| Benedict Carter | Hampton School, Middlesex |
| Dickson Chan | Winchester College, Hampshire |
| Shreya Chandler | German Swiss International Sch., Hong Kong |
| Andrew Chen | Renaissance College, Hong Kong |
| Qiyang Chen | Queen Elizabeths GS, Blackburn, Lancs |
| Lok Kiu Cheng | Sevenoaks School, Kent |
| Lewis Chinery | Taunton School, Somerset |
| Rishi Chotai | Haberdashers' Aske's School for Boys, Elstree |
| Wan Yeung Chui | West Island School (ESF), Hong Kong |
| Matthew Colbrook | The King's School (Seniors), Witney |
| Jennifer Collister | Oxford High School |
| Jack Cooper | Walton HS, Walton-on-the-Hill, Stafford |
| James Dixon | King Edward VI GS, Chelmsford, Essex |
| Rafi Dover | King David HS, Crumpsall, Manchester |
| Chris Drakeford-Lewis | Monkton Combe School, Bath |
| Jonathan Dungay | Steyning Grammar School |
| Suzanna Eames | Stockport Grammar School, Cheshire |

| | |
|---|---|
| Robin Elliott | Reading School, Berkshire |
| Sam Fawcett | Monkton Combe School, Bath |
| Thomas Flynn | Devonport HS for Boys, Plymouth, Devon |
| Takehiro Fujita | Harrow School, Middlesex |
| Cosmos Fung | Tonbridge School, Kent |
| Sarah Gait | Queen Elizabeth GS, Penrith, Cumbria |
| Adam Goucher | Heritage School, Chesterfield, Derbyshire |
| Anna Gould | Ampleforth College Senior School, York |
| Mark Green | Katharine Lady Berkeleys S, Wotton-under-Edge |
| Thomas Hay | Churcher's College, Petersfield, Hants |
| Benjamin Hillman | Penistone Grammar School, Sheffield |
| Eigen Horsfield | Tapton School, Sheffield |
| Charlie Houseago | Westminster School, London |
| Sun Hugo | Warwick School |
| Joshua Hunt | Bryn Celynnog CS, Beddau, Pontypridd |
| Sophia Hyer | Godolphin & Latymer School, London |
| Joshua Inoue | Queen Elizabeth's Hospital, Clifton, Bristol |
| Echo Ji | International College Sherborne S., Dorset |
| Sherry Jiang | Larne Grammar School, Co. Antrim |
| Yibo Jin | Christ's College, East Finchley, London |
| Naomi Kraushar | Tiferes High School, London |
| Lennart Kueck | Malvern College, Worcestershire |
| Michelle Kwok | Headington School, Oxford |
| Joshua Lam | Leys School, Cambridge, Cambs |
| Frank Lam | Oundle School, Glapthorn Road, Oundle |
| Jihoon Lee | Kingston Grammar School, Surrey |
| Dohyeon Lee | Millthorpe School, York |
| Derek Leung | South Island School, Aberdeen, Hong Kong |
| Qinan Li | Simon Langton Boys' GS, Canterbury |
| Shuqing Lian | Caterham School, Surrey |
| Tom Lilburn | King Edward's School, Birmingham |
| Charlotte Bokang Liu | Harrow International School, Beijing |
| Eleanor Loukes | Tonbridge Grammar School, Kent |
| Peerapat Luxsuwong | Ruamrudee International School, Bangkok |
| Alex McBride | Sevenoaks School, Kent |
| Ella Mi | King's School, Peterborough |
| Eleanor Moodey | Brampton College, London |
| Jananan Nathan | Merchant Taylors' School, Middlesex |
| Kevin Ngo | Sir John Cass's & Red Coat S, Tower Hamlets |

| | |
|---|---|
| James Nicholls | Oakham School, Rutland |
| Stephani Oyang | Taipei European School, Taipei |
| Junhyung Park | Fulford School, York |
| Richard Parkinson | Reading School, Berkshire |
| Vishal Patil | King Edward's School, Birmingham |
| Timothy Pearson | Glenalmond College, Perthshire |
| Thomas Pearson | Colyton Grammar School, Devon |
| Matthew Rogers | Wilson's School, Wallington, Surrey |
| Thomas Rychlik | All Saint's RC School, York |
| Kshitij Sabnis | Westminster School, London |
| Thomas Salt | Abingdon School, Oxfordshire |
| Thomas Saunders | St Olave's GS, Orpington, Kent |
| Robert Steane | Bishop Ramsey CE School, Ruislip, Middlesex |
| Oliver Sugg | Royal Grammar School, Guildford, Surrey |
| Andrew Sultana | King's School, Canterbury, Kent |
| Jeffrey Sun | West Island School (ESF), Hong Kong |
| Terence Tang | German Swiss Int. Sch., Hong Kong |
| Yinglun Teng | St John's College, Old St Mellons, Cardiff |
| Stephen Thatcher | King Edward's School, Birmingham |
| Jack Tsai | Wrekin College, Telford, Shropshire |
| Aliraza Visram | King Edward's School, Birmingham |
| Jamie Voros | St Paul's Girls' School, London |
| Barnaby Walker | Wellington College, Crowthorne, Berks |
| Dennis Wang | Altrincham GS for Boys, Cheshire |
| Nicholas Williams | Westminster School, London |
| Harry Winter | Westminster School, London |
| Clement Woo | Harrow School, Middlesex |
| Thomas Wu | International College Sherborne Sch., Dorset |
| Catherine Xu | Sevenoaks School, Kent |
| Lawrence Xu | Merchant Taylors' School, Northwood |
| Ronald Yip | South Island School, Aberdeen, Hong Kong |
| Oliver Yue Jia | West Buckland School, Barnstaple, Devon |
| Xiaoyi Zhang | Marymount Int. S., Kingston upon Thames |
| Michael Zhao | International College Sherborne S, Dorset |

## National Mathematics Summer Schools
## July 4th – 9th and July 11th – 16th, 2010

In 2010, as in recent years there were two summer schools. Participants for the first week were selected predominantly on the basis of performance in the Intermediate Challenge, and were from schools which had not recently been represented at a summer school; those for the second week were predominantly selected on the basis of scores in the Hamilton or Maclaurin Intermediate Mathematical Olympiad papers.

Mary Teresa Fyfe, who has run a week's summer school for many years, was unfortunately unavailable this year. But Vicky Neale stepped in and ran the week extremely successfully.

The programme mostly followed the traditional format that has been developed over the years, with one or two changes. Each morning, things got under way with a masterclass by Philip Coggins. He talked about various aspects of numbers (natural numbers, rational numbers, real numbers, complex numbers, and types of infinity), and introduced the students to a range of new ideas. The seven seniors followed their own programme of masterclasses during these sessions, studying topics such as tilings, sequences, Euclid's algorithm and coding.

The second morning session involved team activities, but these were not quite the traditional competitions. As usual, the students were divided into teams, each led by one of the seniors and named after a mathematician (Germain, Hardy, Jacobi, Klein, Lobachevsky, Möbius and Noether). They tackled a range of activities, designed to give them the chance to develop various mathematical skills, such as investigating, exploring, looking for patterns, asking interesting questions, generalising, making conjectures, giving proofs, explaining ideas, and working collaboratively. Over the course of the week, we asked them to report their progress in various ways, including giving presentations to their teams, sharing ideas with the whole group, and preparing posters. Some of the activities led into afternoon sessions, and they covered a range of mathematical topics. We were impressed by the positive way in which the students responded to these activities, and were especially impressed by the seniors, who were simply fantastic at guiding and encouraging their teams without giving away answers.

The afternoon sessions covered a range of mathematical ideas, including colouring problems, the pigeonhole principle, geometry, polytopes and tilings, group theory, modular arithmetic and mathematical induction. The prize for largest prop goes to John Slater, who brought his (home-made) harpsichord with him to help demonstrate the mathematics of musical scales. We hope that the range of topics and styles of presentation gave everyone something new and interesting to think about, and broadened some mathematical horizons. In addition, Andre Rzym gave a session on Friday morning on mathematics in the financial markets, which illustrated one potential career option for mathematicians.

Some evenings we had mathematical activities: Howard Groves introduced the idea of impartial games to the students, who had great fun analysing Nim and similar games, and Andrew Jobbings gave a range of problems related to dissections, which led to much happy paper cutting. Fortuitously, the bowling trip on the Wednesday evening coincided with a semifinal in the football World Cup, and so the sports enthusiasts were able to follow the progress of two ball games simultaneously. The mathemusical extravaganza on the final evening demonstrated the remarkable non-mathematical skills of the participants, who turned out to be a talented bunch. We had a number of beautiful piano performances, songs, guitar solos, a tuba and ukulele surprise, a very physical demonstration of New Zealand poi, and the traditional rendition of the complex number song, to name but a few items. The atmosphere was, as throughout the summer school, warm, friendly and supportive.

The second week was run by James Gazet with his usual enthusiasm and competence. The students began with "ice-breaker" problems on Sunday. This session was slightly curtailed because of a football match of interest to some [the World Cup Final!] that had been independently timetabled for the same evening. Those who wished to watch it were able to do so. Despite the shortened ice-breaker session, it was clear from the start of the competitions on Monday that all members of the Summer School had quickly identified with their teams. Throughout the week pupils worked hard, concentrated well through a lengthy daily programme and generated a quietly enthusiastic atmosphere.

Richard Atkins' detailed morning Masterclasses on Combinatorics ran from Monday to Friday, culminating in a discussion of Van der Waarden's Theorem. Though pupils had met the basic ideas in this area, the material presented increased in sophistication through the week. Nevertheless, all responded well and made efforts to solve the problems by combinatoric methods, even when other approaches were available. From Monday to Thursday the Masterclass was followed by the team competitions: individual, team & relays. The competitive spirit mounted steadily during the week and overall the Eulerians were the winners. This year the Team Choice time was split equally between team discussion and individual work. The Seniors were particularly adroit at managing the apportioning of individual problems to team members. Last year's innovation of a short post-competition discussion of points raised by the marking of the Team Choice solutions was repeated.

The afternoon session covered a variety of topics: Colouring Problems, Prime Numbers, Conic Sections, Modular Arithmetic, Area of a Triangle, Circle Theorems, Inequalities, and Invariance. On Monday evening there was a trading game, vigorously pursued and enjoyed. On Tuesday evening James Gazet presented some tips for problem-solving and the presentation of solutions. Then Michael Bradley discussed an approach to the solution of Conway's "Soldiers" problem, introduced the previous day.

The seniors had their own academic programme with their own Masterclasses, on Ramsey Theory given by Paul Russell, followed by afternoon sessions given by other members of the staff team.

Non-mathematical activities occupied the two remaining evenings. On Wednesday there was an enjoyable bowling trip (also involving an invigorating walk there and back). This was followed by a truly excellent "Extravaganza of Entertainment". As usual this was music-based with many enjoyable voice, piano and wind performances plus, as an extra this year the Seniors' "Surprise" sketch. The culminating rendition of "The Complex Number Song" was this year preceded by some impromptu brass playing, directed by Richard Atkins. Finally, on Friday morning the Combinatorics Masterclass was followed by a couple of relays and then by the traditonal quiz, in which apparently "ordinary" questions turn out to be mathematics-related after all.

Those running both weeks are extremely grateful for the excellent work of the senior students and staff as well as the hospitality of the Queen's Foundation.

### Pupils in attendance in Week 1

| | |
|---|---|
| Miriam Abraham | St Margaret's School for Girls |
| Greg Anderson | Whalsay School |
| Michael Ansell | Park House School |
| Jordan Bird | Calday Grange Grammar School |
| Konrad Bucher | Douglas Academy, Glasgow |
| James Bukraba | The Kimberley School |
| William Chang | Ysgol Friars |
| Samuel Cheshire | Clifton Comprehensive School |
| Andrew Coker | Caistor Grammar School |
| Tamsin Cornelius | Streatham & Clapham High School |
| Benjamin Dobson | Notre Dame High School |
| Jonathan Dungay | Steyning Grammar School |
| Yuka Esashi | Rye St Antony School |

| | |
|---|---|
| Luke Evans | Belper School |
| Andrew Fernandes | Saffron Walden County High School |
| Zachary Field | Beverley Grammar School |
| Heather Garside | Nottingham High School for Girls |
| Gareth Gould | Antrim Grammar School |
| James Hall | Watford Grammar School for Boys |
| John Howe | Aylesbury Grammar School |
| Matthew Jasper | St Crispin's School |
| Lisa Karlin | Channing School |
| Adam Kelly | Linton Village College |
| Emma Lang | Queen Elizabeth's School |
| Chris Lewis-Brown | Holy Trinity School |
| Aidan McClure | Boston Grammar School |
| Felix McPeake | High School of Glasgow |
| Sakunthala Panditharatne | Wycombe High School |
| Nicola Papastavrou | Cotham School |
| Miles Plaskett | Littleover Community School |
| Anna Randlesome | Sir John Leman High School |
| Sammy Rawson | Richmond School |
| Chris Russell | Mearns Castle High School |
| Emma Russell | Windermere School |
| Amy Saunders | St Alban's High School for Girls |
| Sam Shepherd | Hayes School |
| Paul Sinclair | Madras College |
| Andrew Sultana | King's School |
| Yinglun Teng | St John's College |
| Alex Tsaptsinos | Reading Blue Coat School |
| Samuel Udale-Smith | King Edward's School |
| Beiran Zhang | Fettes College |

**Pupils in attendance in Week 2**

| | |
|---|---|
| Max Baxter Allen | Millfield School |
| Ian Baldwin | Forest School |
| Natalie Behague | Dartford Girls' Grammar School |
| Niloy Biswas | Denbigh High School |
| Sam Brennan | Northgate High School |
| Jaehoon Cho | Mayflower County High School |

| | |
|---|---|
| Jake Cohen-Setton | St Paul's School |
| James Dixon | King Edward VI Grammar School |
| Amy Dosani | North London Collegiate School |
| Suzanna Eames | Stockport Grammar School |
| Robin Elliott | Reading School |
| James Fage | Westminster School |
| Oliver Feng | Olchfa Comprehensive School |
| Humphrey Galbraith | Winchester College |
| Adam Goucher | Heritage School |
| Anna Gould | Ampleforth College Senior School |
| Jennie Han | Redland High School |
| Eleanor Holderness | Latymer Upper School |
| Joshua Inoue | Queen Elizabeth's Hospital |
| Ralph Jordan | Bishops Stortford College |
| James Jordon | Prudhoe Community High School |
| Chava Kaye | Beth Jacob Grammar School |
| Dabin Kwon | Badminton School |
| Baichuan Li | Highgate School |
| Eleanor Loukes | Tonbridge Grammar School |
| Elena Markovitch | Bancroft's School |
| Benjamin Morley | Wells Cathedral School |
| Jananan Nathan | Merchant Taylors' School |
| Kevin Ngo | Sir John Cass's & Red Coat Schools |
| James Nicholls | Oakham School |
| Thomas Salt | Abingdon School |
| Saravanan Sathyanandha | Haberdashers' Aske's School for Boys |
| Thomas Saunders | St Olave's Grammar School |
| Asiya Siddiqua | King Edward VI High School for Girls |
| Josephine Solowiej-Wedderburn | Alleyn's School |
| Joe Tomkinson | Harry Carlton School |
| Vladimir Vankov | Royal Grammar School |
| Jessica Varley | Oundle School |
| Jamie Voros | St Paul's Girls' School |
| Han-Xi Wang | Watford Grammar School for Girls |
| Philip Warren | Sutton Grammar School for Boys |
| Clement Woo | Harrow School |

# Seniors

*Week 1*  Alice Ahn           Glasgow Academy
         Benjamin Barrett    Cardiff High School
         Rachael Booth       Ellen Wilkinson School for Girls
         Adam Dougall        Wymondham High School
         Eigen Horsfield     Tapton School
         Mark Lewis          Royal Latin School

*Week 2*  Lauren Ellison      Red Maids School
         James Munro         St Olave's Grammar School
         David Phillips      St Albans School
         Niral Shah          Merchant Taylors' School
         Angela Xu           Purcell School

# Staff

*Week 1*            *Week 2*
Vicky Neale        Bryn Garrod
Howard Groves      Anne Andrews
Andrew Jobbings    Paul Russell
Jo Harbour         Robin Bhattacharya
Alan Slomson       James Gazet
Mary Fortune       Michael Bradley
Vinay Kathotia     Raphael Fruet
Lizzie Kimber      Paul Smith
Vesna Kadelburg    Richard Atkins
Jo French
Andre Rzym
Phil Coggins
Calum Kilgour
John Slater

# Senior Mathematical Challenge and British Mathematical Olympiads

The Senior Challenge took place on Thursday 5th November 2009. Once again it, and also the BMO events, were sponsored by the Institute of Actuaries. There were 91,940 entries and around 1,200 took part in the next stage, British Mathematical Olympiad Round 1, held on Thursday 3rd December 2009.

## UK SENIOR MATHEMATICAL CHALLENGE

**Thursday 5 November 2009**

Organised by the **United Kingdom Mathematics Trust**

and supported by

**The Actuarial Profession**

making financial sense of the future

**RULES AND GUIDELINES** (to be read before starting)

1. Do not open the question paper until the invigilator tells you to do so.
2. **Use B or HB pencil only**. Mark *at most one* of the options A, B, C, D, E on the Answer Sheet for each question. Do not mark more than one option.
3. Time allowed: **90 minutes**.
   No answers or personal details may be entered on the Answer Sheet after the 90 minutes are over.
4. The use of rough paper is allowed.
   **Calculators, measuring instruments and squared paper are forbidden** .
5. Candidates must be full-time students at secondary school or FE college, and must be in Year 13 or below (England & Wales); S6 or below (Scotland); Year 14 or below (Northern Ireland).
6. There are twenty-five questions. Each question is followed by five options marked A, B, C, D, E. Only one of these is correct. Enter the letter A-E corresponding to the correct answer in the corresponding box on the Answer Sheet.
7. **Scoring rules**: all candidates start out with 25 marks;
   0 marks are awarded for each question left unanswered;
   4 marks are awarded for each correct answer;
   **1 mark is deducted** for each incorrect answer.
8. **Guessing**: Remember that there is a penalty for wrong answers. Note also that later questions are deliberately intended to be harder than earlier questions. You are thus advised to concentrate first on solving as many as possible of the first 15-20 questions. Only then should you try later questions.

**The United Kingdom Mathematics Trust is a Registered Charity.**

*http://www.ukmt.org.uk*

1. What is 20% of 30%?

   A  6%    B  10%    C  15%    D  50%    E  60%

2. Which of the following is not a multiple of 15?

   A  135    B  315    C  555    D  785    E  915

3. What is the value of $1^6 - 2^5 + 3^4 - 4^3 + 5^2 - 6^1$?

   A  1    B  2    C  3    D  4    E  5

4. Steve travelled 150 miles on a motorbike and used 10 litres of petrol. Given that 1 gallon $\approx 4.5$ litres, roughly how many miles per gallon did Steve achieve on his journey?

   A  10    B  20    C  40    D  50    E  70

5. Boris Biker entered the Tour de Transylvania with an unusual bicycle whose back wheel is larger than the front. The radius of the back wheel is 40 cm, and the radius of the front wheel is 30 cm. On the first stage of the race the smaller wheel made 120000 revolutions. How many revolutions did the larger wheel make?

   A  90000    B  $90000\pi$    C  160000    D  $\dfrac{160000}{\pi}$    E  120000

6. A bag contains hundreds of glass marbles, each one coloured either red, orange, green or blue. There are more than 2 marbles of each colour.

   Marbles are drawn randomly from the bag, one at a time, and not replaced.

   How many marbles must be drawn from the bag in order to ensure at least three marbles of the same colour are drawn?

   A  4    B  7    C  9    D  12    E  13

7. A mini-sudoku is a 4 by 4 grid, where each row, column and 2 by 2 outlined block contains the digits 1, 2, 3 and 4 once and once only. How many different ways are there of completing the mini-sudoku shown?

   A 1    B 2    C 4    D 8    E 12

8. The entries to the Senior Mathematical Challenge grew from 87400 in 2007 to 92690 in 2008. Approximately what percentage increase does this represent?

   A  4%    B  5%    C  6%    D  7%    E  8%

9. A square $PQRS$ has sides of length $x$. $T$ is the midpoint of $QR$ and $U$ is the foot of the perpendicular from $T$ to $QS$. What is the length of $TU$?

   A  $\dfrac{x}{2}$    B  $\dfrac{x}{3}$    C  $\dfrac{x}{\sqrt{2}}$    D  $\dfrac{x}{2\sqrt{2}}$    E  $\dfrac{x}{4}$

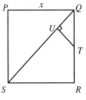

10. Consider all three-digit numbers formed by using *different* digits from 0, 1, 2, 3 and 5. How many of these numbers are divisible by 6?

   A  4         B  7         C  10         D  15         E  20

11. For what value of $x$ is $\sqrt{2} + \sqrt{2} + \sqrt{2} + \sqrt{2} = 2^x$ true?

   A  $\frac{1}{2}$      B  $1\frac{1}{2}$      C  $2\frac{1}{2}$      D  $3\frac{1}{2}$      E  $4\frac{1}{2}$

12. Which of the following has the greatest value?

   A  $\cos 50°$      B  $\sin 50°$      C  $\tan 50°$      D  $\dfrac{1}{\sin 50°}$      E  $\dfrac{1}{\cos 50°}$

13. Suppose that $x - \dfrac{1}{x} = y - \dfrac{1}{y}$ and $x \neq y$. What is the value of $xy$?

   A  4      B  1      C  $-1$      D  $-4$      E  more information is needed

14. $P, Q, R, S, T$ are vertices of a regular polygon. The sides $PQ$ and $TS$ are produced to meet at $X$, as shown in the diagram, and $\angle QXS = 140°$. How many sides does the polygon have?

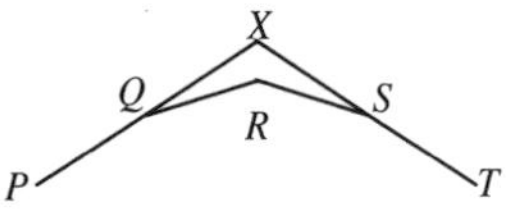

   A  9      B  18      C  24      D  27      E  40

15. For how many integers $n$ is $\dfrac{n}{100 - n}$ also an integer?

   A  1         B  6         C  10         D  18         E  100

16. The positive numbers $x$ and $y$ satisfy the equations $x^4 - y^4 = 2009$ and $x^2 + y^2 = 49$. What is the value of $y$?

   A  1      B  2      C  3      D  4      E  more information is needed

17. A solid cube is divided into two pieces by a single rectangular cut. As a result, the total surface area increases by a fraction $f$ of the surface area of the original cube. What is the greatest possible value of $f$?

   A  $\dfrac{1}{3}$      B  $\dfrac{\sqrt{3}}{4}$      C  $\dfrac{\sqrt{2}}{3}$      D  $\dfrac{1}{2}$      E  $\dfrac{1}{\sqrt{3}}$

18. Which of the following could be part of the graph of the curve $y^2 = x(2 - x)$?

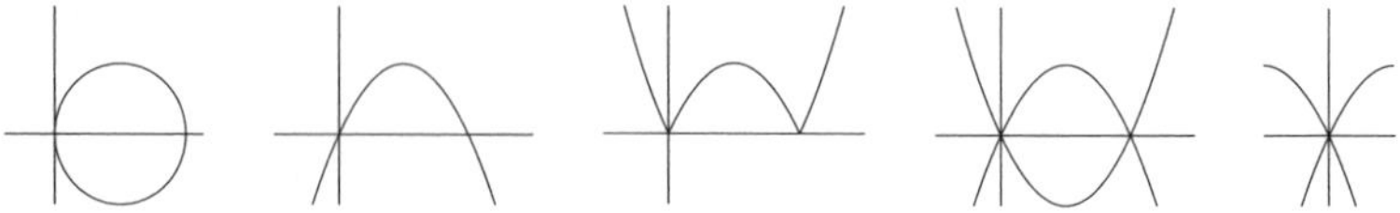

   A         B         C         D         E

19. Hamish and his friend Ben live in villages which are 51 miles apart. During the summer holidays, they agreed to cycle towards each other along the same main road. Starting at noon, Hamish cycled at $x$ mph. Starting at 2 pm, Ben cycled at $y$ mph. They met at 4 pm. If they had both started at noon, they would have met at 2.50 pm. What is the value of $y$?

A  7.5          B  8          C  10.5          D  12          E  12.75

20. A point $P$ is chosen at random inside a square $QRST$. What is the probability that $\angle RPQ$ is acute?

A  $\dfrac{3}{4}$     B  $\sqrt{2}-1$   C  $\dfrac{1}{2}$    D  $\dfrac{\pi}{4}$    E  $1-\dfrac{\pi}{8}$

21. A frustum is the solid obtained by slicing a right-circular cone perpendicular to its axis and removing the small cone above the slice. This leaves a shape with two circular faces and a curved surface. The original cone has base radius 6 cm and height 8 cm, and the curved surface area of the frustum is equal to the area of the two circles. What is the height of the frustum?

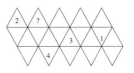

A  3 cm       B  4 cm       C  5 cm       D  6 cm       E  7 cm

22. $M$ and $N$ are the midpoints of sides $GH$ and $FG$, respectively, of parallelogram $EFGH$. The area of triangle $ENM$ is 12 cm². What is the area of the parallelogram $EFGH$?

A  20 cm²   B  24 cm²   C  32 cm²   D  48 cm²   E  more information is required

23. The net shown is folded into an icosahedron and the remaining faces are numbered such that at each vertex the numbers 1 to 5 all appear. What number must go on the face with a  question mark?

A  1          B  2          C  3          D  4          E  5

24. A figure in the shape of a cross is made from five $1 \times 1$ squares, as shown. The cross is inscribed in a large square whose sides are parallel to the dashed square, formed by four of the vertices of the cross. What is the area of the large outer square?

A  9          B  $\dfrac{49}{5}$     C  10          D  $\dfrac{81}{8}$     E  $\dfrac{32}{3}$

25. Four positive integers $a$, $b$, $c$ and $d$ are such that

$$abcd + abc + bcd + cda + dab + ab + bc + cd + da + ac + bd + a + b + c + d = 2009.$$

What is the value of $a + b + c + d$?

A  73          B  75          C  77          D  79          E  81

114

## Further remarks

The 2009 paper was again marked by UKMT (in the same way as the Junior and Intermediate Challenges) rather than being marked in centres. This provided the full profile of marks and a valuable breakdown for the Problems Group. Schools were provided with the usual pupil answer sheet (shown below) and so could give the rapid feedback which is a feature of the Senior Challenge.

| | |
|---|---|
| 1. | |
| 2. | |
| 3. | |
| 4. | |
| 5. | |
| 6. | |
| 7. | |
| 8. | |
| 9. | |
| 10. | |
| 11. | |
| 12. | |
| 13. | |
| 14. | |
| 15. | |
| 16. | |
| 17. | |
| 18. | |
| 19. | |
| 20. | |
| 21. | |
| 22. | |
| 23. | |
| 24. | |
| 25. | |

## UK SENIOR MATHEMATICAL CHALLENGE
### THURSDAY 5 NOVEMBER 2009

### ANSWER SHEET

#### To be completed by the student

SCHOOL/COLLEGE NAME .........................................

UKMT CENTRE NUMBER .........................................

YOUR NAME .........................................

SCHOOL YEAR .........................................

MATHS SET/ TEACHER .........................................

*Enter the option (A, B, C, D or E) which corresponds to the correct answer for each question in the box for that question.*

#### To be completed by the teacher not by the student

Each question is worth *four* marks.

*One* mark is deducted for each wrong answer.

No marks are deducted for questions left unanswered.

The total score is calculated by taking four times the number of correct answers, subtracting the number of wrong answers, and then adding 25.

Number correct ☐ × 4 = ☐

− Number wrong ☐

Difference ☐

+     25

Total score ☐

*NB: Blank papers score 25.*

*Please do NOT return to UKMT*

The solutions are provided in a leaflet which is also set up to facilitate marking in centres who wished to continue to mark in house.

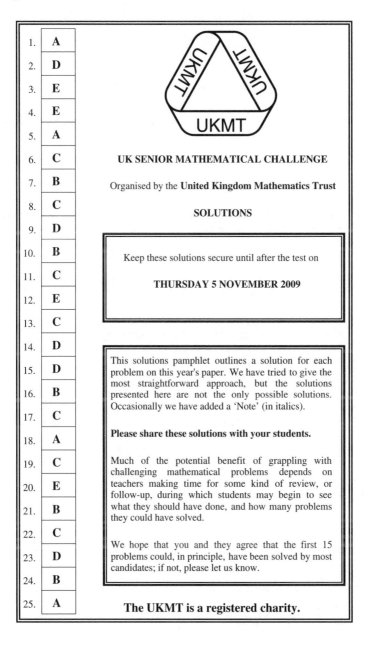

| 1. | A |
| 2. | D |
| 3. | E |
| 4. | E |
| 5. | A |
| 6. | C |
| 7. | B |
| 8. | C |
| 9. | D |
| 10. | B |
| 11. | C |
| 12. | E |
| 13. | C |
| 14. | D |
| 15. | D |
| 16. | B |
| 17. | C |
| 18. | A |
| 19. | C |
| 20. | E |
| 21. | B |
| 22. | C |
| 23. | D |
| 24. | B |
| 25. | A |

UK SENIOR MATHEMATICAL CHALLENGE

Organised by the **United Kingdom Mathematics Trust**

SOLUTIONS

Keep these solutions secure until after the test on

**THURSDAY 5 NOVEMBER 2009**

This solutions pamphlet outlines a solution for each problem on this year's paper. We have tried to give the most straightforward approach, but the solutions presented here are not the only possible solutions. Occasionally we have added a 'Note' (in italics).

**Please share these solutions with your students.**

Much of the potential benefit of grappling with challenging mathematical problems depends on teachers making time for some kind of review, or follow-up, during which students may begin to see what they should have done, and how many problems they could have solved.

We hope that you and they agree that the first 15 problems could, in principle, have been solved by most candidates; if not, please let us know.

**The UKMT is a registered charity.**

## 116

**1.** **A** 20% of 30% = 0.2 × 0.3 = 0.06 = 6%.

**2.** **D** $\dfrac{785}{15} = 52\frac{1}{3}$ hence 785 is not a multiple of 15. But $\dfrac{135}{15} = 9$, $\dfrac{315}{15} = 21$, $\dfrac{555}{15} = 37$, $\dfrac{915}{15} = 61$.

**3.** **E** 1 − 32 + 81 − 64 + 25 − 6 = 5.

**4.** **E** Steve achieved $\dfrac{150}{10}$ × 4.5 miles per gallon which is 15 × 4.5 = 67.5 ≈ 70.

**5.** **A** As the ratio of the radii is 3 : 4 then the number of revolutions made by the larger wheel is 120000 × $\frac{3}{4}$ = 90000.

**6.** **C** If at most two marbles of each colour are chosen, the maximum number we can choose is 8, corresponding to 2 of each. Therefore, if 9 are chosen, we must have at least 3 of one colour, but this statement is not true if 9 is replaced by any number less than 9.

**7.** **B** The top left 2 by 2 outlined block must contain a 3 and a 4 and this can be done in two ways. For each choice there is only one way to complete the entire mini-sudoku.

**8.** **C** The increase in entries from 2007 to 2008 is 92 690 − 87 400 = 5290.
Hence the percentage increase is $\dfrac{5290}{87400}$ × 100% = $\dfrac{5290}{874}$% ≈ $\dfrac{5400}{900}$% = 6%.
(The exact value is $6\frac{1}{19}$.)

**9.** **D** As $T$ is the midpoint of $QR$ then $QT = \frac{1}{2}x$.
Since $\angle UQT = \angle SQR = 45°$ and $\angle QUT = 90°$, $\angle UTQ = 45°$.
Thus triangle $QTU$ is isosceles with $UQ = UT$.
In triangle $QTU$, by Pythagoras' Theorem, $QT^2 = QU^2 + TU^2$.
Hence $\left(\frac{1}{2}x\right)^2 = 2TU^2$ so $TU^2 = \frac{1}{8}x^2$ giving $TU = \dfrac{x}{2\sqrt{2}}$.

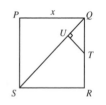

**10.** **B** A number is a multiple of 6 precisely when it is both a multiple of 2 and of 3. To be a multiple of 2, it will need to end with an even digit; i.e. 0 or 2. If it ends with 0, the sum of the other two digits must be a multiple of 3; and only 3 = 1 + 2 or 6 = 1 + 5 are possible. That gives the numbers 120, 210, 150, 510. If it ends with 2, the sum of the others must be 1 = 0 + 1 or 4 = 1 + 3. That gives 102, 132 and 312.

**11.** **C** $\sqrt{2} + \sqrt{2} + \sqrt{2} + \sqrt{2} = 4\sqrt{2} = 2^2 \times 2^{1/2} = 2^{2\frac{1}{2}}$. Hence $x = 2\frac{1}{2}$.

**12.** **E** $\cos 50° < \sin 50° < 1$. Hence $\dfrac{1}{\cos 50°} > \dfrac{1}{\sin 50°} > 1 > \sin 50° > \cos 50°$.
$\tan 50° = \dfrac{\sin 50°}{\cos 50°} < \dfrac{1}{\cos 50°}$ hence $\dfrac{1}{\cos 50°}$ has the greatest value.

**13.** **C** $x - \dfrac{1}{x} = y - \dfrac{1}{y}$ hence $x^2y - y = xy^2 - x$. Thus $xy(y - x) + y - x = 0$.
Therefore $(y - x)(xy + 1) = 0$. As $x \neq y$ then $y - x \neq 0$.
Hence $xy + 1 = 0$ giving $xy = -1$.

**14. D**  Let the external angle of the regular polygon be $x°$.
Hence $\angle XQR = \angle XSR = x°$ and reflex angle
$\angle QRS = (180 + x)°$.
As the sum of the angles in the quadrilateral $QRSX$ is
$360°$ then $140 + x + x + 180 + x = 360$.
Hence $3x = 40$ and the polygon has $\dfrac{360}{40 \div 3} = 27$ sides.

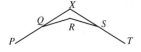

**15. D**  Let $\dfrac{n}{100 - n} = x$ where $x$ is an integer. Hence $n = 100x - nx$.
Hence $n(1 + x) = 100x$ giving $n = \dfrac{100x}{1 + x}$.
Now $x$ and $1 + x$ can have no common factors. Therefore $1 + x$ must be a factor of 100
and can be any of them.
Hence $1 + x \in \{\pm1, \pm2, \pm4, \pm5, \pm10, \pm20, \pm25, \pm50, \pm100\}$ thus the number of
possible integers $n$ is 18.

**16. B**  Since $x^4 - y^4 = 2009$ it follows that $(x^2 + y^2)(x^2 - y^2) = 2009$.
But $x^2 + y^2 = 49$ hence $x^2 - y^2 = \dfrac{2009}{49} = 41$.
Subtracting gives $2y^2 = 8$ hence $y^2 = 4$. Since $y > 0, y = 2$.

**17. C**  The greatest possible value of $f$ is achieved by a rectangular cut through an edge of a
cube and the furthest edge from it. If we take $x$ as the side of the cube, by Pythagoras'
Theorem the extra surface area formed by the cut is $2\sqrt{2}x^2$. Hence $f = \dfrac{2\sqrt{2}x^2}{6x^2} = \dfrac{\sqrt{2}}{3}$.

**18. A**  We have $y^2 = x(2 - x)$. Now $y^2 \geqslant 0$ for all real $y$ hence $x(2 - x) \geqslant 0$.
Hence $0 \leqslant x \leqslant 2$. In fact we can rewrite the equation as $(x - 1)^2 + y^2 = 1$; so this is
a circle of radius 1 with centre $(1,0)$.

**19. C**  The distance cycled by Hamish between noon and 4 pm is $4x$.
The distance cycled by Ben between 2 pm and 4 pm is $2y$.
They meet at 4 pm hence $4x + 2y = 51$ or $2x + 2(x + y) = 51$ (*).
If they had both started at noon then they would have met at 2:50 pm and so $2\frac{5}{6}(x + y) = 51$.
Hence $x + y = 51 \times \dfrac{6}{17} = 18$. Hence from (*) $2x + 2 \times 18 = 51$.
Hence $2x = 15$ giving $x = 7\frac{1}{2}$. Thus $y = 10\frac{1}{2}$.

**20. E**  If $\angle RPQ = 90°$ then $P$ lies on a semicircle of diameter $RQ$.
Let $x$ be the side-length of the square $QRST$.
Hence the area of the semicircle $RPQ = \frac{1}{2}\pi \left(\frac{1}{2}x\right)^2 = \frac{1}{8}\pi x^2$ and the
area of square $QRST$ is $x^2$.
$\angle RPQ$ is acute when $P$ is outside the semicircle $RPQ$.

Hence the probability that $\angle RPQ$ is acute is $\dfrac{x^2 - \frac{1}{8}\pi x^2}{x^2} = 1 - \dfrac{\pi}{8}$.

**21.** **B** Let $r$ be the radius of the small cone and $h$ the height.
Let $l_1$ and $l_2$ be the slant heights of the small and large cones respectively.
By Pythagoras' Theorem $l_2 = \sqrt{6^2 + 8^2} = 10$.
Using similar triangles, $\dfrac{l_1}{r} = \dfrac{10}{6}$ so $l_1 = \dfrac{5}{3}r$ and $\dfrac{h}{8} = \dfrac{r}{6}$ giving $h = \dfrac{4}{3}r$.
Thus the area of the curved surface of the frustum is

$$\pi \times 6 \times 10 - \pi \times r \times \frac{5}{3} \times r = \pi\left(60 - \frac{5r^2}{3}\right).$$

The sum of the areas of the two circles is $\pi \times 6^2 + \pi \times r^2 = \pi\left(36 + r^2\right)$.
Hence $\pi\left(60 - \dfrac{5r^2}{3}\right) = \pi\left(36 + r^2\right)$ and so $24 = \dfrac{8r^2}{3}$ giving $r = 3$, so $h = \dfrac{4}{3} \times 3 = 4$.
Therefore, in cms, the height of the frustum is $8 - 4 = 4$.

**22.** **C** Let the perpendicular distance between $EH$ and $FG$ be $x$ cm and
the area of the parallelogram $EFGH$ be $y$ cm$^2$. Thus $y = FG \times x$.
The area of triangle $EFN$ is $\frac{1}{2}FN \times x = \frac{1}{2} \times \frac{1}{2} \times FG \times x = \frac{1}{4}y$ cm$^2$.
Likewise the areas of triangles $EHM$ and $NGM$ are $\frac{1}{4}y$ cm$^2$ and
$\frac{1}{8}y$ cm$^2$ respectively.
The area of triangle $ENM$ is 12 cm$^2$, hence $y = 12 + \frac{5}{8}y$ and so
$y = 32$. Hence the area of the parallelogram $EFGH$ is 32 cm$^2$.

**23.** **D** Label the rows of the triangles from left to right as follows: $a_1, \ldots, a_5$; $b_1, \ldots, b_{10}$ and
$c_1, \ldots, c_5$.
Now 1 cannot be at $a_4, a_5, b_7, b_8$ or $c_4$ hence 1 must be at $c_3$.
Hence $b_4$ and $b_5$ are 2 and 5 in either order. Hence $a_3$ is 1 or 4.
But 1 cannot be at $a_4$ or $b_7$ hence 1 must be at $a_3$.
4 cannot be at $b_3$ thus 4 is at $a_2$.
Hence the number on the face with the question mark must be 4.

**24.** **B** A shaded triangle is congruent to an unshaded triangle (ASA).
Hence the area of the dashed square is equal to the area of the cross
and both are 5.
Thus the side-length of the dashed square is $\sqrt{5}$.
Hence the sides of a shaded triangle are: $\frac{1}{2}$, 1 and $\frac{1}{2}\sqrt{5}$.
Now the perpendicular distance between the squares is equal to the
altitude, $h$, of the shaded triangle. The area of such a triangle is
$\frac{1}{2} \times \left(\frac{1}{2} \times 1\right) = \frac{1}{4}$ so that $\frac{1}{2} \times \left(\frac{1}{2}\sqrt{5} \times h\right) = \frac{1}{4}$ which gives $h = \dfrac{1}{\sqrt{5}}$.
Hence the length of the sides of the outer square are $\sqrt{5} + 2 \times \dfrac{1}{\sqrt{5}} = \dfrac{5}{\sqrt{5}} + \dfrac{2}{\sqrt{5}} = \dfrac{7}{\sqrt{5}}$.
Thus the area of the large square is $\left(\dfrac{7}{\sqrt{5}}\right)^2 = \dfrac{49}{5}$.

**25.** **A** The left-hand side of the equation can be written as

$$(a + 1)(b + 1)(c + 1)(d + 1) - 1.$$

Hence

$$(a + 1)(b + 1)(c + 1)(d + 1) = 2010.$$

Now expressing 2010 as a product of primes gives $2010 = 2 \times 3 \times 5 \times 67$ hence
$a + b + c + d = 1 + 2 + 4 + 66 = 73$.

## The answers

The table below shows the proportion of pupils' choices. The correct answer is shown in bold. [The percentages are rounded to the nearest whole number.]

| Qn | A | B | C | D | E | Blank |
|---|---|---|---|---|---|---|
| 1 | **92** | 1 | 1 | 0 | 5 | 1 |
| 2 | 2 | 2 | 8 | **86** | 1 | 1 |
| 3 | 3 | 2 | 8 | 4 | **79** | 5 |
| 4 | 2 | 4 | 4 | 4 | **83** | 4 |
| 5 | **52** | 5 | 29 | 5 | 2 | 7 |
| 6 | 3 | 4 | **37** | 26 | 7 | 22 |
| 7 | 11 | **52** | 13 | 7 | 6 | 10 |
| 8 | 6 | 11 | **62** | 8 | 5 | 7 |
| 9 | 9 | 6 | 12 | **36** | 16 | 21 |
| 10 | 17 | **36** | 11 | 8 | 7 | 21 |
| 11 | 5 | 10 | **48** | 5 | 13 | 19 |
| 12 | 7 | 10 | 16 | 14 | **24** | 30 |
| 13 | 2 | 6 | **33** | 2 | 31 | 25 |
| 14 | 20 | 18 | 7 | **9** | 2 | 44 |
| 15 | 17 | 17 | 17 | **8** | 8 | 32 |
| 16 | 3 | **20** | 4 | 5 | 26 | 42 |
| 17 | 20 | 4 | **12** | 8 | 3 | 53 |
| 18 | **28** | 12 | 9 | 11 | 6 | 34 |
| 19 | 4 | 5 | **18** | 4 | 8 | 61 |
| 20 | 15 | 3 | 13 | 4 | **7** | 58 |
| 21 | 3 | **8** | 4 | 4 | 2 | 79 |
| 22 | 1 | 7 | **9** | 8 | 8 | 66 |
| 23 | 3 | 2 | 4 | **5** | 16 | 69 |
| 24 | 14 | **8** | 5 | 4 | 2 | 67 |
| 25 | **4** | 3 | 4 | 4 | 3 | 82 |

**SMC 2009: Some comments on the pupils' choice of answers as sent to schools in the letter with the results**

The average score rose to 51.4 in 2009 from 48.4 in 2008. This is pleasing, but looking more deeply at the distribution of the answers to individual questions, a copy of which you should receive with your results, shows some areas of concern.

The first 5 questions are intended to be very straightforward. The answers to questions 1 to 4 were very encouraging, but it is disconcerting to see that, in answering Question 5 no fewer than 29% of the students thought that the larger wheel would make more revolutions than the smaller wheel! Of course, it is easy to slip up and multiply by 4/3 rather than by 3/4, but we hope students are encouraged to apply a "reality check" to questions with a practical content.

Question 6 does not depend on any techniques. It just needs clear thinking, but 22% of the students failed to answer it, and just under half of those who did give an answer chose the correct option. Some students may have taken one look at Question 12, and been at a loss as to how to answer a question about the values of trigonometric function without a calculator. So we hope you will have the time to go over this question to show that, without any calculations, but just using a general understanding of how the functions behave, it is possible to decide which has the largest value. Indeed, except for the question as to whether $\tan 50°$ is greater or less than $1/\sin 50°$, the relative sizes of all the given function values may be decided quite easily.

The Problems Group aims to make the first 15 questions accessible to all pupils, while the last 10 questions are deliberately intended to be significantly harder, so they can help us to identify students who might make it to the International Mathematical Olympiad.

Two of the later questions, 18 and 19, were solved correctly by a pleasing number of students. The last few questions are really hard and anyone who got even one of these right, without guessing, can feel very pleased with themselves.

As ever, the Problems Group is keen to have teachers' comments on the questions. Are we setting any questions, especially among the early ones, that your pupils could not reasonably be expected to solve? The Problems Group will be meeting in January to set the next paper.

# The SMC marks

As the papers are marked centrally, the full profile of the marks is available and this is shown below.

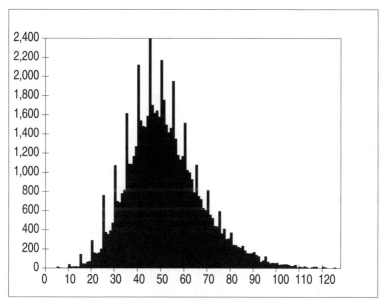

Bar chart showing the actual frequencies in the 2009 SMC

Overall, the paper was slightly easier than in 2008 so the cut-offs were lowered accordingly. On the basis of the standard proportions used by the UKMT, the cut-off marks were set at

GOLD – 79 or over      SILVER – 64 to 78      BRONZE – 54 to 63

# List of high scorers in the 2009 UK Senior Mathematical Challenge

| 125 | Jonis Botan | Rosedale College, Hayes |
| | Andrew Carlotti | Sir Roger Manwood's School, Sandwich |
| | Martin Chan | Westminster School, London |
| | Qiyang Chen | Queen Elizabeths Grammar School, Blackburn |
| | Katherin Chiu | Island School |
| | Ruth Franklin | Manchester High School for Girls |
| | Jordan Millar | Regent House School, Newtownards |
| | Geoffrey Penington | Abingdon School, Abingdon |
| | Tan Ratana | Cambridge Centre for Sixth Form Studies |
| | Weerapat Satitkanitkul | Cambridge Centre for Sixth Form Studies |
| | Jack Smith | King's School, Grantham |
| | Singyung Tse | Cardiff Sixth Form College, Cardiff |
| | Xinlin Zhao | Royal Russell School, Croydon |
| 121 | Park Chui | Winchester College, Winchester |
| | Hyeon ki Jeong | Hanoi International School, Ba Dinh |
| | Nicholas Leung | St Paul's School, Barnes |
| | Edwina Luo | Ashford School, Ashford |
| | Tom Oneill | Devonport High School for Boys, Plymouth |
| | Tanon Protpagorn | Winchester College, Winchester |
| | Fai Tsang | Sevenoaks School, Sevenoaks |
| | Ruoyu Wu | Merchiston Castle School, Edinburgh |
| | Yveline Zhang | Bootham School, Bootham |
| 120 | Duncan Bell | St Olave's Grammar School, Orpington |
| | James Bell | Macmillan Academy, Middlesborough |
| | Luke Betts | Hills Road VI Form College, Cambridge |
| | Nathan Brown | King Edward VI Camp Hill Boys' School, Kings Heath |
| | Woojin Chae | Eton College, Berks |
| | Chen Ding | Quinton House School, Upton |
| | Richard Freeland | Winchester College, Winchester |
| | Nathan Hsu | South Island School, Aberdeen, Hong Kong |
| | Hyunjik Kim | Hampton School, Hampton |

| | | |
|---|---|---|
| | Yuming Mei | Hills Road VI Form College, Cambridge |
| | James Munro | St Olave's Grammar School, Orpington |
| | Nhat Pham | Chelsea Independent College, London |
| | Alex Roberts | Grange School, Hartford |
| | Dilin Wu | Royal Russell School, Croydon |
| | Martin Wu | Ruthin School, Ruthin |
| | Yaw en Yin | Eastbourne College, Eastbourne |
| | Tomas Zeman | Winchester College, Winchester |
| 117 | Alice Ahn | Glasgow Academy |
| | Lawrence Barrott | Royal Grammar School, Guildford |
| | Richard Chen | Harrow School Harrow on the Hill |
| | Andrea Chlebikova | Brighton Hove and Sussex SFC Hove |
| | Xuyang Dang | Harrow International School, Chaoyang District |
| | Minjee Hong | Bangkok Patana School, Sukhumvit 105 |
| | Keyang Hu | Caterham School, Caterham |
| | Jinyang Huang | St Peter's School, York |
| | Chris King | Worcester VI Form College, Worcester |
| | Kirby Lam | Harrow School, Harrow on the Hill |
| | Joshua Lam | Leys School, Cambridge |
| | Andrew Mc clement | Hutcheson's Grammar School |
| | Alex Philpott | The Grammar School at Leeds |
| | Niral Shah | Merchant Taylors' School, Northwood |
| | Bo Wang | Dulwich College, Dulwich Common |
| | Chuwei Zhang | Ruthin School, Ruthin |
| 116 | Jake Chan | Sha Tin College, Sha Tin |
| | Jiasheng Chen | Abbey College, Cambridge |
| | Yuan Feng | Cambridge Tutors College, Croydon |
| | Minsu Jang | Overseas Family School, Singapore |
| | Jeremy Lam | Charterhouse, Godalming |
| | Hwanhee Lee | The British International School, Shanghai |
| | Henry Mak | Charterhouse, Godalming |
| | David Phillips | St Albans School, St Albans |
| | Juan Ryan | Eton College, Berks |

| | | |
|---|---|---|
| | Mark Salmon | Royal Grammar School, High Wycombe |
| | Yuqi Song | John Leggott VI Form College, Scunthorpe |
| | Hugo Sun | Warwick School Warwick |
| | Yuya Tanaka | South Island School, Aberdeen, Hong Kong |
| | Gareth Wilkes | Grange School, Hartford |
| | Angela Xu | Purcell School, Bushey |
| | Hoikang Yang | St Dominic's VI Form Centre, Harrow on the Hill |
| | Charlie Zhou | Eton College, Berks |
| 115 | Thomas Anthony | Hampton School, Hampton |
| | James Ascott | Sir Henry Floyd Grammar School Aylesbury |
| | Jim Ashworth | Trinity School, Croydon |
| | Hu Benhao | Kingswood School, Bath |
| | Yanqing Cheng | Hills Road VI Form College, Cambridge |
| | Johnny Koh | Charterhouse, Godalming |
| | Matei Mandache | Loughborough Grammar School, Loughborough |
| | Sergei Patiakin | Dame Alice Owen's School, Potters Bar |
| | Ram Sarujan | Dr Challoner's Grammar School, Amersham |
| | Angel Wong | Badminton School |
| 113 | Mentor Cheung | Warwick School, Warwick |
| | Oliver Feng | Olchfa Comprehensive School, Sketty |
| | Benjamin Gill | Royal Grammar School, High Wycombe |
| | John Gowers | Eton College, Berks |
| | Metin Ilgen | American Collegiate Institute, Izmir |
| | Edward Kwok | Caterham School, Caterham |
| | Henry Nicholson | Eton College, Berks |
| | Stanley Pinsent | Lawrence Sheriff School, Rugby |
| | Joel Thompson | Stockton Sixth Form College, Stockton-on-Tees |
| | Eujin Yeo | Westminster School, London |
| | Yi Zhang | Abbey College, Cambridge |

A sample of one of the certificates is shown below.

UK SENIOR MATHEMATICAL CHALLENGE

# 2009

of

received a

## GOLD CERTIFICATE

Bernard Silverman

**The Actuarial Profession**
making financial sense of the future

Chairman, United Kingdom Mathematics Trust

---

## THE UNITED KINGDOM SENIOR MATHEMATICAL CHALLENGE

The Senior Mathematical Challenge (SMC) is run by the UK Mathematics Trust. The SMC encourages mathematical reasoning, precision of thought, and fluency in using basic mathematical techniques to solve interesting problems. It is aimed at those in full-time education and with sufficient mathematical competence to undertake a post-16 course.

The problems on the SMC are designed to make students think. Most are accessible, yet still challenge those with more experience; they are also meant to be memorable and enjoyable.

Mathematics controls more aspects of the modern world than most people realise—from iPods, cash machines, telecommunications and airline booking systems to production processes in engineering, efficient distribution and stock-holding, investment strategies and 'whispering' jet engines. The scientific and industrial revolutions flowed from the realisation that mathematics was both the language of nature, and also a way of analysing—and hence controlling—our environment. In the last fifty years old and new applications of mathematical ideas have transformed the way we live.

All these developments depend on mathematical thinking—a mode of thought whose essential style is far more permanent than the wave of technological change which it has made possible. The problems on the SMC reflect this style, which pervades all mathematics, by encouraging students to think clearly about challenging problems.

The SMC was established as the National Mathematics Contest in 1961. In 2008 there were over 90,000 entries from 1918 schools and colleges. Certificates are awarded to the highest scoring 40% of candidates (6% Gold, 13% Silver, 21% Bronze).

Further information on the UKMT and its activities can be found at www.ukmt.org.uk

# The next stage

Subject to certain conditions, candidates who obtained a score of 91 or over in the 2009 Senior Mathematical Challenge were invited to take the British Mathematical Olympiad Round One. Within the UKMT, the British Mathematical Olympiad Subtrust has control of the papers and everything pertaining to them. The BMOS produces an annual account of its events which, for 2009-2010, was edited by James Cranch (University of Leicester) and Jack Shotton (Trinity College, Cambridge). Much of this report is included in the following pages.

United Kingdom Mathematics Trust

## British Mathematical Olympiad

### Round 1 : Thursday, 3 December 2009

**Time allowed**  *Three and a half hours.*

**Instructions**  • *Full written solutions – not just answers – are required, with complete proofs of any assertions you may make. Marks awarded will depend on the clarity of your mathematical presentation. Work in rough first, and then write up your best attempt.*

*Do not hand in rough work.*

• *One **complete** solution will gain more credit than several unfinished attempts. It is more important to complete a small number of questions than to try all the problems.*

• *Each question carries 10 marks. However, earlier questions tend to be easier. In general you are advised to concentrate on these problems first.*

• *The use of rulers and compasses is allowed, but calculators and protractors are forbidden.*

• *Start each question on a fresh sheet of paper. Write on one side of the paper only. On each sheet of working write the number of the question in the top **left**-hand corner and your name, initials and school in the top **right**-hand corner.*

• *Complete the cover sheet provided and attach it to the front of your script, followed by your solutions in question number order.*

• *Staple all the pages neatly together in the top **left**-hand corner.*

**Do not turn over until told to do so.**

United Kingdom Mathematics Trust

## 2009/10 British Mathematical Olympiad
## Round 1: Thursday, 3 December 2009

1.  Find all integers $x$, $y$ and $z$ such that
    $$x^2 + y^2 + z^2 = 2(yz + 1) \text{ and } x + y + z = 4018.$$

2.  Points $A$, $B$, $C$, $D$ and $E$ lie, in that order, on a circle and the lines $AB$ and $ED$ are parallel. Prove that $\angle ABC = 90°$ if, and only if, $AC^2 = BD^2 + CE^2$.

3.  Isaac attempts all six questions on an Olympiad paper in order. Each question is marked on a scale from 0 to 10. He never scores more in a later question than in any earlier question. How many different possible sequences of six marks can he achieve?

4.  Two circles, of different radius, with centres at $B$ and $C$, touch externally at $A$. A common tangent, not through $A$, touches the first circle at $D$ and the second at $E$. The line through $A$ which is perpendicular to $DE$ and the perpendicular bisector of $BC$ meet at $F$. Prove that $BC = 2AF$.

5.  Find all functions $f$, defined on the real numbers and taking real values, which satisfy the equation $f(x)f(y) = f(x + y) + xy$ for all real numbers $x$ and $y$.

6.  Long John Silverman has captured a treasure map from Adam McBones. Adam has buried the treasure at the point $(x, y)$ with integer co-ordinates (not necessarily positive). He has indicated on the map the values of $x^2 + y$ and $x + y^2$, and these numbers are distinct. Prove that Long John has to dig only in one place to find the treasure.

# The British Mathematical Olympiad 2009-2010

The paper was marked by volunteers in December. Below is a list of the prize winners from Round 1.

## Round 1 Prize Winners
The following contestants were awarded prizes:

### Gold Medals

| | |
|---|---|
| Benjamin Barrett | Cardiff High School |
| Luke Betts | Hills Road VI Form College, Cambridge |
| Nathan Brown | King Edward VI Camp Hill Boys' School |
| Sam Cappleman-Lynes | Shebbear College, Devon |
| Ruth Franklin | Manchester High School for Girls |
| Richard Freeland | Winchester College |
| Edward Godfrey | Thomas Hardye School, Dorset |
| Jacqueline Keyang Hu | Caterham School, Surrey |
| Andrew Hyer | Westminster School |
| Sahl Khan | St Paul's School, London |
| Joshua Lam | Leys School, Cambridge |
| Jordan Millar | Regent House School, County Down |
| James Munro | St Olave's Grammar School, London |
| Sergei Patiakin | Dame Alice Owen's School, Hertfordshire |
| Geoffrey Penington | Abingdon School, Oxfordshire |
| David Phillips | St Alban's School |
| Maithra Raghu | Henrietta Barnett School, London |
| Aled Walker | King Edward VI Camp Hill Boys' School |
| Tomas Zeman | Winchester College |

### Silver Medals

| | |
|---|---|
| Thomas Anthony | Hampton School, London |
| James Bell | Macmillan Academy, Middlesbrough |
| Andrew Carlotti | Sir Roger Manwood's School, Kent |
| Martin Chan | Westminster School |
| Andrea Chlebikova | Brighton Hove and Sussex Sixth Form College |
| Oscar Cunningham | Portsmouth Grammar School |
| Xuyang Dang | Harrow International School |
| Yuhan Gao | Loughborough Grammar School |
| Eigen Horsfield | Tapton School, Sheffield |
| Daniel Hu | City of London School |
| Li Yun Ju | Dulwich College, London |
| Kelvin Wong | Colchester Royal Grammar School |

| | |
|---|---|
| Matthew Leach | Perse School, Cambridge |
| Benjamin Lee | Methodist College, Belfast |
| Mark Lewis | Royal Latin School, Buckingham |
| Jason Long | Glasgow Academy |
| David Mestel | Hills Road Sixth Form College, Cambridge |
| Wesley Mok | Tonbridge School, Kent |
| Zhi Qiao | St Marylebone CE School, London |
| Kshitij Sabnis | Westminster School |
| Ram Sarujan | Dr Challoner's Grammar School, Bucks |
| Stephen Smith | King's College School, London |
| Michael Smith | Reading School |
| Jack Smith | King's School, Grantham |
| Rosa Sun | King Edward VI Grammar School, Essex |
| Minh Thanh Tran | Bellerbys College, Cambridge |
| Bo Wang | Dulwich College, London |
| Kenan Wang | Hurtwood House, Surrey |
| Yizhou Wang | Abbey College, London |
| Angela Xu | Purcell School, Hertfordshire |
| Shukei Yeun | Badminton School, Bristol |
| Chuwei Zhang | Ruthin School, Denbighshire |
| Zhitian Zhou | Abbey College, London |
| Yaoyu Zhu | King's School, Oxford |

## Bronze Medals

| | |
|---|---|
| Alice Ahn | Glasgow Academy |
| Matthew Arran | Landau Forte College, Derby |
| Indranil Banik | Harvey Grammar School, Kent |
| Fred Blundun | Westminster School |
| Archie Bott | Winchester College |
| Douglas Buisson | Hills Road Sixth Form College, Cambridge |
| Feifan Chen | Cambridge Tutors College |
| Jiasheng Chen | Abbey College, London |
| Lisa Cheng | Queenswood School, Hertfordshire |
| Xie Di | Loughborough College |
| Minh Trang Duong | Cambridge Tutors College |
| Zhucheng Fang | Repton School, Derbyshire |
| Jaichen Fu | MPW College, Cambridge |
| Sunil Ghosh | Royal Grammar School, Guildford |
| Rebecca Hann | Judd School, Kent |
| David Harper | Ormskirk School, Lancashire |

| | |
|---|---|
| Will Hu | Ashford School, Kent |
| Zizheng Huang | Oundle School, Peterborough |
| Hyunjik Kim | Hampton School, London |
| Jun Ho Ku | Cheltenham College |
| Tran Le | Atlantic College, South Wales |
| Howon Lee | Whitgift School, Croydon |
| Yongbo Leong | Dulwich College, London |
| Nicholas Leung | St Paul's School, London |
| Qikun Liu | Abbey College, London |
| Yi Luan | MPW College, Cambridge |
| Henry Mak | Charterhouse, Surrey |
| Ryan Mullarkey | Royal Grammar School, Guildford |
| Grace Murphy | St Paul's Girls' School, London |
| Minh Tran Nguyen | Bosworth College, Leicester |
| Nina Ngyuen | MPW College, Cambridge |
| Watcharaphol Paritimongkol | |
| | Cambridge Tutors College |
| Thomas Parton | Wolgarston High School, Staffordshire |
| Alex Philpott | The Grammar School at Leeds |
| Tanon Protpagorn | Winchester College |
| Alex Roberts | Grange School, Hertford |
| Weerapat Satitkanikul | Cambridge Centre for Sixth Form Studies |
| Chris Smithers | Portsmouth Grammar School |
| Baskaran Sripathmanatha | Latymer School, London |
| Yixuan Wang | Dulwich College, London |
| Danny Wang | Bellerbys College London |
| Gareth Wilkes | Grange School, Hertford |
| Yutian Wu | Merchiston Castle School, Edinburgh |
| Martin Wu | Ruthin School, Denbighshire |
| Ruoyu Wu | Merchiston Castle School, Edinburgh |
| Jason Wyatt | Colyton Grammar School, Devon |
| Qichen Xu | Dauntseys School, Wiltshire |
| Xingjian Yang | Lord Wandsworth College, Hampshire |
| Yaw en Yin | Eastbourne College, East Sussex |
| Vincent Yu | Sha Tin College, Hong Kong |
| Yi Zhang | Abbey College, London |
| Jiayu Zhang | Abbey College, London |
| James Zhang | Dean Close Senior School, Cheltenham |
| Jason Zhang | Queen Mary's Grammar School, Walsall |
| Xin Lin Zhao | Royal Russell School, Croydon |

United Kingdom Mathematics Trust

# British Mathematical Olympiad

## Round 2 : Thursday, 28 January 2010

**Time allowed** *Three and a half hours.*
*Each question is worth 10 marks.*

**Instructions** • *Full written solutions – not just answers – are required, with complete proofs of any assertions you may make. Marks awarded will depend on the clarity of your mathematical presentation. Work in rough first, and then draft your final version carefully before writing up your best attempt.*
*Rough work **should** be handed in, but should be clearly marked.*

• *One or two **complete** solutions will gain far more credit than partial attempts at all four problems.*

• *The use of rulers and compasses is allowed, but calculators and protractors are forbidden.*

• *Staple all the pages neatly together in the top **left**-hand corner, with questions 1, 2, 3, 4 in order, and the cover sheet at the front.*

In early March, twenty students eligible to represent the UK at the International Mathematical Olympiad will be invited to attend the training session to be held at Trinity College, Cambridge (8-12 April). At the training session, students sit a pair of IMO-style papers and 8 students will be selected for further training. Those selected will be expected to participate in further correspondence work and to attend further training sessions. The UK Team of six for this summer's International Mathematical Olympiad (to be held in Astana, Kazakhstan, 6-12 July) will then be chosen.

**Do not turn over until told to do so.**

United Kingdom Mathematics Trust

## 2009/10 British Mathematical Olympiad
## Round 2: Thursday, 28 January 2010

1.  There are $2010^{2010}$ children at a mathematics camp. Each has at most three friends at the camp, and if $A$ is friends with $B$, then $B$ is friends with $A$. The camp leader would like to line the children up so that there are at most 2010 children between any pair of friends. Is it always possible to do this?

2.  In triangle $ABC$ the centroid is $G$ and $D$ is the midpoint of $CA$. The line through $G$ parallel to $BC$ meets $AB$ at $E$. Prove that $\angle AEC = \angle DGC$ if, and only if, $\angle ACB = 90°$.
    *The centroid of a triangle is the intersection of the three medians, the lines which join each vertex to the midpoint of the opposite side.*

3.  The integer $x$ is at least 3 and $n = x^6 - 1$. Let $p$ be a prime and $k$ be a positive integer such that $p^k$ is a factor of $n$. Show that $p^{3k} < 8n$.

4.  Prove that, for all positive real numbers $x$, $y$ and $z$,
$$4(x + y + z)^3 > 27(x^2y + y^2z + z^2x).$$

# The British Mathematical Olympiad 2009-2010
## Round 2

The second round of the British Mathematical Olympiad was held on Thursday 28th January 2010. Some of the top scorers from this round were invited to a residential course at Trinity College, Cambridge.

### Leading Scores

| | | |
|---|---|---|
| 39 | Jack Smith | King's School, Grantham |
| 30 | Luke Betts | Hills Road VI Form College, Cambridge |
| | Andrew Carlotti | Sir Roger Manwood's School, Kent |
| | Andrew Hyer | Westminster School |
| | Sergei Patiakin | Dame Alice Owen's School, Hertfordshire |
| 29 | Richard Freeland | Winchester College, Hampshire |
| | Aled Walker | King Edward VI Camp Hill Boys' S., Birmingham |
| 27 | Jordan Millar | Regent House School, County Down |
| 23 | David Phillips | St Alban's School, Hertfordshire |
| 21 | Hyunjik Kim | Hampton School, Middlesex |
| | Geoffrey Penington | Abingdon School, Oxfordshire |
| | Maithra Raghu | Henrietta Barnett School, London |
| 20 | Nathan Brown | King Edward VI Camp Hill Boys' S., Birmingham |
| | Martin Chan | Westminster School |
| | Ruth Franklin | Manchester High School for Girls |
| | Yuhan Gao | Loughborough Grammar School |
| | Daniel Hu | City of London School |
| | Zhi Qiao | St Marylebone CE School, London |
| | Tomas Zeman | Winchester College, Hampshire |
| | Chuwei Zhang | Ruthin School, Denbighshire |
| 19 | Benjamin Elliott | Godalming College, Surrey |
| | Matei Mandache | Loughborough Grammar School |
| | David Mestel | Hills Road VI Form College, Cambridge |
| | Ram Sarujan | Dr Challoner's Grammar School |
| | Will Hu | Ashford School, Kent |
| 16 | Oscar Cunningham | Portsmouth Grammar School |
| 13 | Benjamin Barrett | Cardiff High School |
| | James Bell | Macmillan Academy, Middlesbrough |
| | Jack Buckingham | Marlwood School, Bristol |
| | Joshua Lam | Leys School, Cambridge |
| | Nicholas Leung | St Paul's School, London |
| | Sam Porritt | Greenhead College, West Yorkshire |
| | Gareth Wilkes | Grange School, Cheshire |

# IMO 2010

The 2010 International Mathematical Olympiad took place in Almaty and Astana, Kazakhstan from the 6th to the 12th of July. The Team Leader was Dr Geoff Smith, University of Bath and the Deputy Leader was Dr James Cranch, University of Leicester. A full account of the 2010 IMO and the UK preparation for it appears later in this book.

The members of the UK team were: Luke Betts; Nathan Brown; Andrew Carlotti; Richard Freeland; Sergei Patiakin and Aled Walker. The reserves were: Andrew Hyer and Jordan Millar.

In addition to the Leader and Deputy Leader, the team were accompanied by Dr Joseph Myers, CodeSourcery as observer with leader; Dr Ceri Fiddes, Millfield School as observer with students. For the pre-IMO phase, when Dr Fiddes was unavailable, Miss Jacqui Lewis of St Julian's School, Lisbon acted as observer with students.

## Introduction to the BMO problems and full solutions

The following 'official' solutions are the result of many hours' work by a large number of people, and have been subjected to many drafts and revisions. The contestants' solutions included here will also have been redrafted several times by the contestants themselves, and also shortened and cleaned up somewhat by the editors. As such, they do not resemble the first jottings, failed ideas and discarded pages of rough work with which any solution is started.

Before looking at the solutions, pupils (and teachers) are encouraged to make a concerted effort to attack the problems themselves. Only by doing so is it possible to develop a feel for the question, to understand where the difficulties lie and why one method of attack is successful while others may fail. Problem solving is a skill that can only be learnt by practice; going straight to the solutions is unlikely to be of any benefit.

It is also important to bear in mind that solutions to Olympiad problems are not marked for elegance. A solution that is completely valid will receive a full score, no matter how long and tortuous it may be. However, elegance has been an important factor influencing our selection of contestants' answers.

# BMO Round 1 – Questions and Solutions

1.  Find all integers $x$, $y$ and $z$ such that
$$x^2 + y^2 + z^2 = 2(yz + 1) \text{ and } x + y + z = 4018.$$

(*Proposer: Paul Jefferys, UBS*)

---

This question can be done in several ways. However, probably the fastest, and the most common among students, is to observe that the identity $(y - z)^2 = y^2 - 2yz + z^2$ can be used to tidy up the more complicated of the two equations.

*Solution by the editors*

Our first step is to observe that we have a $2yz$ and also a $y^2 + z^2$ in the first equation. We know that $y^2 - 2yz + z^2$ factorises, so we rearrange to get
$$x^2 + y^2 - 2yz + z^2 = 2,$$
and then factorise this as
$$x^2 + (y - z)^2 = 2.$$
All squares are non-negative, and only 0 and 1 are less than or equal to 2. So we must have
$$x^2 = 1 \text{ and } (y - z)^2 = 1.$$
This means that $x$ is 1 or $-1$; also, $y - z$ is 1 or $-1$. This gives four possibilities; we shall try each in turn.

*Case* 1: $x = 1$, $y - z = 1$

In this case, we have a system of three linear equations

$$x = 1 \tag{1}$$

$$y - z = 1 \tag{2}$$

$$x + y + z = 4018. \tag{3}$$

We subtract (1) from (3) to get

$$y - z = 1$$
$$y + z = 4017.$$

Finally we can add and subtract these two to get

$$2y = 4018$$
$$2z = 4016,$$

from which we deduce that $x = 1$, $y = 2009$, $z = 2008$.

*Case* 2: $x = 1$, $y - z = -1$

This case is similar. Again we subtract the linear equations to get

$$y - z = -1$$

$$y + z = 4017,$$

from which we get $x = 1$, $y = 2008$, $z = 2009$.

*Case* 3: $x = -1$, $y - z = 1$

This is once again similar. After eliminating $x$ we get

$$y - z = 1$$

$$y + z = 4019,$$

which gives $x = -1$, $y = 2010$, $z = 2009$.

*Case* 4: $x = -1$, $y - z = -1$

This is the last case. After subtracting to get rid of $x$ we find that

$$y - z = -1$$

$$y + z = 4019,$$

which gives $x = -1$, $y = 2009$, $z = 2010$.

It is quick to check that these solutions all work.

2. Points $A$, $B$, $C$, $D$ and $E$ lie, in that order, on a circle and the lines $AB$ and $ED$ are parallel. Prove that $\angle ABC = 90°$ if, and only if, $AC^2 = BD^2 + CE^2$.

(*Proposer: David Monk, ex-University of Edinburgh*)

*Solution by the editors*

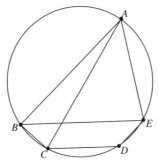

The equation $AC^2 = BD^2 + CE^2$ suggests using Pythagoras' theorem – however, the lengths $AC$, $BD$ and $CE$ do not form the sides of a triangle as they stand. Looking at triangle $ACE$, we see that if we knew that $AE = BD$ (i.e. that two opposite sides of the cyclic trapezium $ABDE$ are equal), then we could apply Pythagoras. Let's try and prove this.

Since $ABDE$ is cyclic, we know that $\angle AEB = \angle ADB$ and $\angle ABE = \angle ADE$. Because $AB$ and $ED$ are parallel, $\angle ABE = \angle ADE = \angle BAD$. So triangles $AEB$ and $BDA$ are congruent by AAS congruency, whence $AE = BD$, which is what we wanted.

Now, $\angle ABC + \angle AEC = 180°$, and so $\angle ABC = 90°$ if, and only if, $\angle AEC = 90°$. By Pythagoras' theorem and its converse, applied in triangle $ACE$, $\angle AEC = 90°$ if, and only if, $AC^2 = AE^2 + CE^2 = BD^2 + CE^2$. Therefore $AC^2 = BD^2 + CE^2$ if, and only if, $\angle ABC = 90°$, as required.

3.  Isaac attempts all six questions on an Olympiad paper in order. Each question is marked on a scale from 0 to 10. He never scores more in a later question than in any earlier question. How many different possible sequences of six marks can he achieve?

*(Proposer: Jeremy King, Tonbridge School)*

---

There appears to be nothing special about the numbers six and 10, except that the Olympiad paper sounds suspiciously like a BMO1 paper. Thus it is natural to experiment with numbers smaller than six and 10.

For example, if there are three questions, and scores can be at most two, then there are ten possibilities:

| | | | | |
|---|---|---|---|---|
| 0, 0, 0; | 1, 0, 0; | 1, 1, 0; | 1, 1, 1; | 2, 0, 0; |
| 2, 1, 0; | 2, 1, 1; | 2, 2, 0; | 2, 2, 1; | 2, 2, 2; |

and if scores can be at most three, then there are ten more possibilities (for a total of twenty):

| | | | | |
|---|---|---|---|---|
| 3, 0, 0; | 3, 1, 0; | 3, 1, 1; | 3, 2, 0; | 3, 2, 1; |
| 3, 2, 2; | 3, 3, 0; | 3, 3, 1; | 3, 3, 2; | 3, 3, 3. |

Proceeding in this manner, we could gather numerical data into a table (indexed by the number of questions and the maximum permitted score):

| | | Number of questions | | | |
|---|---|---|---|---|---|
| | | 1 | 2 | 3 | 4 |
| Max score | 0 | 1 | 1 | 1 | 1 |
| | 1 | 2 | 3 | 4 | 5 |
| | 2 | 3 | 6 | 10 | 15 |
| | 3 | 4 | 10 | 20 | 35 |
| | 4 | 5 | 15 | 35 | 70 |

This evidence has no logical status as a proof; however, it makes the following proofs easier to discover.

*Solution 1 by the editors*

The well-trained student will recognise the numbers in the table above as the binomial coefficients: given numbers $n$ and $k$ the *binomial coefficient* $\binom{n}{k}$ is the number of ways of choosing $k$ objects out of a set of $n$ objects.

The numerical value of $\binom{n}{k}$ is $\dfrac{n!}{k!\,(n-k)!}$ for $0 \leqslant k \leqslant n$. It is easy to check that the number in row $i$, column $j$ of the table above is $\binom{i+j}{i}$.

So we guess that our number will be $\binom{16}{6}$: to prove this we need to express any score as a choice of six objects from a set of sixteen. With this in mind, imagine graphing scores on a bar chart. The following figure shows bar graphs for three sequences of scores, namely $(6, 6, 3, 2, 2, 1)$, $(10, 10, 8, 3, 0, 0)$ and $(6, 5, 5, 4, 2, 0)$:

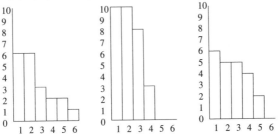

As the next figure shows, each bar graph yields a walk from the top left of the chart to the bottom right, which travels only to the right and downwards.

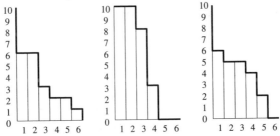

Each such walk consists of sixteen steps, of which exactly six are to the right (and the other ten are downwards). Moreover, it is not difficult to see that any such walk determines a unique sequence of scores.

Thus the number of different sequences of scores is the same as the number of walks from the top left to the bottom right. But this is the same as the number of ways of choosing six steps to be 'rightwards' out of the set of sixteen. This is, by definition, the binomial coefficient $\binom{16}{6}$.

We can compute this binomial coefficient by the standard method:

$$\binom{16}{6} = \frac{16!}{6!\,10!} = \frac{16 \times 15 \times 14 \times 13 \times 12 \times 11}{6 \times 5 \times 4 \times 3 \times 2 \times 1} = 8008.$$

*Solution* 2 *by the editors*

A more direct solution along the same lines is to consider what happens when we add 6 to Isaac's score for Q1, 5 to his score for Q2, 4 to his score for Q3, 3 to his score for Q4, 2 to his score for Q5, and 1 to his score for Q6.

Then we have a sequence of six scores between 16 (the maximum possible, for Q1) and 1 (the minimum possible, for Q6). Also, all these scores are now different: they are strictly decreasing in order from Q1 to Q6. So they form a subset of the numbers from 1 to 16.

Moreover, any such subset yields a sequence of scores (by subtracting 6 from the largest, 5 from the next largest, and so on). So the number of sequences of six appropriate scores is exactly $\binom{16}{6}$, the number of six-element subsets of a sixteen-element set, which (as seen in the previous solution) is 8008.

*Solution* 3 *by the editors*

Without any knowledge of binomial coefficients, one might notice that, in the table of results above, each number is the sum of those above it and to the left of it.

So, if we write $A(m, q)$ for the number of sequences of $q$ scores where the maximum permitted score is $m$, we might try to prove that

$$A(m, q) = A(m - 1, q) + A(m, q - 1).$$

However, if we have a sequence of $q$ scores where the maximum permitted score is $m$, then either the first score is $m$ or it is less than $m$. In the first case, what follows can be any sequence of $q - 1$ scores where the maximum permitted score is $m$. In the second case we have a sequence of $q$ scores all of which are at most $m - 1$. This proves the recurrence.

Also, we have $A(m, 0) = 1$ for all $m$ (since there is only one empty sequence) and $A(0, q) = 1$ for all $q$ (since the scores must all be zeroes).

This enables us to build up quickly a large table as in the preamble, and show that $A(10, 6) = 8008$.

4.  Two circles, of different radius, with centres at $B$ and $C$, touch externally at $A$. A common tangent, not through $A$, touches the first circle at $D$ and the second at $E$. The line through $A$ which is perpendicular to $DE$ and the perpendicular bisector of $BC$ meet at $F$. Prove that $BC = 2AF$.

*(Proposer: David Monk, ex-University of Edinburgh)*

---

Let the two circles have radii $r_1$ and $r_2$. Since the circles are of different radius, we may assume, without loss of generality, that $r_2 > r_1$. Let $FA$ meet $DE$ at $L$ and let the midpoint of $BC$ be $M$.

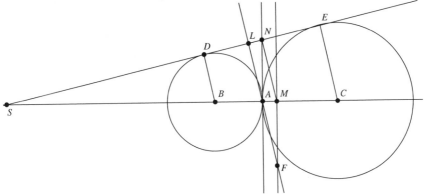

*Solution 1 by the editors*

In a configuration like this, it is often a good idea to extend $ED$ to meet $CB$ at a point, $S$. This point, the 'external centre of similitude', is the point from which the smaller circle can be enlarged to obtain the larger circle. Then triangles $SBD$, $SAL$ and $SCE$ are all similar, as they all have the angle at $S$ and a right angle in common.

The idea is to compute the length $AF$ using all these similar triangles. Since $\angle FMA = 90° = \angle SLA$ and $\angle FAM = \angle SAL$, triangles $FAM$ and $SAL$ are similar. So $\dfrac{AF}{AM} = \dfrac{SA}{AL}$ and this ratio is equal to $\dfrac{SB}{SD}$. Now because $\dfrac{SB}{BD} = \dfrac{SC}{CE}$, these are in turn equal to $\dfrac{SC - SB}{CE - BD} = \dfrac{r_2 + r_1}{r_2 - r_1}$. We can now calculate that $AM = BM - BA = \tfrac{1}{2}(r_2 - r_1)$, and so

$$AF = \tfrac{1}{2}(r_2 - r_1) \times \frac{r_2 + r_1}{r_2 - r_1} = \tfrac{1}{2}(r_2 + r_1) = \tfrac{1}{2}BC,$$

as required.

142

*Solution* 2 *by the editors*

This solution makes use of the common tangent at $A$ to the two circles. Suppose this tangent intersects $DE$ at $N$. The two common tangents from a fixed point to a circle have equal length, and so $ND = NA$ and $NA = NE$. Therefore $N$ is the midpoint of $DE$. It follows that $MN$ is parallel to $CE$ and $BD$, and $MN = \frac{1}{2}(CE + BD) = \frac{1}{2}(CA + BA) = \frac{1}{2}BC$. Also, $FM$ is perpendicular to $BC$, as is $AN$, and so $FM$ is parallel to $AN$. Hence, since $FA$ is parallel to $MN$, $ANMF$ is a parallelogram. Opposite sides of a parallelogram are equal, which gives $AF = NM = \frac{1}{2}BC$, as required.

5. Find all functions $f$, defined on the real numbers and taking real values, which satisfy the equation $f(x)f(y) = f(x + y) + xy$ for all real numbers $x$ and $y$.

*(Proposer: David Monk, ex-University of Edinburgh)*

---

The most important idea with a question such as this is to specialise. The equation we are given is very general: it is easiest to read off information from special cases. Choosing useful special cases is an art form, but the following solution contains some methods which are frequently useful.

*Solution by the editors*

We start by making some substitutions which seem likely to give helpful bits of information. Setting $y = 0$ gives

$$f(x)f(0) = f(x)$$

whence $f(x)(f(0) - 1) = 0$, so either $f(x) = 0$ for all $x$, or $f(0) = 1$. The former is untenable (for example, from substituting $x = y = 1$), so we can conclude that $f(0) = 1$.

We can make use of this by substituting $y = -x$: we get

$$f(x)f(-x) = f(0) - x^2 = 1 - x^2,$$

and so in particular

$$f(1)f(-1) = 1 - 1^2 = 0.$$

Thus we have $f(1) = 0$ or $f(-1) = 0$.

If $f(1) = 0$, then we can make use of this by substituting $y = 1$ to get

$$0 = f(x)f(1) = f(x + 1) + x,$$

so $f(x + 1) = x$ or equivalently $f(x) = 1 - x$. It is easy to check that this is indeed a valid solution.

On the other hand, if $f(-1) = 0$, then we can substitute $y = -1$ and get

$$0 = f(x)f(-1) = f(x - 1) - x,$$

so $f(x - 1) = x$ or equivalently $f(x) = 1 + x$. Again, this is easily checkable.

So in summary we have just the two solutions $f(x) = 1 + x$ and $f(x) = 1 - x$.

144

6. Long John Silverman has captured a treasure map from Adam McBones. Adam has buried the treasure at the point $(x, y)$ with integer co-ordinates (not necessarily positive). He has indicated on the map the values of $x^2 + y$ and $x + y^2$, and these numbers are distinct. Prove that Long John has to dig only in one place to find the treasure.

(Proposer: Jeremy King, Tonbridge School)(Proposer: Jeremy King, Tonbridge School)

---

*Solution by the editors*

The question asks us to show that the equations $x^2 + y = a$ and $x + y^2 = b$ can have at most one solution in integers if $a$ and $b$ are distinct. Suppose not, so that there are two different solutions $(x_1, y_1)$ and $(x_2, y_2)$. Then we have $x_1^2 + y_1 = x_2^2 + y_2$ and $x_1 + y_1^2 = x_2 + y_2^2$, giving

$$x_1^2 - x_2^2 = y_2 - y_1 \qquad (1)$$

$$y_1^2 - y_2^2 = x_2 - x_1. \qquad (2)$$

Multiplying these and factorising, we get

$$(x_1 - x_2)(x_1 + x_2)(y_1 - y_2)(y_1 + y_2) = (x_1 - x_2)(y_1 - y_2).$$

Now, if $x_1 = x_2$, then it is easy to see from (1) and (2) that $y_1 = y_2$, so the solutions weren't different! Therefore we can assume $x_1 \neq x_2$ and, similarly, $y_1 \neq y_2$. This allows us to cancel factors $(x_1 - x_2)$ and $(y_1 - y_2)$ from the above equation to get

$$(x_1 + x_2)(y_1 + y_2) = 1.$$

It follows that $x_1 + x_2 = y_1 + y_2 = \pm 1$. Plugging this into (1) gives

$$x_1 - x_2 = \pm(y_2 - y_1) \qquad (3)$$

$$x_1 + x_2 = y_1 + y_2. \qquad (4)$$

Adding (3) and (4) shows that either $x_1 = y_2$ and $x_2 = y_1$ or $x_1 = y_1$ and $x_2 = y_2$. In either case, this contradicts the condition that $x_1^2 + y_1 = x_2^2 + y_2$ and $x_1 + y_1^2 = x_2 + y_2^2$ are distinct. Therefore the equations written down by Adam McBones can have at most one integer solution.

## BMO Round 2 – Questions and Solutions

1. There are $2010^{2010}$ children at a mathematics camp. Each has at most three friends at the camp, and if $A$ is friends with $B$, then $B$ is friends with $A$. The camp leader would like to line the children up so that there are at most 2010 children between any pair of friends. Is it always possible to do this?

   *(Proposer: Paul Jefferys, UBS)*

---

One serious difficulty with this question is whether to try to prove 'yes' or 'no'. A good strategy with such questions is to guess one, and try it. This might be lucky but, if not, the failure might suggest how to prove the other way.

If trying to prove that it is not always possible, a natural thing to do is to find an arrangement which is likely to be as hard as possible to arrange on a line. We should thus try to arrange the friendships to have as few coincidences as possible: so that friends do not share friends, and friends of friends do not share friends, and suchlike. (This is because every such coincidence is likely to make things easier to fit onto a line.)

Trying to make such an arrangement leads naturally to the following solution.

*Solution based on that of Aled Walker, King Edward VI Camp Hill Boys' School, Birmingham*

We will show that it is *not* always possible. We consider a person $X$ who has friendships arranged according to this diagram:

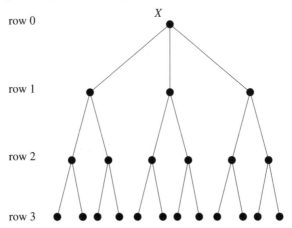

146

This pattern cannot be maintained forever (we will run out of children!) but we will show that it can go far enough to break the condition that pairs of friends must be separated by at most 2010 children.

We will aim for a contradiction: suppose that we do have the children arranged in a line, satisfying this condition. Person $X$ is somewhere along the line. His three friends (in Row 1) must be within 2011 places of him. This means we have $1 + 3$ children in at most $1 + 2 \times 2011$ possible places.

Now consider the six people in Row 2. They are all within 2011 places of their friends in Row 1, and so within $2 \times 2011$ places of Person $X$. This means we have ten people (person $X$, his three friends in Row 1, and the six people in Row 2) fitting in at most $1 + 2 \times 2 \times 2011$ different places.

If we continue to Row $n$, we have considered a total number of children given by

$$1 + 3 + (3 \times 2) + (3 \times 2^2) + \ldots + (3 \times 2^n)$$
$$= 1 + 3(1 + 2 + \ldots + 2^n)$$
$$= 1 + 3(2^{n+1} - 1)$$
$$= 3 \times 2^{n+1} - 2.$$

But since all the children in rows up to $n$ are connected to Person $X$ by a chain of at most $n$ friendships, they can be at distance at most $2011n$ from Person $X$, and so can be sitting in at most $1 + 2n \times 2011$ different places.

Now, for sufficiently large $n$, we will have

$$(3 \times 2^{n+1}) - 2 > 2n \times 2011,$$

since the left-hand side grows exponentially and the right-hand side linearly.

Indeed, take $n = 19$. Then $3 \times 2^{n+1} - 2 > 3\,000\,000$ since $2^{20} > 1\,000\,000$, while $2 \times 19 \times 2011 < 80\,000$.

So there are not enough places to seat all these children, breaking the condition. Note that $3 \times 2^{19+1}$ is much smaller than $2010^{2010}$, so we have enough children to arrange in this way.

2. In triangle *ABC* the centroid is *G* and *D* is the midpoint of *CA*. The line through *G* parallel to *BC* meets *AB* at *E*. Prove that ∠*AEC* = ∠*DGC* if, and only if, ∠*ACB* = 90°.

   *The centroid of a triangle is the intersection of the three medians, the lines which join each vertex to the midpoint of the opposite side.*

   (*Proposer: David Monk, ex-University of Edinburgh*)

---

There are very many ways to attack this problem. One of the simplest is given below. It makes crucial use of the observation that, under the hypothesis ∠*AEC* = ∠*DGC*, *BEGC* is cyclic. In problems like this it is always a good idea to look for cyclic quadrilaterals.

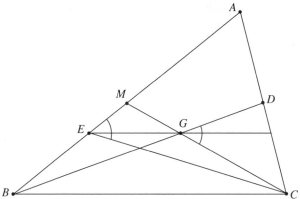

*Solution by the editors*

Suppose ∠*AEC* = ∠*DGC*. Then ∠*BEC* = ∠*BGC*, so *BEGC* is cyclic. Also, *BEGC* is a trapezium; a cyclic trapezium is isosceles (see the solution to BMO1 question 2), and so *BEGC* is isosceles. If *CG* and *AB* meet at *M*, then *AM* = *BM*. But *BEGC* is isosceles, so ∠*EBC* = ∠*GCB* and triangle *BMC* is isosceles. Therefore *AM* = *BM* = *CM* and *M* is the circumcentre of *ABC*. Thus *AB* is a diameter, and so ∠*ACB* = 90°.

Conversely, suppose ∠*ACB* = 90°. Then *M* is the circumcentre of *ABC*, and so *AM* = *BM* = *CM* (since *CM* is a median). Thus *BEGC* is isosceles, and is therefore cyclic. Hence ∠*BEC* = ∠*BGC*, giving ∠*AEC* = ∠*DGC*, as required.

148

3. The integer $x$ is at least 3 and $n = x^6 - 1$. Let $p$ be a prime and $k$ be a positive integer such that $p^k$ is a factor of $n$. Show that $p^{3k} < 8n$.

*(Proposer: Paul Jefferys, UBS)*

The key to this problem is to exploit the rich properties of the *cyclotomic polynomials* thoroughly: these are the factors of the polynomials $x^m - 1$. In the case where $m = 6$, the polynomial $x^6 - 1$ has four factors, all of a form pleasant enough to allow us to draw strong conclusions.

*Solution by Sergei Patiakin, Dame Alice Owen's School, Hertfordshire*

In what follows, we will use the notation $p^i \,\|\, N$ to mean '$p^i \mid N$ but $p^{i+1} \nmid N$'. We assume that $p^k \,\|\, n$, since choosing smaller values of $k$ only makes the problem easier.

Clearly $p$ does not divide $x$, or else $n$ will be $-1$ (mod $p$) and therefore not divisible by $p^k$.

We can factorise

$$n = x^6 - 1 = (x^2 - 1)(x^2 + x + 1)(x^2 - x + 1).$$

Note that

$$x^2 - x + 1 < x^2 - 1 < x^2 + x + 1 < 2x^2 - 1. \qquad (1)$$

Suppose (for a contradiction) that

$$p^{3k} \geq 8n = 8(x^6 - 1) > 8(x^2 - 1)^3,$$

which means that $p^k > 2(x^2 - 1)$ and so $p^k \geq 2x^2 - 1$.

Then, by equation (1), $p$ must divide at least two of the numbers $x^2 - x + 1$, $x^2 - 1$ and $x^2 + x + 1$.

We consider three cases, one for each pair.

(i) $p \mid x^2 - x + 1$ and $p \mid x^2 + x + 1$.

Then $p$ also divides their difference $2x$. Since $p \nmid x$, this means $p = 2$. But then $x$ is odd, so both $x^2 - x + 1$ and $x^2 + x + 1$ are odd, which contradicts their being divisible by the even prime $p$.

(ii) $p \mid x^2 + x + 1$ and $p \mid x^2 - 1 = (x + 1)(x - 1)$.

As above, $p$ cannot be 2, since it divides the odd number $x^2 + x + 1$. Thus $p$ cannot divide both $x - 1$ and $x + 1$. We split into subcases:

(a) $p \mid x + 1$

   In this case $p$ divides $(x^2 + x + 1) - (x + 1) = x^2$, so $p \mid x$, which is a contradiction.

(b) $p \mid x - 1$

   In this case $p$ divides $(x^2 + x + 1) + (x - 1) = x(x + 2)$, so $p \mid x + 2$. Since we also have $p \mid x - 1$, we must have $p = 3$. But then $9 \mid (x - 1)(x + 2) = x^2 + x - 2$, so $x^2 + x + 1 \equiv 3 \pmod{9}$. If $3^j \| x - 1$, then $3^{j+1} \| (x - 1)(x^2 + x + 1) = x^3 - 1$, so
$$3^{j+1} \| (x^3 - 1)(x^3 + 1) = (x^6 - 1),$$
and so $k = j + 1$. Then $3^k = 3 \cdot 3^j \leqslant 3(x - 1) \leqslant 2x^2 - 1$ (the latter inequality holding for all $x \geqslant 3$) which is a contradiction.

(iii) $p \mid x^2 - x + 1$ and $p \mid x^2 - 1$.

As before, we can split into two cases:

(a) $p \mid x - 1$

   In this case $p$ divides $(x^2 - x + 1) + (x - 1) = x^2$, so $p \mid x$, which is a contradiction.

(b) $p \mid x + 1$

   In this case $p$ divides $(x^2 - x + 1) - (x + 1) = x(x - 2)$, so $p \mid x - 2$. Since we also have $p \mid x + 1$, we must have $p = 3$. But then $9 \mid (x + 1)(x - 2) = x^2 - x - 2$, so $x^2 - x + 1 \equiv 3 \pmod{9}$. If $3^j \| x + 1$, then $3^{j+1} \| (x + 1)(x^2 - x + 1) = x^3 + 1$, so $3^{j+1} \| (x^3 + 1)(x^3 - 1)$, so $k = j + 1$. Then
$$3^k = 3 \cdot 3^j \leqslant 3(x + 1) \leqslant 2x^2 - 1$$
(the latter inequality holding for all $x \geqslant 3$), which is another contradiction.

In all cases we have reached a contradiction, so we are done.

4.  Prove that, for all positive real numbers $x$, $y$ and $z$,

$$4(x + y + z)^3 > 27(x^2y + y^2z + z^2x).$$

*(Proposer: Adrian Sanders, formerly of Trinity College, Cambridge)*

---

Don't be fooled by the length of the solution below: this problem is difficult, and was only fully solved in the exam by one person. The idea is to try and rearrange the inequality into a form where it says a sum of positive things – such as non-zero squares – is positive. A fair bit of trial and error or cunning is then required to find the right way of rearranging the expression. It is useful to note that the inequality is cyclically symmetric, and so one might try to rewrite it as a cyclic sum of positive terms, such as

$$x(ax + by + cz)^2 + y(ay + bz + cx)^2 + z(az + bx + cy)^2 > 0,$$

and solve for $a$, $b$ and $c$.

*Solution by Jack Smith, King's School, Grantham*

If $x$, $y$, $z > 0$, then

$$x(2x - 4y - z)^2 + y(2y - 4z - x)^2 + z(2z - 4x - y)^2 \geqslant 0.$$

Equality only occurs if $2x - 4y - z$, $2y - 4z - x$, $2z - 4x - y$ are all equal to zero; solving these simultaneous equations gives $x = y = z = 0$, which cannot happen for $x$, $y$, $z > 0$.

So for $x$, $y$, $z > 0$, we have strict inequality above. Expanding gives the inequality

$$4x^3 + 4y^3 + 4z^3 - 15x^2y - 15y^2z - 15z^2x + 12xy^2 + 12yz^2 + 12zx^2 + 24xyz > 0,$$

adding $27x^2y + 27y^2z + 27z^2x$ to each side gives

$$4(x^3 + y^3 + z^3) + 12(x^2y + y^2z + z^2x + xy^2 + yz^2 + zx^2) + 24xyz > 27(x^2y + y^2z + z^2x)$$

and factorising gives

$$4(x + y + z)^3 > 27(x^2y + y^2z + z^2x).$$

# Olympiad Training

Various training camps are held throughout the year to select and prepare students for participation in the UK team at forthcoming International Mathematical Olympiads and other international events.

The training programme for the academic year 2009-10 began in September with a camp at The Queen's College, Oxford (previously held at the University of Bath), for students new to IMO preparation.

Since 2001, there has been a visit to Budapest over the New Year to train with the Hungarian IMO squad, and this tradition continued in 2009-10, with 20 British and 20 Hungarian students attending.

The traditional Easter training and selection camp was once again held at Trinity College, Cambridge, and the UKMT are most grateful to Trinity College for its generous hosting of the event.

Twenty young UK mathematicians came to Cambridge for the Trinity College Training Session and IMO Squad selection exams. The group included all candidates for the current year's IMO team along with some younger students with great potential for future IMO's. There were 4 or 5 sessions per day covering material useful for IMO problems. Part way through and at the end of the 5-day camp, students sat two IMO-style 4 ½ hour papers, after which a final small UK IMO squad was selected for intensive training.

The final team of 6 for the IMO was finalised towards the end of May after a highly intensive training and selection camp held at Oundle School.

The UK are sometimes also invited to participate in competitions abroad, and this year we were fortunate enough to be invited to participate in the Romanian Master in Mathematics competition in February 2010; the Balkan Mathematical Olympiad, this year held in Moldova in early May; and the Italian Team Mathematical Competition in late May.

152

## Trinity College IMO camp, 8th to 12th April 2010
## Outline Programme

Twenty young UK mathematicians gathered in Cambridge for the Trinity College Training Session and IMO Squad selection exams. We were joined by Claude Deschamps from France.

The programme below outlines the main scheduled activities. This had a parallel structure with 'innocents' and 'experienced' (Mint and Used – in a philatelic sense) having sessions tailored to their needs.

### Thursday 8th April

| | | |
|---|---|---|
| 14:00 | Welcome and Introductions | (GCS) |
| 14:30 | Mint: Combinatorics 1 | (CF) |
| | Used: Algebra 1 | (RB) |
| | *Tea* | |
| 16:45 | Mint: Algebra 1 | (JC) |
| | Used: Combinatorics 1 | (JM) |
| 19:00 | *Dinner followed by Mathematical Relays* | (RA) |

### Friday 9th April

| | | |
|---|---|---|
| 09:00 | Mint: Geometry 1 | (GCS) |
| | Used: Number Theory 1 | (NK) |
| | *Tea* | |
| 11:00 | Mint: Number Theory 1 | (IL) |
| | Used: Geometry 1 | (TL) |
| 13:00 | *Lunch* | |
| 14:00 | Trinity prize-giving | (BB) |
| 15:15 | Mint: Convex Functions | (HM) |
| | Used: Combinatorics 2 | (JC) |
| | *Tea* | |
| 17:15 | Mint: Combinatorics 2 | (JM) |
| | Used: Algebra 2 | (PAR) |
| 19:00 | *Dinner followed by Social Event* | (BB) |

## Saturday 10th April

| | | |
|---|---|---|
| 08:30 | First Selection Test 1 | |
| 13:00 | *Lunch* | |
| 14:00 | Free Time | |
| | | |
| 15:15 | Mint: Geometry 2 | (GCS) |
| | Used: Number Theory 2 | (IL) |
| | *Tea* | |
| 17:15 | Mint: Functional Equations | (CD) |
| | Used: Geometry 2 | (TL) |
| 19:00 | *Dinner followed by Quiz* | (RB) |

## Sunday 11th April

| | | |
|---|---|---|
| 09:00 | Mint: Geometry 3 | (VK) |
| | Used: Algebra 3 | (IL) |
| | *Tea* | |
| 11:00 | Mint: Number Theory 2 | (PAR) |
| | Used: Geometry 3 | (GCS) |
| 13:00 | *Lunch* | |
| 14:15 | Mint: Algebra 2 | (KB) |
| | Used: Reflections and Rotations | (HM) |
| | *Tea* | |
| 16:45 | Mint: Number Theory 3 | (DY) |
| | Used: Functional Equations | (CD) |
| | | |
| 19:00 | *Dinner and social event* | |
| | | |
| 20:15 | Presenting Solutions (DY); Romanian Debrief (Many) | |
| | The French IMO training system (CD) | |
| | Forthcoming camps (GCS) | |

## Monday 12th April

| | | |
|---|---|---|
| 08:30 | First Selection Test 2 | |
| 13:00 | *Lunch* | |
| 14:00 | Background problems debrief | |
| 16:00 | Tea and farewell | |

154

## Participants

| | |
|---|---|
| Alice Ahn | Glasgow Academy |
| Luke Betts | Hills Road VI Form College, Cambridge |
| Nathan Brown | King Edward's Camp Hill, Birmingham |
| Andrew Carlotti | Sir Roger Manwood's School, Kent |
| Martin Chan | Westminster School, London |
| Andrea Chlebikova | Brighton Hove and Sussex SFC Hove |
| Ben Elliot | Godalming College, Surrey |
| Ruth Franklin | Manchester High School for Girls |
| Richard Freeland | Winchester College, Hampshire |
| Andrew Hyer | Westminster School, London |
| Daniel Hu | City of London School |
| Sahl Khan | St Paul's School, London |
| Hyunjik Kim | Hampton School, Hampton |
| Matei Mandache | Loughborough Grammar School, Loughborough |
| Jordan Millar | Regent House School, Newtownards |
| Sergei Patiakin | Dame Alice Owen's School, Potters Bar |
| David Phillips | St Alban's School, Hertfordshire |
| Jack Smith | King's School, Grantham |
| Maithra Raghu | Henrietta Barnett School, London |
| Aled Walker | King Edward's Camp Hill, Birmingham |

## Staff

| | | | | | |
|---|---|---|---|---|---|
| Richard Atkins | RA | Robin Bhattacharyya | RB | Bela Bollobas | BB |
| Claude Deschamps | CD | James Cranch | JC | Ceri Fiddes | CF |
| Vesna Kadelburg | VK | Nathan Kettle | NK | Imre Leader | IL |
| Tom Lovering | TL | Heather Macbeth | HM | Joseph Myers | JM |
| Paul Russell | PAR | Jack Shotton | JS | Geoff Smith | GCS |
| Dominic Yeo | DY | | | | |

Subsequent to this, the team plus reserves were selected. Final selection of the team was at Oundle school during the Spring half-term holiday.

# The International Mathematical Olympiad

In many ways, a lot of the events and activities described earlier in this book relate to stages that UK IMO team members will go through before they attend an IMO. At this stage, it is worth explaining a little about the structure of the Olympiad, both for its own sake as well as to fit the following report into a wider context.

An IMO is a huge event and takes several years to plan and to execute. In 2010, teams from more than 100 countries went to Kazakhstan to participate. A team consists of six youngsters (although in some cases, a country may send fewer). The focus of an IMO is really the two days on which teams sit the contest papers. The papers are on consecutive days and each lasts $4\frac{1}{2}$ hours. Each paper consists of three problems, and each problem is worth 7 marks. Thus a perfect score for a student is 42/42. The students are ranked according to their personal scores, and the top half receive medals. These are distributed in the ratios gold:silver:bronze = 1:2:3. The host city of the IMO varies from year to year. Detailed contemporary and historical data can be found at

http://www.imo-official.org/

But, whilst these may be the focus, there are other essential stages, in particular the selection of the problems and, in due course, the co-ordination (marking) of scripts and awarding of medals.

As stated, an IMO team is built around the students but they are accompanied by two other very important people: the Team Leader and the Deputy Leader. (Many teams also take Observers who assist at the various stages. Some Observers may turn out to be future Leaders.) Some three or four days before the actual IMO examinations, the Team Leaders arrive in the host country to deal with the task of constructing the papers. Countries will have submitted questions for consideration over the preceding months and a short list of questions (and, eventually, solutions) are given to Team Leaders on arrival. The Team Leaders gather as a committee (in IMO parlance, the Jury) to select six of the short-listed questions. This can involve some very vigorous debate and pretty tough talking! But it has to be done. Once agreed, the questions are put into the papers and translations produced into as many languages as necessary, sometimes over 50.

At some stage, the students, accompanied by the Deputy Leader, arrive in the host country. As is obvious, there can be no contact with the Team Leader who, by then, has a good idea of the IMO papers! The Leaders and the students are housed in different locations to prevent any contact, casual or otherwise.

On the day before the first examination, there is an Opening Ceremony. This is attended by all those involved (with due regard to security). Immediately after the second day's paper, the marking can begin. It may seem strange that students' scripts are 'marked' by their own Leader and Deputy. In fact, no actual marks or comments of any kind are put on the scripts themselves. Instead, having looked at scripts and decided what marks they think should be awarded, the Leader and Deputy have to justify their claim to others, called co-ordinators, who are supplied by the host country. Once all the marks have been agreed, sometimes after extremely protracted negotiation, the Jury decides where the medal boundaries should go. Naturally, this is a crucial part of the procedure and results in many tears as well as cheers.

Whilst the co-ordination of marks is going on, the students have time to relax and recover. There are often organised activities and excursions and there is much interaction and getting to know like-minded individuals from all corners of the world.

The grand finale is always the closing ceremony which includes the awarding of medals as well as speeches and numerous items of entertainment – some planned but others accidental.

# The 51st International Mathematical Olympiad
## Almaty and Astana, Kazakhstan
## 2nd to 14th July, 2010
## Geoff Smith (UK IMO Team Leader)

This year the annual world championship of secondary school mathematics was held at various sites in Kazakhstan during July 5th – July 14th. The six students sit two exams, each of duration four hours 30 minutes under strictly controlled conditions. This year the UK team consisted of six boys and, unusually, five of them are being educated in the maintained sector.

The team was selected by competitive examination, and consisted of the following:

| | |
|---|---|
| Luke Betts | Hills Road Sixth Form College, Cambridge |
| Nathan Brown | King Edward's Camp Hill, Birmingham |
| Andrew Carlotti | Sir Roger Manwood's School, Kent |
| Richard Freeland | Winchester College, Hampshire |
| Sergei Patiakin | Dame Alice Owen's School, Hertfordshire |
| Aled Walker | King Edward's Camp Hill, Birmingham |

The results of our team members were as follows.

|                  | P1 | P2 | P3 | P4 | P5 | P6 | S   | award              |
|------------------|----|----|----|----|----|----|-----|--------------------|
| Luke Betts       | 7  | 1  | 1  | 7  | 1  | 0  | 17  | bronze             |
| Nathan Brown     | 7  | 0  | 1  | 7  | 7  | 0  | 22  | silver             |
| Andrew Carlotti  | 7  | 0  | 0  | 7  | 0  | 6  | 20  | bronze             |
| Richard Freeland | 7  | 0  | 0  | 7  | 0  | 0  | 14  | honourable mention |
| Sergei Patiakin  | 7  | 0  | 6  | 7  | 7  | 0  | 27  | gold               |
| Aled Walker      | 7  | 0  | 0  | 7  | 0  | 0  | 14  | honourable mention |
| totals           | 42 | 1  | 8  | 42 | 15 | 6  | 114 |                    |

The medal cut-offs were 15 for bronze, 21 for silver and 27 for gold.

This result had us ranked 25th in terms of points scored, at the back of the peloton. A dramatic underperformance on Problem 2, a geometry question, served to undermine some excellent work on the far more demanding problems 3, 5 and 6. The scores of the leading countries were as follows: 1 People's Republic of China 197; 2 Russian Federation 169; 3 United States of America 168; 4 Republic of Korea 156; 5= Kazakhstan 148; 5= Thailand 148; 7 Japan 141; 8 Turkey 139; 9 Germany 138; 10 Serbia 135; 11= Vietnam 133; 11= Italy 133; 13= Canada 129; 13= Hungary 129; 15 Australia 128; 16= Romania 127; 16= Islamic Republic of Iran 127; 18 Peru 124; 19 Taiwan 123; 20 Hong Kong 121; 21 Bulgaria 118; 22= Ukraine 117; 22= Singapore 117; 24 Poland 116; 25 United Kingdom 114; 26 Uzbekistan 112; 27 Belarus 110; 28 Azerbaijan 109; 29 New Zealand 106; 30 France 105.

As usual, the performance of China was excellent, and they had the only student with a perfect score. Australia performed very well this year, and the results of New Zealand are truly exceptional, given their modest population base and their performances in the past. I should also draw your attention to the performance of Saudi Arabia. The Kingdom is making a great training effort, and this year secured 55 marks and two bronze medals. This is more than double the number of marks they obtained in all five previous participations combined.

As for the UK, if we had performed well on Problem 2 and, say, scored 21 points, then that would have given an overall score of 134. As I have noted before, the rank statistic is extremely sensitive to small perturbations in performance for those teams which finish in the range 10th–30th. Two of our students have that rarest of distinctions, a double honourable mention.

158

In most years, 14 points are enough to get a bronze medal, and they can count themselves unlucky to have lost out.

Congratulations are due to all of our students, and one must mention the special performances of Nathan and Sergei in obtaining silver and gold medals respectively.

Detailed results and statistics can be found at the official IMO site:

http://www.imo-official.org

It is with sorrow that I must report that the jury disqualified the team of North Korea following allegations that some of their students had produced solutions which were exceptionally close to those in the official solutions booklet.

Here are the six problems of the 51st Mathematical Olympiad. The problems should be taken in two groups of three, and for each three questions the time limit is 4 hours 30 minutes.

## Day 1

### Problem 1
Determine all functions $f : \mathbb{R} \to \mathbb{R}$ such that the equality

$$f(\lfloor x \rfloor y) = f(x) \lfloor f(y) \rfloor$$

holds for all $x, y \in \mathbb{R}$. (Here $\lfloor z \rfloor$ denotes the greatest integer less than or equal to $z$.)

### Problem 2
Let $I$ be the incentre of triangle $ABC$ and let $\Gamma$ be its circumcircle. Let the line $AI$ intersect $\Gamma$ again at $D$. Let $E$ be a point on the arc $BDC$ and $F$ a point on the side $BC$ such that

$$\angle BAF = \angle CAE = \tfrac{1}{2}\angle BAC$$

Finally, let $G$ be the midpoint of the segment $IF$. Prove that the lines $DG$ and $EI$ intersect on $\Gamma$.

### Problem 3
Let $N$ be the set of positive integers. Determine all functions $G : \mathbb{N} \to \mathbb{N}$ such that

$$(g(m) + n)(m + g(n))$$

is a perfect square for all $m, n \in \mathbb{N}$.

## Day 2

### Problem 4

Let $P$ be a point inside the triangle $ABC$. The lines $AP$, $BP$ and $CP$ intersect the circumcircle $\Gamma$ of triangle $ABC$ again at the points $K$, $L$ and $M$ respectively. The tangent to $\Gamma$ at $C$ intersects the line $AB$ at $S$. Suppose that $SC = SP$. Prove that $MK = ML$.

### Problem 5

In each of six boxes $B_1$, $B_2$, $B_3$, $B_4$, $B_5$, $B_6$ there is initially one coin. There are two types of operation allowed:

*Type* 1: Choose a nonempty box $B_j$ with $1 \leqslant j \leqslant 5$. Remove one coin from $B_j$ and add two coins to $B_{j+1}$.

*Type* 2: Choose a nonempty box $B_k$ with $1 \leqslant k \leqslant 4$. Remove one coin from $B_k$ and exchange the contents of (possibly empty) boxes $B_{k+1}$ and $B_{k+2}$.

Determine whether there is a finite sequence of such operations that results in boxes $B_1$, $B_2$, $B_3$, $B_4$, $B_5$ being empty and box $B_6$ containing exactly $2010^{2010^{2010}}$ coins. (Note that $a^{b^c} = a^{(b^c)}$.)

### Problem 6

Let $a_1$, $a_2$, $a_3$, ... be a sequence of positive real numbers. Suppose that for some positive integer $s$, we have

$$a_n = \max\{a_k + a_{n-k} \mid 1 \leqslant k \leqslant n - 1\}$$

for all $n > s$. Prove that there exist positive integers $\ell$ and $N$, with $\ell \leqslant s$ and such that $a_n \leqslant a_\ell + a_{n-\ell}$ for all $n \geqslant N$.

These problems were submitted by France, Hong Kong, USA, Poland, Netherlands and Iran respectively.

### Leader's Diary

Readers are warned that sometimes this diary is more accurate than seems likely. It is intended to entertain and inform, and I trust that no-one will take offence.

This year the IMO produced its own official diary, and various editions can be downloaded from http://www.imo2010org.kz using the top right tab labelled 'Diary of Olympiad'. These are large files, for the diary is in glorious colour, and has many pictures. I urge the reader to examine these documents as an accompaniment to my more subversive commentary. The first edition has some impressive pictures of the architecture of Astana, and much else besides.

**June 30** I make a very early start to get to Heathrow Airport. I am carrying almost all the passports, and the consequences of being late are too horrible to contemplate. My bags are very heavy because they are stuffed with IMO detritus for the team. I reach Paddington on time and reverse direction using the Heathrow Express, arriving at Terminal 1 before 09:00.

I am first to arrive because pre-IMO pastoral supremo Jacqui Lewis is having trouble finding a Hotel Hoppa bus. Joseph 'Combinatorics' Myers is first to show up, wearing a UK Panama hat lovingly preserved from IMO Vietnam. Then Jacqui arrives, and the team start to trickle in. There is much swapping of goods to be done, so we open our bags. The sadly absent Vesna Kadelburg has sorted out some natty team uniforms, and these are distributed. I pass out Union Flags for the ceremonies. The Panama hats for 2010 have not arrived, and I suspect sabotage, but say nothing. The last parent says good-bye, and we are ready to face the IMO.

After a while we finally get our computer-generated boarding cards, we go to hand in our luggage, and the nice check-in people explain that it doesn't matter which seats you select using the check-in machines, because they have the power to reassign seats.

We have managed to arrange the party in a loose clump on the packed aeroplane. We have an uneventful flight to Moscow. There we need to enter the transit area, which means going through a security check. The relevant agent is not to be found, so we wait for while, but eventually we are admitted to the Moscow Domodedovo playground. This is not a bad place, but it has a parochial policy on cash. They take roubles and nothing else. Neither dollars nor euros work, though credit cards will do nicely. We find an Italian outfit where the team can grind their way through pizzas, until at midnight we board a Transaero flight to Astana, Kazakhstan.

I spot the Vietnamese leader Hà Huy Khoái, but he is presumably en route to Almaty whereas we are going to Astana.

**July 1** We arrive in Astana very early in the morning. There is no hurry, and we find ourselves at the back of the immigration queues. At this point a whirlwind called Madina arrives. She is a local organizer, and marches us to the front of the queue. An IMO 2010 sign is then slapped on an immigration portal and we are whisked through at speed. There is a friendly lady from the Ministry of Education and Science standing there to oversee the process. The immigration officer is genial, and discards my immigration card as being unnecessary. I have doubts about this, because I fear that the lady from the Ministry will not be there on the way out, and I may meet a less generous border guard who doesn't happen to know how important I am, and may feel that I ought to be brandishing a doubly stamped immigration card. In fact I am being quite prescient. Read on.

Then the IMO officials and the lady from the Ministry attempt to march us through the green channel of customs. I explain that I have read the Kazakh customs regulations, and that I wish to declare a large sum of foreign currency. Once again I am informed that the regulations do not apply, and we are marched through customs. I have a sinking feeling. The local organizers are clearly making a big effort, and this bodes well for the rest of the IMO. Since we are four days earlier than most of the teams, they are practising the art of greeting on us. Well done, and thank you.

The airport is much like the rest of what we see in Astana. It is an excellent building, but is not supported by the usual clutter of infrastructure – hotels, car hire firms, giant car parks and petrol stations are absent. This is an airport surrounded by empty space, an asset with which Kazakhstan is richly endowed. I knew about this in advance, having failed to find anything when searching the internet using the keywords: Astana Airport Hotel. I then tried a map tool and discovered that with Astana Airport, you get what it says on the tin. Nothing else.

We have booked a driver to transfer us to the Imperia G hotel. I have been informed that the driver will carry an 'Imperia G' sign. We don't see him immediately because 'Imperia G' is written in the Cyrillic alphabet. The organizers promise to come to see us soon, and we are driven into town. The hotel is in the old city, the naturally occurring place called Akmola which has been extended by Presidential fiat into the new city called Astana.

At first sight, Astana seems to be the capital of Mars. It is a showcase of contemporary architecture. The shapes are a festival of geometry. Stately pleasure domes erupt from the steppe at startling angles. Postmodern shopping centres, apartment blocks and sports arenas do not jostle at all. Giant administrative buildings curve and glint, and are rarely simply connected. In non-mathematical terms, think Gruyère cheese, or the work of Henry Moore, or polo mints. Kisho Kurokawa and Lord Foster have been set loose. Norman Foster has supplied the Khan Shatyr Entertainment Centre, the Palace of Peace and Reconciliation and the Pyramid of Peace.

We check in, and have breakfast. The Australians are staying at the same hotel, and we run into them shortly before going upstairs for showers and bed. We get up at lunchtime, to try to force ourselves into the local timezone. By evening, the Australians have yet to return, so we explore. A nearby market allows us to change some cash into the local currency (1 euro = lots of tenge). We find a Turkish restaurant, and let the team loose on the menu. It is very satisfactory, including kebabs, ice-cream and other health foods. The host doesn't quite understand about giving clients space, and proceeds to join us at our table. I think that we are so far East that Brits remind him of Turkey.

**July 2** Next day we hook up with the Australians over breakfast. Angelo and Ivan are their leaders. We plan to have practice exams together. The hotel quoted us a silly price for the hire of appropriate facilities, but our excellent IMO guides have obtained the use of a local school. Joseph Myers and I must transfer to the jury site today, so we bid farewell to the students as they leave for their first training exam.

The IMO guides persuade us that it is pointless and expensive to take a taxi to the airport, and a schoolteacher escorts me, Joseph, Angelo and our bags on the necessary pair of bus journeys. As a grotesque foreigner, I am a source of entertainment for local toddlers, and I spend quite a bit of time with my fingers clenched in tiny Kazakh hands. The Australian leader Angelo is with us, and given his unmarried and relatively youthful state, seems to be making excellent progress with the young women of Central Asia.

The flight to Almaty is uneventful. There is a lot of cloud, but when we do get to see the ground we observe that it is empty grassland, steppe in all directions. Air Astana are excellent. We are met at Almaty airport, and the local organizers put the three of us, and all our bags, into one medium-sized car. This is not actually possible, but it happened. The driver clearly had ambitions in Formula One, but was inhibited by being placed in rush hour traffic. Nonetheless, he managed several inappropriate and entertaining changes of lane.

After a little more than an hour we reached the sanatorium where the jury was based. I have some experience of hotels in the former Soviet Union, and this place is top of the range. The food is not the universal hotel diet, but is all the better for that. I have a bedroom on the 7th floor and, to my delight, I discover that I have a floor lady, just as it was in the USSR. A woman sits in charge of each floor all the time. They have shifts, but she is always there. She never does anything. The system was part of the full-employment economics of Soviet la-la-land, and presumably the ladies could also report if counter-revolution was breaking out on their floor. Why are they still doing this, twenty years on? Presumably there was no moment at which it seemed appropriate to change this bizarre arrangement.

Although the food is wholesome, and I am attuned to the former Soviet obsession with buckwheat, some people clearly find the diet a little strange. There was also a tuck shop, where dissolute sanatorium clients could purchase chocolate, vodka, brandy and beer, or so I was told.

This is one of the happiest times of the IMO, when you get to see old friends again, and engage in ruthless teasing and mockery until settling down to see what events may bring.

After some effort, we get our hands on copies of the short-list, the proposals from which the problems on the papers will likely be chosen, and we go to work. I am concerned about G1, the easiest geometry problem, because I can solve it immediately. It turns out to be a lovely exercise by my UK colleague Christopher Bradley, but it is a little too easy, even for a first question. If you work forwards and backwards at the same time, from where you start and also from what you want to be, you quickly meet in the middle by the use of cyclic quadrilaterals and chasing angles. Fortunately G2 looks about right for a geometry problem. It will yield easily if you recall that if two points are mutually inverse with respect to a circle, then that circle is a circle of Apollonius with respect to those points.

There are very many excellent medium-level combinatorics problems. We are blessed with an excellent choice this year. There are a few monstrous questions too. Other than a shortage of easy questions, it is a good selection, but there is no 'grasshopper problem' as memorable as the one used in 2009.

**July 3** We continue to work on the problems. I have set up camp on my balcony. The view is magnificent. We are on the edge of the Zailisky Alatau Mountains, and sufficiently high that insects are not a problem. The air is clean, and towards the end of the day the Kazakh brandy is delicious.

As we work on the problems, we confront the fact that the IMO is happening in parallel with the World Cup. Late at night, the jury room is darkened, and we can watch matches on a giant screen. Relevant leaders take a keen interest in proceedings.

**July 4** UK Observer A, Joseph Myers, has sunk C7, the most difficult of the combinatorics proposals. He supplies chapter and verse of a paper published by the American Mathematical Society which includes the result. I ask permission for Joseph to address the jury, and this is granted. Joseph normally speaks at the same rate that he thinks, and for most people this causes serious bandwidth problems, especially people who are not native speakers of English. Joseph manages to slow down enough to get his point across, and unfortunately a very attractive problem is removed.

Eventually we start to select the papers. This is done in the order easy, hard and finally medium. We choose a functional equation with an unusual solution set and a nice geometry problem for the easy problems. For the hard problems we find an intriguing question which is, in a way, another functional equation, but it has a peculiar method of solution. We also select a hard algebra problem.

Next we turn to the two medium problems. Since we have not yet chosen a combinatorics problem, and we have a raft of excellent combinatorics problems of this level, we do have the option of choosing both medium problems to be combinatorics, but of course there is the geometry lobby. They have their way, and we select G4. Next we agonize over the combinatorics question. In the end, when it comes down to a choice between two problems, and it is clear that support for the problems is equally divided, we make the choice on the basis that one problem is likely to be much easier to co-ordinate than the other.

There is a notation phase, and eventually the English Language Committee meetings to sort out the wording. We produce rival versions of questions for the jury's perusal. In fact we offer to recast Problem 3 in terms of sequences because, in its current formulation, it is a little too close to being another functional equation problem. However, the jury decides to go with the original formulation.

**July 5** Individual language groups proceed with the translations of their papers, with the official languages done first.

There are elections to the advisory board. Nazar Agakhanov of Russia will be the new IMOAB chair following two terms by the excellent József Pelikán. There are eight candidates for the two remaining vacancies on the board. There is a two-stage electoral process for the two seats, and I had played a significant role in the design of this system last year. Joseph Myers seemed very amused when I forgot the details of the process and accidentally spoilt my ballot on the first round. Myung-Hwan Kim of South Korea is re-elected, and I am elected for the first time. IMOAB elections are a little strange, because you generally want everyone to win, especially your opponents.

**July 6** The principal value of travelling the world is to meet and try to understand radically diverse cultures. As much of western and central Europe is converging, Kazakh priorities are very different. This is clear from the amazing effort that they put into ceremonial activities. The DVD of the IMO will have a few brief shots of young people doing mathematics or playing sport, but it is dominated by formal public events; parades, medal ceremonies and middle-aged people making speeches.

In order to attend the Opening Ceremony, Leaders and Observers A have to board buses at 3 a.m. for a long journey from Almaty to Astana.

At length the Opening Ceremony begins. We leaders are at the front and the students are at the back. The students parade across the stage carrying flags, and there is a significant amount of folkloric activity. This involves formal dancing, and girls wearing remarkable hats resembling those tall thin desserts with a vertical axis of symmetry which, in 1960 at least, were forever dusted with dessicated coconut and sat on a wafer base. At one point hundreds of children fill the stage and each performs on the traditional Kazakh two-string lute.

There was also some dramatic drumming. Kazakh percussionists dress in shiny olive green clothes, big boots, and hats with giant ear flaps. The programme gently morphs into a traditional Kazakh heavy-metal set by Ulytau. Eventually, the Minister for Education and Science makes a splendid speech of welcome, and the ceremony comes to a close.

We adjourn to our hotel about lunchtime, and there is complete chaos. Hundreds of people all want to check in at the same time and, bless 'em, the Kazakhs have retained Soviet era stuff about filling in cards, handing in passports and so on. The hotel have laid on no extra staff to assist with this process, nor has anyone in the IMO organization given any thought as to how to make this business easier. The rooms are filled with extra beds, because the students had been jammed into the same hotel the previous night. There are no extra staff, so the hotel is having difficulty reconfiguring to normal patterns of bedroom use. Also many bedrooms have no desks, because they have been blagged for the jury room.

In such circumstances, I normally head for the bar, and wait for the foyer to clear. However, after the very early start, I cannot face a drink. I scout around and find upstairs a nice big sofa outside the hotel manager's swish office. I reason that this person is partly responsible for the turmoil below, and that he or she would probably be annoyed if a slob of a guest sets up camp outside their office. I remove my shoes and enjoy a prolonged kip.

After five hours I wander downstairs to find the queue has finally disappeared. Apparently one of the guides had eventually taken charge of the situation. By handing out registration cards, and getting people to fill them in while in the queue, she had dramatically sped up the process. She deserves a gold medal. I check in, and discover (at 18:30) that my room is yet to be made up. I don't care. The staff are onto it quickly enough, and at

166

length I have an extremely comfortable room on the fourth floor, not far from Joseph Myers.

**July 7** This is the day of the first exam. The jury sits awaiting the first message from the students. The students are allowed to send questions of clarification to the jury during the first 30 minutes of the exam. IMO internet Tsar Matjaž Željko is trying to look serene, but the Kazakh 'just in time' philosophy of communications management is not completely attuned to his more cautious approach. Matjaž is clearly doubtful that communications between the sites will work smoothly. The first student message is from an Australian student. It is a complaint about the conditions under which they are living. After that there are some sensible mathematical questions.

After the question phase is over, text messages start to filter in from the deputies. At this stage, it would normally not be appropriate for informal communications to take place between the two sites, but clearly some of the deputies and observers C are very concerned. They are not at the same site as the students, and there is as yet no means of the deputies getting to the students. This was bad enough for deputies, but for observers C this was outrageous. The designated purpose of observers C is to stay with the students. This is particularly important for countries such as the UK where parents have the expectation that their offspring will be protected and cherished by a designated person from their own country. Our observer C was Ceri Fiddes. She had travelled at great expense a quarter of the way round the world in order to look after our students, and now she was denied access.

I took comfort in the fact that I knew that Ceri had access to funds, and if necessary could simply pull the team out and take them home. Since I was not there, I cannot incorporate events at the student site into this diary, but I hope that Ceri and James will make a public report.

In the evening Joseph and I get access to the UK solution scripts, and go to work. I take the geometry problem 2, and the scripts are simply dreadful. Joseph reports, by way of contrast, that they all seem to have solved problem 1. Sergei seems to have done problem 3, and a couple of students each have some useful scraps which should be worth a mark. I wonder if other teams experienced the same dismal performance at problem 2, and asking around, it seems that almost every team has done better than us. Our old geometric weakness has resurfaced. Shudder.

**July 8** The second exam begins, and there is a decent collection of questions from the students. The set-square issue comes up again, left over from 2009. After the exam starts, it becomes completely legitimate for deputies and observers at or near the student site to communicate with us, and text messages pour in.

The UK has won the Mathematical Ashes again. This is a private competition held just before the IMO between the UK and Australia. The urn can stay in the northern hemisphere for another year. We find out that it is now possible for deputies and observers to get access to the student site, but that there are security guards trying to discourage this process. I rest easier, since it seems that now we probably won't need to make an early departure.

In the afternoon we hear that an emergency jury meeting is being called in the evening, but no agenda is supplied. Rumours of an irregularity allegation circulate. My heart sinks.

For several days I have been waging a campaign to get hold of a large number of boxes posted to Astana from UKMT. These will contain all sorts of presents for IMO people, including the much-sought-after BMO solutions booklet by James Cranch. There should also be a plentiful supply of David Monk's master-work *New Problems in Euclidean Geometry*. David has been supporting the UK IMO effort since 1968, and he is the author of more IMO problems than anyone else. Now he has produced this lovely book, full of really interesting problems. The boxes will no doubt also contain whatever trinkets are lying around the UKMT office. I have asked repeatedly, and been told every time that these boxes have not arrived.

Prompted by the ever-helpful Mary Wimbury in the UKMT office, we get the courier company to confirm that the materials were received, and to supply the details as to where and when the delivery took place. Then I present this information to the friendly Kazakh IMO leader Almaz Kungozhin. He goes into overdrive, and with the help of IMO organizer Evgeniya Kalchevskaya, they track down the consignment. Soon a van appears at the hotel entrance, and a dozen boxes are taken to my room. When I open them, I discover that the booklets and books are all present, and that UKMT had tidied its office by clearing out pens and key-fobs. I set about distributing the goodies to the rest of the IMO.

In the early evening the deputy leaders turn up after a long journey. They have moved to our hotel to assist with co-ordination. They tell stories which are quite disturbing, but also reassuring. When you have very limited information, you tend to worry that conditions might be simply awful. The reality is rarely quite so bad, and even James Cranch's story about getting into the students' site by pushing his way through security guards sounds quite normal. The team can rely on Ceri now that James is here. Gordon Lessells, the Irish deputy, had hired a van and driver to provide a bus service for other deputies while there was no IMO one provided. Well done Gordon!

I don't propose to give a blow-by-blow account of the jury meeting which concerned the allegations against DPRK. The regulations were followed, and North Korea were disqualified for this year. On reflection, the procedures could have been more transparent, and I hope that this unpleasant experience will lead to the introduction of a more refined process to deal with allegations of impropriety.

The long process of exam paper construction involves the problems being seen by a hundred leaders, and plenty of co-ordinators, members of the problem selection committee and observers A. All this happens over a lengthy period, so that any corrupt people have ample time to transmit problems, and to prepare alternative model answers. Maybe it is not really happening, but in fact sufficiently many leaders believe that this sometimes happens that the atmosphere is soured. We must develop a streamlined method of paper construction which involves only a very few trusted, experienced and expert eyes seeing the paper in advance.

There must be sanctions against leaders who exaggerate the ingenuity and accuracy of a student's script. It is a relatively easy thing to give a slightly false account, especially if student has written in a language which is not widely understood. I would favour an ethics committee which would examine the scans of scripts during the period between IMOs. If a student has secured high marks on a script which is worth little, then the leader of that country can be asked to explain how this happened to the jury of a subsequent IMO.

Host countries must take their pastoral responsibilities seriously. Deputies, and especially observers C, must have ready access to the students. When this happens, there will be no need for any unsupervised communications at inappropriate times.

**July 9–10** These are the co-ordination days. We divide the work between us, and I take all the geometry. I will address the problems in numerical order, though that is not how they were scheduled. Sometimes we called for breaks and had sessions re-scheduled.

I was to lead on Problem 1, though Joseph was also very familiar with the scripts. The co-ordinators conceded three 7s immediately, but wanted to talk about the other papers. In the time available we were able to go through two of the remaining scripts line by line, and collected two more 7s. There remained the script of Nathan 'seven lemmas' Brown. We knew his script to be correct, and he had broken the argument up into many small pieces, and had correctly explained how to put the parts together. The difficulty was that he had written his solution in tiny handwriting, and it was very difficult to read, especially for co-ordinators who were used to Cyrillic script. I volunteered to write it all out again, with associated notes of explanation, and so we adjourned for a second meeting. When we resumed, the co-ordinators first convinced themselves that my version was a fair representation of the original, and then Joseph Myers took them through it, correcting a couple of gratuitous errors that I had inserted. The co-ordinators finally agreed and we had six 7s.

Problem 2 was the geometry problem on which we had bombed badly. Luke Betts got a single mark for accidentally observing a correct triangle similarity which was relevant to what had become known as the 'Iranian Solution'.

Problem 3 was of more interest. Two candidates got a mark for proving that the function must be injective. Sergei Patiakin had solved the problem, but lost a mark for giving a dodgy justification of one of the steps.

Problem 4 was the second geometry problem, and so I led. We agreed four 7s straight away. The disputes were that I wanted a 7 for Luke Betts, and the co-ordinators were only offering 3 because they thought that there was a hole in his argument. On the other hand, they wanted to give Andrew Carlotti a 7 but I was only prepared to take 3. I explained to them the weakness in Carlotti's argument, and they looked a little surprised. I asked them about the alleged weakness in Betts's script, and I couldn't understand what they were worried about. I suggested an overnight adjournment so that we could both make detailed preparations, and we met again the next day.

When we met again, I explained that Luke had quoted the result that when two points are inverse with respect to a circle, then that circle is an Apollonius circle with respect to these points. Fortunately, when the marking scheme was being designed, I spoke in the jury and asked if an educated student quoted this result (or an equivalent one about orthogonal circles), whether it would be allowed. I was worried that a student might do this since I had explained it in a geometry session a couple of months before. The problem captain had accepted that this was allowed. In our second meeting, the co-ordinators rapidly agreed that Luke was right.

Finally we came to Andrew Carlotti's script. He had used an inversion map which, unfortunately, did not exist. If it existed, all would be well, and he had supplied a persuasive argument that it ought to exist. My difficulty was that the map didn't exist. However, since our previous meeting I had realised that you could dodge the problem by composing with a homothety with scale factor $-1$ about the attempted centre of inversion, and that would fix the problem. I now thought the script was worth about 5 or 6. The co-ordinators had found the fix as well, but insisted that this manoeuvre was simply a 'negative inversion', and that other scripts had got full marks for this argument, and so we had to accept full marks too. I put up some resistance, but finally we conceded for the sake of the IMO.

James Cranch led on Problem 5. When we walked into co-ordination we were pleased to see Géza from Hungary who is an excellent mathematician and speaks wonderful English. James quickly agreed two 7s for Sergei and Nathan. He then went into grovelling mode in an attempt to get a mark for Luke Betts. In the course of trying to prove the wrong thing, Luke had accidentally invented the Ackermann function. James thought that this was such a wonderful thing to do that it might be worth a mark. Indeed, it turned out to be in the mark scheme, and the mark was banked.

For Problem 6, only Andrew Carlotti had solved the problem. James began by remarking that he had translated the first part of Andrew Carlotti's problem 6 script 'into English from Idiot', to which the Kazakh coordinators did not react but which caused Ilya Bogdanov at the next table to burst out laughing. Eventually James and Joseph managed to extract the correct score of 6 marks for Andrew.

We have given UKMT presents to all the co-ordinators, and now an interesting thing happens. Word has got out about David Monk's book, and we receive a stream of supplicants asking for extra copies. Fortunately we have enough copies to keep everyone happy.

**July 11** There are various excursions today, but I decide to rest. For me the high point of the day will be a meeting concerning the launch in 2012 of a European Girls' Event at Murray Edwards College Cambridge.

After dinner we have the final jury meeting, and the medal boundaries are determined. There are fulsome tributes to the work of József Pelikán, and he gets a standing ovation.

The incoming IMOAB chair Nazar Agakhanov makes a short speech in which he proposes some IMO reform. The decisions must be taken next year, and we have 12 months to reflect on the best way forward. Secretary John Webb explains that there is a problem in 2013, and we currently have no host country for that year. This will obviously be the first item on the agenda of the incoming Advisory Board.

**July 12** Today is the day that we get to see the students again, but the procedure is to go on an excursion in order to meet them. The main event is an equine festival out of town.

We are so keen to see the students again, that I agree to go on the excursion. We sit on a bus at the appointed time, and wait for 30 minutes. Then the bus drives us to the back of the hotel and we get out again, because this is where the first stage of the excursion takes place. This is a model of Kazakhstan, with all the most important mausoleums, power stations, palaces and railway stations so that you could experience the treasures of the country without having to visit it.

At last we paid a lingering farewell to this homage to Brouwer's fixed-point theorem, and made our way to the buses. Less than an hour later, we were at the equine sports centre. We sat in the stadium and after a while the students arrived from the other site, after a long and tiring journey. It was delightful to see Ceri and the team again, but for reasons connected with who was supposed to eat where, student delegations and leaders were ordered to sit in different parts of the stadium.

We watched some excellent Kazakh horsepersonship, including some 'riding two horses at once', which takes some doing, and some magnificent 'pick something up from the ground while riding at full pelt' which was also impressive. Then there was an event of dubious political correctness, where a Kazakh girl on horseback was chased down by a male rider who wrestled her from her horse, and pulled her to the ground in a rather robust form of kiss-chase.

Soon everyone poured out, and the local organizers tried to usher leaders into luxurious yurts (tents) for lunch. I resisted at first, because I was far more interested in talking to the team than having lunch. It was delightful to chat to them again after our long separation, and to hear edited highlights of their adventures.

At length the UK leaders adjourned to a yurt. This had been magnificently prepared by primary school children. We were serenaded by musicians. We ate salads for a while, and then a dish of rice and sheep was presented. We shared food and had a wonderful time. We thanked the artists for all the trouble that they had taken, and asked them to pass on our thanks to the schoolchildren.

The students would now move their base to Astana city, and stay in a hotel near to where the leaders are based.

**July 13** The closing ceremony is held mid-afternoon. There is a vast pedestrian concourse in front of the Palace of Independence, and a long red carpet runs out of the Palace doors, down the steps, and all the way across the concourse to the road. There is a guard of honour on each side of the carpet, and musicians are waiting outside the palace.

In a wonderful ceremonial gesture, it turns out that the red carpet is for the teams. Each of them marches along behind a guide carrying their country's name. The students carry flags, and as they get close to the palace, the incessant Kazakh music becomes overwhelming. The jaunty firemen have giant trumpets, in the spirit of a vuvuzela, but three times the length. Stacks of speakers bring the music to the threshold of pain.

We have no idea if we will be asked to assist in the medal ceremony, so we sit there and hope to be left alone. The teams parade across the stage once more, in a reprise of the opening ceremony. Then Prime Minister Karim Massimov comes in, and presents a prize to the only student who acheived a perfect score, Zipei Nie of China.

The astonishing Lisa Sauermann of Germany scored 36/42, and so earned another gold medal. She now has one silver and three golds, and will soon surpass the German deputy Christian Reiher who retired from competition in 2003 with one bronze and four golds. I think Lisa has a couple more IMO chances, and no doubt she will enjoy trying to overtake Christian.

Past Kazakh IMO competitors present the bronze medals. Various academic luminaries hand out the silver ones, and the Minister of Education and Science bestows the gold medals. These are accompanied by laptops, thanks to Exxon Mobil, one of the principal sponsors of this IMO. At this point UK gold medallist Sergei Patiakin is holding his Union Jack inverted, a traditional distress signal in the Royal Navy. Sergei is in trouble, and I surmise that his crew have yellow fever or perhaps he has been captured by Barbary pirates. I gesture to him, and he quickly rectifies the situation. False alarm.

József Pelikán made his farewell speech as chair, and made very gracious remarks wishing good luck to the new Advisory Board. We owe József an enormous debt of gratitude.

After the ceremony we return to the leaders' hotel. The closing banquet is held in a large room round the back of the complex. It is a splendid affair, and adults even get a little wine. There is the presentation of the Golden Microphone. This has been won by the leader of the Netherlands, Johan Konter. As usual the comical overblown ceremony goes very well.

We go to bed early because we have an early flight the next day. The IMO organization has laid on a bus for us at 03:00. They wanted to pick up our students first at 02:00 but Ceri and James refused, and arranged a taxi for 03:30 instead, and told the organization about this. Nonetheless, an attempt was made to drag our team out of bed for a bus, and poor Sergei Patiakin had to mediate because of his Russian language skills. Sergei is a very well-mannered young man, not versed in the art of telling people, very firmly, to go away.

Joseph, James and I go by bus from our hotel, and meet up with the main party at the airport. As expected, the border guard takes a very dim view of my lack of an immigration card stamped in two places until I mutter the magic words 'International Mathematical Olympiad', and he lets me out. Joseph Myers had a similar problem.

The flight to Moscow is fine, and we have only a couple of hours in transit in Domodedovo. We have a light breakfast, and then find that we are very fortunate for our final leg. We have a giant plane with very few passengers. We spread out, and doze.

Arrival is easy enough, and we are met by friendly families.

**Conclusion**

A great many people worked very hard to create IMO 2010, and I would like to single out the guides for special praise. It seems that they were often acting without full information, and were under pressure to control the activities of the teams. Of course it would have been more sensible if the guides had been better informed, and then they could have taken on their proper role as facilitators and assistants with greater ease. Even so, all reports I had were that the guides were trying their best to be helpful and kind.

The Kazakh organization DARYN put in an immense effort to run this event, a sustained project which lasts many years of course, and considerable resources were expended. The Kazakh state was clearly committed to the project, and the warm and wise words of two Ministers were very welcome.

Thanks to the students, their families, fellow UKMT volunteeers and employees who have been involved this year. We now have a rich cycle of events, involving more and more students in various national and international competitions.

As I step back from the task of leading the UK IMO team, I would like to make a couple of points. First I must thank my successor James Cranch for agreeing to take on the role, and the various deputies, observers and trainers who have helped with IMO participation in recent years. I would explicitly like to thank Vesna Kadelburg. She wisely decided not to go to Kazakhstan while her health was vulnerable, but continued to support the enterprise in many ways.

UKMT continues to prosper. It is a large and multi-faceted organization, engaging in various aspects of secondary school mathematics enrichment. All of these activities are successful and, moreover, the financial structure which underpins UKMT and the British Mathematical Olympiad continues to function well. BMOS welcomes financial support from elsewhere, for example the generous support from Winton Capital Management, but we are not dependent upon it. However we do rely on the continuing goodwill of UKMT and BMOS and a legion of other volunteers.

Mathematics in the UK is enjoying a boom both in terms of secondary school participation, and in terms of recruitment to undergraduate mathematics courses. It would be gross hubris to attribute this marvellous circumstance solely to the activities of UKMT, but surely the complex and sustained mathematics enrichment programme that has been built under the UKMT flag in recent years has played at least a part in the revival of interest in mathematics in this country.

We must stay together, working for the good of the subject, and nurturing each generation of mathematical talent as it passes through. We must build UKMT, both in terms of volunteer effort and financial clout, until it sits as a permanent and powerful force behind mathematics at school level.

*Postscript*

There is always one final UK IMO event which happens after the end of the UKMT year. This event is a celebration of the performances of the UK IMO team members. In 2010, it was held in the Royal Society on Monday 20th September. The audience consisted of pupils, teachers and parents. In latter years, the team members have concocted their version of the IMO, accompanied by much hilarity and their medals are re-presented. There is a mathematical talk which this year was given by Professor Imre Leader of Trinity College, Cambridge.

# UKMT Mentoring Schemes (Administered by BMOS)

The UKMT Mentoring Schemes have continued to expand this year and pupils from well over 400 UK schools now use the material to inspire and challenge their brightest pupils and to introduce them to problem-solving and topics outside their standard curriculum. These have been ably administered by Janet Clark at the Maths Challenges Office at Leeds.

We are grateful to our patrons Professor Tim Gowers and Professor Imre Leader for their continued support and guidance and to all the mentors and teachers who give freely of their time and expertise to encourage and help all the school pupils as they tackle the sheets each month.

This year a deliberate attempt was made to introduce more people to the schemes, and after both the Junior Challenge and the Intermediate Challenge, schools with high scorers in these competitions received letters inviting them to participate in the schemes. There was an excellent response to this and the number of schools participating in the Junior Scheme has risen by a massive 50% from 300 last year to over 450 this year. There have also been increases at the higher levels as well.

Our aim continues to be to inspire school pupils across the UK with challenging problems and to help them to realise that there is a whole world of mathematics out there beyond their regular schoolwork which is waiting to be explored. We realise we are setting the bar quite high, but the aim is to encourage them with graded problems - easier ones to build confidence and help them to realise that they can achieve success with ingenuity and persistence and a bit of knowledge - and moving on to much harder ones which require the same things but need more ingenuity, more persistence and more knowledge. Every problem solved is not just an exercise in applying a formula correctly, but requires insight and creativity so that when it is solved, there is a real sense of achievement which can build self-confidence and a desire to delve deeper.

The schemes cater for pupils from Years 7 to 13. Each person is linked up with a mentor who can offer help, guidance and encouragement and they read and give feedback on the solutions offered by their mentees. At the Junior and Intermediate levels, we encourage teachers to mentor their own pupils because regular contact is important at this stage. At the Senior and Advanced levels, mentees are mentored by undergraduates, postgraduates and teachers who are more familiar with problem-solving techniques, though of course any teacher who is willing to act as a mentor to their own pupils is warmly encouraged to do so. Anyone who is interested in either being a mentee, a mentor or using the sheets with their classes is welcome to register with Janet Clark who administers the schemes from the UKMT Leeds office. The e-mail address is mentoring@ukmt.org.uk .

There are four schemes, which run from October through to May. In each scheme a sheet of about eight graded problems is issued at the beginning of each month and just before the end of the month mentees submit to their mentor the solutions or partial solutions they have managed to achieve. These are then read and returned with helpful feedback and comments.

*Junior Scheme*

This is used in 450 schools and is run by John Slater and Julian Gilbey. It caters for those of roughly Years 7 to 9 who have perhaps done well in the Junior Maths Challenge and are looking at Junior Olympiad papers. A few hints are given with the questions which aim to introduce pupils to problem-solving at an accessible level, though the later questions will usually be quite challenging. All pupils are currently mentored by their teachers and teachers are welcome to enrol in order to use the problem sheets with their classes. This is often a good way to stimulate the interest of a whole class, rather than just one or two individuals, though it is likely that only one or two will rise to producing good solutions to the later questions. Thanks are due to all teachers and others who have acted as mentors this year.

*Intermediate Scheme*

This is used in 400 schools and is run by Richard Atkins. It is aimed at those approximately in Years 9 to 11, who have done well in the Intermediate Maths Challenge and are preparing for Intermediate Olympiad papers or who have attended one of the UKMT National Mathematics Summer Schools. There is quite a gradient in these problems, from some which can be approached without knowledge of any special techniques to others which require modular arithmetic, some knowledge of number theory and geometrical theorems etc. The aim is gradually to introduce these techniques through the year. As mentees come across these, we hope they will ask questions or look at the internet to find out about these methods. Most pupils are mentored by their teachers, but some external mentors are available where necessary.

Thanks are due to all teachers who have acted as mentors, and to the external mentors: Anne Andrews, Neill Cooper, Yi Feng, Vesna Kadelburg, Vicky Neale, Ian Slater, and Pavel Stroev.

*Senior Scheme*

This is used in over 200 schools and is run by André Rzym and James Cranch. It is aimed approximately at those in Years 11 to 13 and the questions are set at quite a challenging level, aimed at those who are tackling BMO papers or who have outgrown the Intermediate scheme. Typically just two or three people at any school might enrol with this scheme and most of the mentors are undergraduates or postgraduates, though it is good to see that several teachers are keen to act as mentors at this level. Doing the questions is a stimulating experience for any teacher and in my view one of the best ways to add freshness and innovation to one's regular teaching. An important role of mentors at this level is to encourage their mentees because the questions are generally more taxing than anything they confront at A-level, and each problem solved is a distinct achievement which should give huge satisfaction. Thanks are due to all teachers involved and the external mentors: Anne Andrews, Teresa Barata, Chris Bryant, Neill Cooper, Owen Cotton-Barratt, James Cranch, Janet Dangerfield, Ben Fairbairn, Ildar Gaisin, Julian Gilbey, Victoria Gregson, Michael Griffiths, Tim Hennock, James Holloway, Vicky Hoskins, Ina Hughes, Michael Illing, Vinay Kathotia, Kate Land, Robert Lasenby, James Lawrence, Jonathan Lee, Kelvin Lee, Charles Leedham-Green, Michael Lipton, Freddie Manners, Gerry Netto, Peter Neumann, Jerome Ripp, Julia Robson, André Rzym, Dirk Schlueter, Peter Scott, Jack Shotton, Paul Smith, Balazs Szendroi, Stephen Tate, Oliver Thomas, Alan Thompson, James Welham, Weijun Xu, Dominic Yeo, Rong Zhou and Alison Zhu.

*Advanced Scheme*

This scheme, which is run by Tom Rogerson, is aimed at UK IMO squad members and those who have outgrown the Senior scheme, the questions being very hard and mainly of interest to those who are aiming for selection for the UK team in the annual International Mathematics Olympiad. This comprised 20 people this year and huge thanks are due to the select band of mentors who are able to cope with questions at this level: Robin Bhattacharyya, Yimin Ge, Paul Jefferys, Nathan Kettle, Henry Liu, Tom Lovering, Max Menzies and Joseph Myers.

*Mentoring Conference & Dinner*

This year for the first time we held our conference and dinner in Oxford, at St Anne's College. We are grateful to Balazs Szendroi and James Cranch for addressing the conference and to Peter Neumann for organising the event. It was a welcome opportunity to build some more mentoring links with Oxford. In 2010 our conference and dinner will be back in Cambridge.

Richard Atkins, Director of Mentoring

# UKMT Team Maths Challenge 2010

*Overview*

The Team Maths Challenge (TMC) is a national maths competition which gives pupils the opportunity to participate in a wide range of maths activities and compete against other pupils from schools in their region. The TMC promotes team working unlike the individual challenges (the Junior, Intermediate and Senior). Students work in groups and are given practical tasks as well as theoretical problems to add another dimension to mathematics.

The TMC is designed for teams of four pupils in:

- Y8 & Y9 (England and Wales)
- S1 & S2 (Scotland)
- Y9 & Y10 (Northern Ireland)

with no more than two pupils from the older year group.

Sample TMC material is available to download from the TMC section of the UKMT website (www.ukmt.org.uk) for use in school and to help teachers to select a team to represent their school at the Regional Finals.

*Report on the 2010 TMC*

The eighth year of the TMC saw the competition encounter significant challenges to participation, including new 'rarely cover' guidelines in state schools and the volcanic ash crisis, which left many teachers (including some event coordinators!) stranded abroad and unable to attend Regional Finals. However, determined marketing efforts along with the introduction of new venues (increasing the number of Regional Finals from 60 to 66) served to minimise the potential downward effect and a total of 1448 teams entered the competition (compared to 1500 last year), of which 1341 turned up to participate on the day.

The CD-ROM of materials from the 2009 TMC was sent in September to all schools that participated in that year's competition and was also included in the general mailing of 2010 competition details and entry forms to schools in early October. As usual, full details of the competition (including Regional Final dates, venues and availability of places) were also made available on the UKMT website, along with additional past materials for the use of schools in selecting and preparing their team of four. Participants from the 2009 TMC also received a copy of the winning poster from the 2009 National Final, originally created by The King's School (Worcester) and professionally reproduced by Andrew Jobbings.

Each team signed up to participate in one of the 66 Regional Finals, held between late February and the middle of May at a widely-spread set of venues. Each Regional Final comprised four rounds which encouraged the teams to think mathematically in a variety of ways. The Group Round is the only round in which the whole team work together and they are faced with a set of ten challenging questions. In the Crossnumber the team splits into two pairs; one pair get the across clues and the other pair get the down clues. The two pairs then work independently to complete the Crossnumber using logic and deduction. For the Head-to-Head, teams are paired up and compete against their opponents to be the first to correctly answer a series of questions, with each pair working on different questions and the solution of each question dependent on the previous answer. The final round of the day, the Relay, is a fast and furious race involving much movement to answer a series of questions in pairs. Each Regional Final was run by a regional lead coordinator with support from an assistant coordinator and, at some venues, other local helpers. The teachers who accompanied the teams were fully occupied too – they were involved in the delivery and marking of all the rounds.

*TMC National Final*

Winners from the 66 Regional Finals (including one tie for first place) and a small number of runners-up were invited to the National Final on 21$^{st}$ June 2010. Having outgrown the previous venue (the Camden Centre), the event was held in the grand surroundings of the Lawrence Hall, one of the prestigious Royal Horticultural Halls in Westminster, London. As in the Regional Finals there were 4 main rounds, but as usual the Group Round was replaced by the Group Circus (a similar round but with the addition of some practical materials for use in solving the questions) and the day began with a Poster Competition, which was judged and scored separately from the main event. The Poster theme for 2010 was 'Quadrilaterals' and the extra space in the new venue also allowed for an exhibition of the teams' posters during the remainder of the day.

The following schools participated at the National Final (a ratio of 6:4 state to independent schools):

| | |
|---|---|
| All Hallows Catholic School | Farnham, Surrey |
| Altrincham Girls' Grammar School | Altrincham, Cheshire |
| Altrincham Grammar School for Boys | Altrincham, Cheshire |
| Amery Hill School | Alton, Hampshire |
| Aylesbury High School | Aylesbury, Buckinghamshire |

| | |
|---|---|
| Bablake School | Coventry, Warwickshire |
| Balfron High School | Balfron, Glasgow |
| Bancroft's School | Woodford Green, Essex |
| Bedford Modern School | Bedford |
| Bedford School | Bedford |
| Beverley Grammar School | Beverley, East Yorkshire |
| Bishop Perowne College | Worcester |
| Bournemouth School | Bournemouth |
| Bristol Grammar School | Clifton, Bristol |
| Buxton Community School | Buxton, Derbyshire |
| Cherwell School | Oxford |
| Christleton High School | Chester |
| Clifton College | Clifton, Bristol |
| Clitheroe Royal Grammar School | Clitheroe, Lancashire |
| Clyst Vale Community College | Broadclyst, Exeter |
| Colchester Royal Grammar School | Colchester, Essex |
| Commonweal School | Swindon |
| Conyers School | Yarm, Stockton-on-Tees |
| Debenham High School | Debenham, Suffolk |
| Dowdales School | Dalton in Furness, Cumbria |
| Durham Johnston School | Durham |
| Durrington High School | Worthing, West Sussex |
| Emmanuel College | Gateshead, Tyne & Wear |
| Ewell Castle School | Epsom, Surrey |
| Fulford School | York |
| Glebelands School | Cranleigh, Surrey |
| Gleniffer High School | Paisley, Glasgow |
| Guernsey Grammar School | Guernsey |
| Guildford High School | Guildford, Surrey |
| Haberdashers' Aske's School for Boys | Elstree, Hertfordshire |
| Highgate School | Highgate, London |
| Hobart High School | Lodden, Norfolk |
| Hutcheson's Grammar School | Glasgow |
| Ivanhoe College | Ashby de la Zouch, Leicestershire |
| King Edward VI Camp Hill Boys' School | Kings Heath, Birmingham |
| King Edward's School | Birmingham |
| King's School | Macclesfield, Cheshire |

| | |
|---|---|
| King's School Bruton | Bruton, Somerset |
| Lancing College | Lancing, West Sussex |
| Liverpool Blue Coat School | Liverpool |
| Llanishen High School | Llanishen, Cardiff |
| Loreto Grammar School | Altrincham, Cheshire |
| Lumen Christi College | Derry, N Ireland |
| Madras College | St Andrews, Fife |
| Magdalen College School | Oxford |
| Monmouth School | Monmouth, Gwent |
| North Halifax Grammar School | Halifax |
| Nottingham High School for Girls | Nottingham |
| Perse School for Girls | Cambridge |
| Plymouth College | Plymouth |
| Queen Elizabeth High School | Gainsborough, Lincolnshire |
| Queen Elizabeth Grammar School | Penrith, Cumbria |
| Queen Elizabeth Grammar School | Wakefield, West Yorkshire |
| Queen Elizabeth's School | Barnet, Hertfordshire |
| Reading Blue Coat School | Reading |
| Reigate Grammar School | Reigate, Surrey |
| Robert Gordon's College | Aberdeen |
| Rye College | Rye, East Sussex |
| School of St Helen and St Katharine | Abingdon Oxfordshire |
| Sir Harry Smith Community College | Whittlesey, Peterborough |
| Stanwell School | Penarth, Cardiff |
| St Paul's Girls' School | Hammersmith, London |
| St Paul's School | Barnes, London |
| Tapton School | Sheffield |
| The Grammar School at Leeds | Leeds |
| The Hazeley School | Hazeley, Milton Keynes |
| The King's School Worcester | Worcester |
| Torquay Boys' Grammar School | Shiphay, Devon |
| Townley Grammar School for Girls | Bexleyheath, Kent |
| Walton Priory County Middle School | Stone, Staffordshire |
| Wellington School | Wellington, Somerset |
| Wilson's School | Wallington, Surrey |
| Wolverhampton Girls' High School | Wolverhampton |
| Yarm School | Yarm, Stockton-on-Tees |

A special mention also goes to the following schools, which were invited to participate but sadly could not attend: Friends' School Lisburn (Antrim); Harvey Grammar School (Folkestone, Kent); Packwood Haugh School (Ruyton-XI-Towns, Shropshire); Queen Mary's Grammar School (Walsall, West Midlands); Truro School (Cornwall).

We were delighted to have in attendance Robin Wilson, Emeritus Professor of Pure Mathematics at the Open University, who presented the prizes at the end of the day, as well as Frances Kirwan, Chair of the UKMT Council, and Emma Watkins representing Winton Capital Management, joint competition sponsors along with Helix. We are also grateful to Arbelos for providing additional prizes for the event and to UKMT volunteer Andrew Bell for capturing the day's excitement in his additional role as official photographer. Congratulations go to the 2010 Team Maths Challenge champions, Magdalen College School (Oxford), and the winners of the Poster Competition, Altrincham Grammar School for Boys (Cheshire).

As usual, thanks are due to a great number of people for ensuring another successful year of the TMC: the team of volunteers (listed at the back of this book) who generously give up their time to write, check and refine materials, run Regional Finals and readily carry out countless other jobs behind the scenes; the staff in the UKMT office in Leeds for the way in which the competition is administered (particularly Nicky Bray who has responsibility for the central coordination of the competition, assisted by Jo Williams) and the team of packers for their efficient and precise preparation and packing of materials; the teachers who continue to support the competition and take part so willingly, some of whom also organise and host a Regional Final at their own school and, of course, the pupils who participate so enthusiastically in the competition at all levels. Our thanks also go to additional contacts at schools and other host venues responsible for organising and helping with Regional Finals (listed at the back of this book).

The venues for the 2010 Regional Finals (some of which hosted two events) were:

| | |
|---|---|
| Aberdeen | University of Aberdeen |
| Bath | Royal High School |
| Belfast | Rockport School, Holywood |
| Berkshire | Furze Platt School, Maidenhead |
| Berkshire | Horris Hill School, Newbury |
| Birkenhead | Birkenhead School |

| | |
|---|---|
| Blackpool | Arnold School |
| Bradford | Bradford Grammar School |
| Bristol | St Katherine's School |
| Cambridge (2 events) | Centre for Mathematical Sciences, University of Cambridge |
| Cardiff | Cardiff University Students' Union |
| Carlisle | Caldew School |
| Channel Islands | St Helier Parish Assembly Hall, Jersey |
| Cornwall | Penair School, Truro |
| Cumbria | Barrow in Furness Sixth Form College |
| Derbyshire | Swanwick Hall School |
| Derry | St Columb's College |
| Devon | Exmouth Community College |
| Doncaster | Danum School |
| Dorset | Corfe Hills School, Broadstone |
| Durham | Durham University Students' Union |
| East Sussex | Robertsbridge Community School |
| Edinburgh | University of Edinburgh |
| Essex | Bancroft's School, Woodford Green |
| Falkirk | Forth Valley College |
| Glasgow | University of the West of Scotland, Paisley Campus |
| Gloucester | Wycliffe College |
| Hertfordshire | Ashlyns School, Berkhamsted |
| Hertfordshire | Haberdashers' Aske's School for Girls, Elstree |
| Hull | Newland School for Girls |
| Keele | Keele University |
| Kent | Hartsdown Technology College, Margate |
| Kent | Tonbridge Grammar School |
| Leeds | Lawnswood School |
| Leicester | Grace Dieu Manor School, Thringstone |
| Liverpool | St Edward's College |
| London, Central (2 events) | City of London School |
| London, East | The Octagon, Queen Mary, University of London |

184

| | |
|---|---|
| London, North | Preston Manor High School, Wembley |
| London, Outer | St Olave's Grammar School, Orpington |
| London, South | Trinity School, Croydon |
| Manchester (2 events) | University of Manchester |
| Middlesbrough | Macmillan Academy |
| Norfolk | Swaffham Hamond's High School |
| Northampton | Caroline Chisholm School |
| Northumberland | Knott Hall, Heddon-on-the-Wall |
| Oxford | University of Oxford |
| Peterborough | The King's School |
| Plymouth | Plymouth Guildhall |
| Rugby | Rugby High School |
| Shropshire | Moreton Hall School, Oswestry |
| Somerset | Millfield School |
| Stockport | Poynton High School |
| Suffolk | Framlingham College |
| Swindon | Wootton Bassett School |
| Warwick | Myton School |
| West Sussex | Ardingly College |
| West Sussex | Lancing College |
| Winchester (2 events) | St Swithun's School |
| Wolverhampton (2 events) | Jennie Lee Centre |
| York | The Mount School |

*TMC Regional Finals Material*

Each of the 66 Regional Finals held across the UK involved four rounds:

1. Group Round
2. Crossnumber
3. Head-to-Head
4. Relay Race

*Group Round*

Teams are given a set of 10 questions, which they should divide up among themselves so that they can answer, individually or in pairs, as many as possible in the allotted time (45 minutes).

Question 1

The lock of Claire's locker has a three-digit code such as 5, 2, 4. She has forgotten the code but she knows that all three digits are different. She also knows that if she divides the first digit by the second digit and then squares the result she gets the third digit. Find all possible three-digit codes for her lock.

Question 2

All the letters in this question represent different positive integers.

If F = 5, O = 3 and X = 4 then FOX = 60, BIBLE = 66 and BALL = 28.

Find the value of LIBEL.

Question 3

Find two integers, neither of which has a zero digit, whose product is 1 000 000.

Question 4

Richard had to arrive at the airport at exactly 10 am. If he is able to drive at an average speed of 60 miles per hour he would arrive early at 9 am. If he drives at an average speed of 40 miles per hour he would arrive late at 11am. How fast should he travel to arrive at the airport at 10 am exactly?

*You need to assume that Richard sets out at the same time in each scenario. You are not told what this time is and are not asked for it, but could work it out from the information given. You are asked to work out what his average speed should be if, after setting out at the same time as in the first two examples, he is to arrive exactly on time.*

Question 5

*a*, *b* and *c* are all positive.

$$a \times b = 2$$
$$b \times c = 24$$
$$c \times a = 3$$

What is the value of $a + b + c$ ?

186

## Question 6

Shakira chooses, at random, two different single digit numbers, not including zero. She then works out their sum. What is the probability that the sum is a single digit number?

*Please give your answer as a fraction in its lowest terms.*

## Question 7

*ABCD* is a square. *P* and *Q* are squares drawn in the triangles *ADC*, *ABC* as shown.

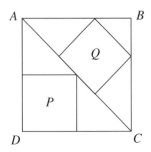

What is the ratio of the area of square *P* to the area of square *Q*?

Give your answer in the form *a* : *b* where *a* and *b* are integers with no common factor greater than 1.

## Question 8

One pump used on its own fills a swimming pool in 2 hours. A second pump used on its own fills the same pool in 3 hours. A third pump can be used to empty all the water from the same pool in 90 minutes.

How long would it take to fill the pool if all three pumps were in use at the same time?

## Question 9

The number of diagonals of a regular polygon equals twice the number of sides. How many sides does the polygon have?

## Question 10

The mean of five integers is 4, the median is 3 and the only mode is 1.

List all possible sets of integers as working below.

Give as the final answer, on your answer sheet, the largest product which can be found using just two of the integers in any one of your sets.

*Crossnumber*

Teams are divided into pairs, with one pair given the across clues and one pair given the down clues. Each pair answer as many questions as possible on the grid, showing their answers to the supervising teacher who either confirms or corrects them. The correct version is then shown to both pairs. Pairs only communicate through the supervisor, but they may make a request for particular clues to be solved. This round lasts up to 45 minutes.

| 1 | 2 | | 3 | ■ | 4 | | 5 | ■ |
|---|---|---|---|---|---|---|---|---|
| ■ | | ■ | 6 | | | ■ | 7 | |
| 8 | | 9 | ■ | ■ | 10 | 11 | | ■ |
| | ■ | 12 | 13 | | ■ | | ■ | 14 |
| 15 | | ■ | | | 16 | ■ | 17 | |
| | ■ | 18 | | 19 | | 20 | ■ | |
| ■ | 21 | | 22 | ■ | ■ | 23 | 24 | |
| 25 | | ■ | 26 | | 27 | ■ | | ■ |
| ■ | 28 | | | ■ | 29 | | | |

*Across*:

1. A prime factor of 8765 (4)
4. The interior angle of a regular polygon; its digits have a product of twelve (3)
6. A Fibonacci number whose digits add up to twenty-four (3)
7. A prime number which is one greater than a square number (2)
8. Ninety-nine greater than the number formed by reversing the order of the digits (3)

188

10. A multiple of 25 Across (3)
12. 9 Down multiplied by seven (3)
15. A number with seven factors (2)
17. The third side of a right-angled triangle with hypotenuse 9 Down and other side 25 Across (2)
19. (10 Across) per cent of 8 Across (3)
21. An odd multiple of nine (3)
23. The product of the seventh prime number and the eleventh prime number (3)
25. An even number (2)
26. The lowest common multiple of 25 Across and 11 Down (3)
28. A multiple of eleven, and also the mean of 12 Across, 16 Down, 19 Across, 24 Down and 27 Down (3)
29. A power of nineteen (4)

*Down*:
2. An even square number (3)
3. One third of 21 Across (2)
4. The interior angle of the regular polygon which has twice as many sides as the regular polygon whose interior angle is 4 Across (3)
5. One less than a multiple of eleven (3)
8. A power of nine (4)
9. The mean of 3 Down, 7 Across, 13 Down, 17 Across and 27 Down (2)
11. Ninety-one less than 10 Across (2)
13. The sum of the squares of the digits of 23 Across (2)
14. A factor of 4567 (4)
16. The difference between 11 Down and 3 Down (2)
18. The square root of 8 Down (2)
20. The highest common factor of 10 Across and 24 Down (2)
21. The total number of days in a year in the months whose names do not contain the letter A (3)
22. A prime number that is ten less than a cube number (3)
24. A square number multiplied by five; the product of its digits is forty (3)
27. A triangle number which is the sum of two prime numbers that differ by eight (2)

*Head-to-Head*

Teams are divided into pairs, with one pair given Questions 1 and 3 (along with the record sheet on which to record their answers) and the other pair given Questions 2 and 4. The first pair work on Question 1 and then pass their answer to the other pair who use it to help them answer Question 2, for which they can first carry out some preparatory work. This continues with the second pair passing the answer to Question 2 back to the first pair and so on until a full set of answers is presented for marking.

Each team is paired up with another team for this activity and bonus points are awarded to the first team in each pair to present a correct set of answers before their opponents. Four of these mini relays are attempted in the time given.

**A1**   Write down 10% of 20% of 30% of 40% of 50% of 10000.

**A2**   *T is the number that you will receive.*

The number $1000T$, when expressed as a product of prime factors, can be written in the form $2^a \times 3^b \times 5^c$, where $a$, $b$ and $c$ are integers.

Write down the value of $a + b + c$.

**A3**   *T is the number that you will receive.*

Write down the lowest common multiple of $\sqrt{64}$, $\sqrt{100}$ and $\sqrt{T}$.

**A4**   *T is the number that you will receive.*

A cuboid with length 10 cm and width 2 cm is made up from $T$ centimetre cubes.

Write down the total surface area, in cm$^2$, of the cuboid.

**B1**   Write down the value of
$$\frac{2010}{2 + 0 + 1 + 0} + \frac{201 + 0}{2 + 0 + 1 + 0} + \frac{20 + 10}{2 + 0 + 1 + 0}.$$

**B2**   *T is the number that you will receive.*

The number *T* is an example of a palindromic number – one which is unchanged if the order of its digits is reversed.

Write down the number of palindromes between 300 and *T* inclusive.

**B3**   *T is the number that you will receive.*

The diagram shows a triangle drawn on a square grid made up of nine smaller squares. The area of the shaded triangle is *T* cm².

Write down the area, in cm², of one of the smaller squares.

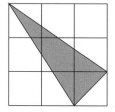

**B4**   *T is the number that you will receive.*

Write the number *T* as a word in the gap shown in the following sentence and then write down the answer to the question:

Out of the first _____ letters in this sentence, what fraction are vowels?

---

**C1**   Starting in the box in the left, apply the operations in the order given and write down your final answer.

$$\boxed{15} \Rightarrow \boxed{\text{square}} \Rightarrow \boxed{-57} \Rightarrow \boxed{\div 7} \Rightarrow \boxed{\times 5} \Rightarrow \boxed{\div 2}$$

**C2**   *T is the number that you will receive.*

I had budgeted for *T* items at £1.98 each, but in the sale they were only £1.80.

How many was I able to buy?

**C3**  *T is the number that you will receive.*

The diagram shows a magic square in which the numbers in each column, row and two main diagonals add up to the same number. Write down the value of the number that should be written in the shaded square.

|     | $T$   |       |
|-----|-------|-------|
| $T+2$ | $T+4$ |       |
| $T+3$ |       | $T+1$ |

**C4**  *T is the number that you will receive.*

A right-angled triangle with sides in the ratio 3 : 4 : 5 has perimeter equal to $T$ cm. Semicircles are drawn on each of the three sides.

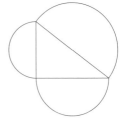

Write down the total perimeter, in cm, of the resulting shape, giving your answer as a multiple of $\pi$.

---

**D1**  John runs to the park at a constant speed, and back at twice that speed, taking a total of 18 minutes.

How many minutes would it have taken him if he had not speeded up?

**D2**  *T is the number that you will receive.*

A clock has a minute hand which is $T$ cm long. In one hour the area swept out by the minute hand is 48 times the area swept out by the hour hand.

What is the length, in cm, of the hour hand?

**D3**  *T is the number that you will receive.*

Marina notices that there are four times as many plain biscuits as chocolate biscuits in the tin. In fact, if she were to eat T plain biscuits, there would be an equal number of each type left.

How many chocolate biscuits are there?

192

**D4**    *T is the number that you will receive.*

The diagram shows five identical rectangles arranged to form a larger rectangle. If the width of the larger rectangle is $(T + 11)$ cm, as shown, write down the total area, in cm$^2$, of the larger rectangle.

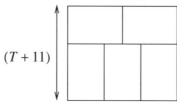

$(T + 11)$

---

*Relay Race*

The aim here is to have a speed competition with teams working in pairs to answer alternate questions. Each team is divided into two pairs, with each pair seated at a different desk away from the other pair and their supervising teacher. This round lasts up to 45 minutes.

One member of Pair A from a team collects question A1 from the supervising teacher and returns to his/her partner to answer the question together. When the pair are certain that they have answered the question, the runner returns to the front and submits their answer. If it is correct, the runner is given question B1 to give to the other pair (Pair B) from their team. If it is incorrect, Pair A then have another go at answering the question, then the runner returns to the front to receive question B1 to deliver to pair B. (Pair A can only have one extra attempt.) The runner then returns, empty handed, to his/her partner. Pair B answer question B1 and a runner from this pair brings the answer to the front, as above, then takes question A2 to Pair A. Pair A answer question A2, return it to the front, collect question B2 for the other pair and so on until all questions are answered or time runs out. Thus the A pairs answer only A questions and the B pairs answer only B questions. Only one pair from a team should be working on a question at any time and each pair must work independently of the other.

**A1**    All of the integers from 1 to 100 inclusive are written down. How many times does the digit 1 (one) appear?

**A2**    What is the value of:
number of sides of 9 heptagons
+ number of sides of 2 dodecagons?

**A3**   Before decimalisation, British money had pounds, shillings and pence, with 20 shillings in a pound and 12 pence in a shilling.

How much change would I get from a five pound note if my bill was two pounds, four shillings and seven pence?

**A4**   I am a three digit number. All my digits are different. The sum of my digits is 6. My tens digit is greater than my units digit. My tens digit and my units digit in that order form a two-digit prime number. Who am I?

**A5**   A drink is made from orange juice, lime juice and lemonade in the ratio 5:1:20 respectively.

How much of the drink can I make if I have 80ml of orange juice, 18ml of lime juice and 350 ml of lemonade?

**A6**   Five different whole numbers have a mean and median of 6 and a range of 8.

Three of the numbers are prime.

What are the five numbers?

**A7**   A worker earns £26000 per year. Calculate his monthly pay after deducting 22% tax.

**A8**   Mark runs the first lap of a race at 3 km/hr and the second lap at 6 km/hr. What was his average speed over the course of the race?

**A9**   A sunflower in my garden doubles its height every 24 hours.

It is 1.5 metres tall just before midnight on Sunday.

On which day did it measure 10 cm?

**A10**   The letters of the word "supercalifragilisticexpialidocious" are written on tiles and placed in a bag. One tile is taken out at random. What is the probability that it is a vowel?

**A11**   Sue and Ann share a packet of sweets.

Ann eats a third of the sweets and Sue eats three quarters of the rest.

Six sweets are left in the packet. How many were there when it was full?

**A12**   For his yearly wages a medieval servant was promised 100 ducats and a cloak.

However, the servant left his master's house after only 7 months and received 20 ducats and the cloak as his due.

How much was the cloak worth?

**A13** A gardener puts edging all round a rectangular lawn 11 metres wide and 16 metres long, and around the circular pond, radius 3 metres, in the middle.

The edging is sold in multiples of 5 metres.

How many metres must she buy?

**A14** If $\dfrac{1}{a} = \dfrac{2}{3} + \dfrac{3}{2}$ what is the value of $a$?

**A15** How many days, to the nearest day, are there in a million seconds?

**B1** Four clocks all give different times. I know that one is accurate, one 5 minutes slow, one 5 minutes fast and one 15 minutes fast.

They show 5:59, 5:54, 5:49 and 6:09.

What is the correct time?

**B2** Find the sum of all the interior angles of a triangle, a pentagon and a hexagon.

**B3** What percentage of the numbers from 1 to 25 inclusive are primes?

**B4** All of the numbers from 100 to 300 inclusive are written down.

How many times does the digit 6 appear?

**B5** Paul and his friend share a litre bottle of water. Paul drinks $\frac{1}{5}$ of the bottle and his friend drinks $\frac{3}{10}$ of the remainder. What fraction is left?

**B6** Calculate $\dfrac{1^2 + 2^2 + 3^2 + 4^2}{1^3 + 2^3 + 3^3 + 4^3}$.

**B7** Before decimalisation, British money had pounds, shillings and pence, with 20 shillings in a pound and 12 pence in a shilling.

How much change would I get from a ten pound note if my bill was six pounds, fourteen shillings and three pence?

**B8** In 8 years from now Sam will be three times as old as he was 12 years ago. What is his age now?

**B9** On my walk I counted 12 people each walking 1 dog, 3 people walking 2 dogs and 1 person walking 4 dogs. All the other dog-walkers had 3 dogs, and the mean number of dogs per walker was 2.

How many dog-walkers did I meet altogether?

**B10** A man bought a picture. He expected to sell it at a 10% profit on his purchase price. However, he had to sell it for £500 less than his expected selling price and as a result made a loss of 15% on what it cost him.

How much did he pay for the picture?

**B11** A mathematical grandmother decorates a rectangular quilt 90cm long and 60cm wide for her new grandson with braid, which is sold in multiples of 50cm. The braid goes all around the edge and along both diagonals.

How much braid must she buy?

**B12** What is one tenth of one fifth of one half of £250?

**B13** Find the values of the numbers $A$, $B$, $C$, $D$ and $E$.

$$2A + B = 100$$
$$B = 2A$$
$$C + 2D = B$$
$$A = D + E$$
$$4E = D$$

**B14** How many years, to the nearest ten years, are there in a million hours?

**B15** What is the value of:

$$\frac{1}{3} + \frac{1}{4} + \frac{1}{5} + \frac{1}{9} + \frac{1}{12} + \frac{1}{15} ?$$

Give your answer as a simplified fraction.

*TMC National Final Material*

At the National Final, the Group Round was replaced by the Group Circus.

*Group Circus*

Teams move around a number of stations (ten at the 2010 National Final) to tackle a variety of activities, some of which involve practical materials.

Station 1

The 3 × 3 square below contains all of the digits 1 to 9. One of these digits goes in each of the squares. Each digit is used once only.

The 3-digit number in the middle row is double that in the top row. The number in the bottom row is three times the number in the top row.

Using the blank 3 × 3 square and digit cards (1 to 9) provided, find two other ways of arranging the digits 1 to 9 so that the 3-digit row numbers are related in the same way.

| 1 | 9 | 2 |
|---|---|---|
| 3 | 8 | 4 |
| 5 | 7 | 6 |

(There are 3 marks for one, 6 marks for two.)

Station 2

You have been given 10 dominoes:

0-0, 0-1, 0-2, 0-3, 1-1, 1-2, 1-3, 2-2, 2-3, 3-3.

Arrange these ten dominoes (two have been placed) in the pattern shown below so that:

– the total number of spots on each of the four sides of the square is the same (corner numbers count in both directions);
– none of the joins match, for example domino 0-1 directly next to 1-2,

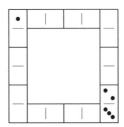 is not allowed.

Station 3

Each of the letters used below is representing a different single digit.

Example: $AB + 2 = AC$

[the answer could be $A = 1, B = 3, C = 5$ because $13 + 2 = 15$.]

If $ABCD \times 9 = DCBA$
find $A$, $B$, $C$ and $D$.

Station 4

You have a 'four-block' in front of you as shown in the diagram below. This is just four standard dice placed together on the table.

Arrange the four dice, still keeping them in the form of a four-block, so that the total number of dots around the side faces is equal to the number of dots on the top face added to the number of dots which are in contact with the table.

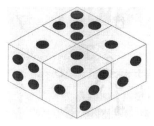

Station 5

You have an arrangement of playing cards as shown in the diagram below. One of the cards has been turned over so we are unable to see it.

Find the pattern in this arrangement and write down a description of the card which has been turned over.

| 6♦ | 4♣ | 2♥ | K♠ |
|------|------|------|------|
| 8♠ | ? | 3♠ | J♦ |
| 10♥ | Q♣ | A♦ | 9♣ |
| A♣ | 3♦ | 5♠ | 7♥ |

198

Station 6

Find the maximum number of red counters that can be placed on the grid applying the rules below.

Place the red counters on squares of the 3 × 12 grid provided, with no more than one counter in each square, so that no two counters are directly next to each other, not even diagonally. Each row of 12 squares must contain at least one red counter.

Station 7

You have a paper trapezium in front of you. This trapezium consists of a square and half another identical square.

Divide this paper trapezium into four pieces, all exactly the same shape and size.

Show these clearly by

- folding the paper, or
- drawing the relevant lines to give the four pieces.

Station 8

You have a large circle in front of you.

You can draw six straight lines across this circle. Each line must cross the circle completely. For instance, three parallel lines drawn one way and three in another direction can divide the circle into 16 distinct regions as shown in the diagram below.

Find the greatest number of distinct regions that can be obtained using six lines across the circle. Your lines do not have to be parallel. You may obtain your answer by either reasoning or drawing.

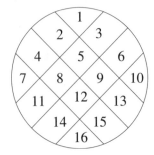

Station 9

At this station there must be no placement of matches directly on top of one another. Each match must form one of the congruent squares with no loose matches anywhere.

(i) Move (but do not remove) three matches to make *only* four congruent squares.

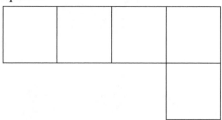

(ii) Move (but do not remove) three matches to make five congruent squares.

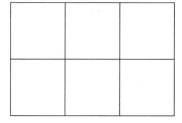

Station 10

You have 27 interlocking cubes in front of you. There are three each of nine different colours. The challenge is to fit them all together to make one cube with all nine colours showing on each face.

*Crossnumber*

*Across*:

1. A power of eleven (5)
4. A square number which is the sum of a three-digit cube number and a three-digit fourth power (3)
6. The sum of five consecutive Fibonacci numbers (3)
7. The lowest common multiple of 1 Down and 21 Down (4)
10. A prime factor of 32123 (3)
11. The number of dots in the sixtieth pattern in this sequence: (4)
13. Twenty-five more than a multiple of seven and twenty-five less than a multiple of seventeen (2)
14. The difference between two cube numbers (2)
15. One more than a multiple of four; its digits are the same as those of 4 Down but not in the same order (4)
16. An odd number with ten factors; its digits are consecutive (3)

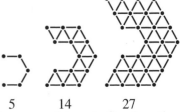

5    14    27

17. (13 Across) percent of 12 Down; the product of its digits is ten (4)
20. The square of 21 Down (3)
22. The area of a rhombus whose perimeter is 120 and the lengths of whose diagonals are in the ratio 3 : 4 (3)
23. A multiple of eleven with two distinct digits, each occurring more than once (5)

*Down*:
1. A prime factor of 23432 (3)
2. A prime number, the product of whose digits is (13 Across) percent of (13 Across) (3)
3. The sum of two Fibonacci numbers (2)
4. A number, the product of whose digits is zero (4)
5. A power of 111 (5)
8. The total of the interior angles (in °) of a polygon (3)
9. The number of line segments in the fortieth pattern in this sequence: (4)

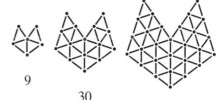

9     30     63

12. A number more than 15 Across but less than 15 Down (4)
13. A multiple of four whose five digits are distinct and have a range of four (5)
14. An even multiple of the sixth and twelfth prime numbers (3)
15. A multiple of eleven (4)
18. The longest side of a right-angled triangle whose shorter sides are 13 Across and 14 Across (3)
19. Half of the mean of 2 Down, 3 Down, 10 Across and 16 Across (3)
21. The square root of 20 Across (2)

*Head-to-Head*

**A1**  Write down the value of $N$ that makes this equation correct:
$$27 \times 120 \times N = 96 \times 75 \times 36.$$

**A2**  *T is the number that you will receive.*
The exterior angles of a hexagon have a sum of 360 degrees. Three of the exterior angles are equal to $\frac{1}{2}T°$, $T°$ and $2T°$. The three remaining exterior angles are in the ratio 1 : 4 : 5.
Write down the size, in degrees, of the smallest exterior angle.

**A3**  *T is the number that you will receive.*
The mean of a list of $T$ numbers is 15.
One more number is added to the list and the mean is recalculated as 14.
Write down the value of the extra number.

**A4**  *T is the number that you will receive.*
Write down the value of
$$\left( \frac{(2T+1)^2 - 1}{2} - 2T \right)^2.$$

**B1**  Write down the value of this expression (your answer should be a positive whole number):
$$\sqrt{\left( \left( \left( \left( \frac{3}{4} \right)^2 \div \frac{2}{5} \right) \times \frac{8}{9} \right) \div \frac{5}{16} \right)}.$$

**B2**  *T is the number that you will receive.*
A solid steel cuboid measuring 3 metres by 8 metres by $T$ metres is melted down and recast into smaller cuboids measuring 30 cm by 50 cm by 160 cm.
How many smaller cuboids is it possible to make?

**B3**  *T is the number that you will receive.*
A set of $T$ squares, each with area 1 cm$^2$ are packed together into a rectangle with area $T$ cm$^2$. Rectangles of six different shapes can be created in this way.
Write down the difference, in centimetres, between the smallest and largest perimeters of these rectangles.

**B4**  *T is the number that you will receive.*
Write down the lowest common multiple of $T$ and 156.

**C1**   The grid below shows squares of area 1.

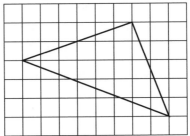

T is the area of the triangle shown.
Write down the value of T.

**C2**   *T is the number that you will receive.*
The calculation:

$$\left(1-\frac{1}{2}\right)\times\left(1+\frac{1}{3}\right)\times\left(1-\frac{1}{4}\right)\times\left(1+\frac{1}{5}\right)\times\left(1-\frac{1}{6}\right)\times\left(1+\frac{1}{7}\right)\times...\times\left(1-\frac{1}{T-1}\right)\left(1+\frac{1}{T}\right)$$

gives a fraction $\frac{a}{b}$, which is in its lowest terms. Write down the value of $b - a$.

**C3**   *T is the number that you will receive.*
A mathematician drills a cylindrical hole of radius 1cm straight through the middle of a cube of side $\frac{1}{2}T$ cm.

The resulting shape has total surface area $(a + b\pi)$ cm², where $a$ and $b$ are whole numbers.

Write down the value of $a - b$.

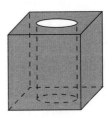

**C4**   *T is the number that you will receive.*
The exterior angles of any regular polygon have a sum of 360 degrees.

The points $A$, $B$, $C$ and $D$ are consecutive vertices on a regular $T$-sided polygon.

How many degrees is angle $ACD$?

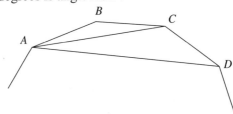

204

**D1** Twins Anna and Bob each have toy building blocks with the letters of their names on them.

Bob can make three different "words" from his:

$\boxed{B}\boxed{O}\boxed{B}$   $\boxed{B}\boxed{B}\boxed{O}$   $\boxed{O}\boxed{B}\boxed{B}$

How many different "words" could Anna make from hers?

$\boxed{A}\boxed{N}\boxed{N}\boxed{A}$

**D2** *T is the number that you will receive.*

$a = T$, $b = 2T$ and $c = -3T$, write down the value of $\sqrt{b^2 - 4ac}$.

**D3** *T is the number that you will receive.*

John cycles at $T$ km per hour for 15 minutes, rests for 3 minutes, and then cycles at $(T + 1)$ km per hour for 12 minutes.

What is the average speed for the whole journey in km per hour?

**D4** *T is the number that you will receive.*

At current exchange rates, 20 Bibbles equal 24 Babbles, and 18 Babbles equal 32 Bobbles.

How many Bobbles equal $(2T + 1)$ Bibbles?

*Relay Race*

**A1** What is the sum of the prime factors of 2010?

**A2** A box weighs 242 kg when full and 188 kg when half full. How much does it weigh, in kilograms, when empty?

**A3**

$PQRST$ is a regular pentagon. $PU$ is perpendicular to $PT$. What is the size of angle $QUP$?

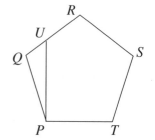

**A4** Three tenths of a number is one more than two sevenths of the number. What is the number?

**A5** How many millilitres of water must be added to 360 ml of orange cordial containing 50% juice to make a drink containing 30% juice?

**A6**    St Trinian's school day starts at 8:40 am and ends at 3:30 pm. How many degrees does the hour hand of a clock turn through in a school day?

**A7**    The four members of the winning team at a Regional TMC final each received a pencil case. Two were red, one green, and one blue. Two of the team were twins, and wanted different coloured cases. In how many different ways could the cases have been awarded?

**A8**    Three tiles meet at a point without leaving a gap or overlapping. They are a square, a regular hexagon, and another regular polygon. How many sides does the other polygon have?

**A9**    Find the value of

$$\sqrt{3^4 \times 2^3 \times 5 + 2^3 \times 3^2 \times 5}.$$

**A10**    A pie chart is being prepared, showing the numbers of various tree types in a park. The table shows the angles for the four main types. The "Other" section represents 12 trees.

| Tree type | Oak | Ash | Lime | Sycamore | Other |
|---|---|---|---|---|---|
| Pie chart angle | 90° | 135° | 60° | 45° | |

How many trees are there altogether in the park?

**A11**    What are the letters, in order, of the diagonal from top left corner to bottom right corner of this grid if each row, column and 2 × 2 block shown contains the letters UKMT?

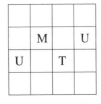

**A12**    The teacher with a TMC team has a bag of sweets. She eats one, and gives half the remainder to the pupil with most right answers, then repeats the eating one and giving half to each of the other three team members in order. The final 3 sweets left in the bag she offers to the scorers. How many sweets were in the bag initially?

**A13**    In 1610 Galileo discovered the four largest moons of Jupiter: Io, Ganymede, Europa and Callisto. The mass of the Earth is $6.0 \times 10^{24}$ kg. The mass of Europa is $1.48 \times 10^{23}$ kg.

To one decimal place, what percentage is this of the Earth's mass?

**A14**  A mathematical granny has 5 grandchildren whose ages are 1, 6, 7, 10 and 12. She bakes an apple tart in a circular dish, and decides to divide it between them in the ratio of their ages. How many degrees bigger is the biggest slice than the smallest?

**A15**  The letters *A* to *F* represent different digits from 0 to 5 in these two multiplications.

What is the 6 digit number *A B C D E F*?

$$\begin{array}{r} A\,F\,F\,D \\ E\times \\ \hline E\,F\,A\,F \end{array} \qquad\qquad \begin{array}{r} A\,B\,C \\ A\,D\times \\ \hline E\,F\,A\,F \end{array}$$

**B1**  Harry counts the money in his piggy bank at the end of each month. On March 31st he had £4.00. On April 30th the total had decreased by 10%. During May his savings increased by 15%. How much was in his piggy bank on 31st May?

**B2**  The National Final of the Senior Team Maths Challenge was on the third of February this year. Many of the teachers writing the dates on forms were interested to see that they wrote four consecutive descending numbers, with a bit of punctuation.

How many months from that date will be the next date with four consecutive decreasing numbers?

**B3**  Nicky gives her cats, Sid and Lou, a dish of munchy biscuits. One third of the biscuits are green, and the rest are brown. Sid eats 2 green biscuits for each 3 that Lou eats, and 4 brown biscuits for each 3 that Lou eats.

What fraction of the biscuits does Sid eat?

**B4**  Three squares are attached at their corners and strung between two vertical poles as shown. Find the value of *x*.

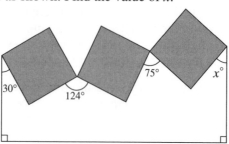

**B5** What are the letters, in order, of the diagonal from top left corner to bottom right corner of this grid if each row, column and 2 × 2 block shown contains the letters UKMT?

|   |   | K |   |
|---|---|---|---|
|   |   |   | U |
| U |   |   |   |
| M | T |   |   |

**B6** Boris and Michael are jogging in the same direction around a lake. It takes Boris 6 minutes to complete a lap and Michael 8 minutes. After completing each lap the boys take a rest, Boris for 1 minute and Michael for two minutes. They then continue jogging. If they start jogging together, how long, in minutes, does it take until they are next together?

**B7** During a cold winter, half the 600 litres of water in my rectangular pond froze. The volume of water increases by 10% when it turns to ice. My pond is 1.5 metres wide and 2 metres long. How many centimetres higher was the level after freezing than before?

(1 litre of water occupies 1000 cm3.)

**B8** Hamilton High School starts at 8:30 am and finishes at 3:30 pm each day. What is the number of times the hour and minute hand form a right angle on the school clock during a school day?

**B9** A distracted postman has 4 letters to deliver to 4 different houses. He puts one at random through each letterbox. What is the probability that they are all delivered correctly?

**B10** If $2T + M = C$ and $C + M = 3T$ what is the value of $T \div M$?

**B11** A set of axes is drawn on one-centimetre squared paper. The points $A$, $B$ and $C$ have coordinates (2,0), (4,3) and (0,5).
What is the area of the triangle $ABC$?

**B12** In 1610 Galileo discovered the four largest moons of Jupiter: Io, Ganymede, Europa and Callisto. The mass of the Earth is $6.0 \times 10^{24}$ kg. The mass of Callisto is $1.08 \times 10^{23}$ kg.
To one decimal place, what percentage is this of the Earth's mass?

**B13** A slug in my garden moves in a straight line from one corner of the 2m by 1m rectangular plot where it has eaten a lettuce to the diagonally opposite corner to eat a strawberry.
To the nearest 10 cm, how far did it travel?

**B14** A bag contains coloured counters. Each counter has a positive whole number on it. One third of the counters are yellow and the rest are blue. The probability that a yellow counter has an even number on it is three eighths and the probability that a blue counter has an even number on it is one quarter.

Calculate the probability that a counter, drawn at random, has an even number on it. Give your answer as a simplified fraction.

**B15** What is the value of

$$\sqrt{90\tfrac{1}{4}} - \sqrt{\sqrt{39\tfrac{1}{16}}} \ ?$$

## *Solutions from the Regional Finals*

*Group Round*

Solution

1. Possible codes (can be written as, e.g., 214 or 2,1,4):
   214, 634, 319, 629
2. LIBEL = 132
3. Numbers are 64 and 15625
4. Speed required: 48 miles per hour
5. $a + b + c = 10.5$ or $10\tfrac{1}{2}$ or $\tfrac{21}{2}$
6. Probability: $\tfrac{4}{9}$
7. Ratio of areas, $P : Q = 9 : 8$
8. Time taken: 6 hours
9. Number of sides: 7
10. Maximum product: 56

## Crossnumber

| 1 **1** | 2 **7** | **5** | 3 **3** | | 4 **1** | **6** | 5 **2** | |
|---|---|---|---|---|---|---|---|---|
| | **8** | | 6 **9** | **8** | **7** | | 7 **3** | **7** |
| 8 **6** | **4** | 9 **5** | | | 10 **1** | 11 **4** | **0** | |
| **5** | | 12 **3** | 13 **7** | **1** | | **9** | | 14 **4** |
| 15 **6** | **4** | | **8** | | 16 **1** | | 17 **4** | **5** |
| **1** | | 18 **8** | | 19 **9** | **0** | 20 **3** | | **6** |
| | 21 **1** | **1** | 22 **7** | | | 23 **5** | 24 **2** | **7** |
| 25 **2** | **8** | | 26 **1** | **9** | 27 **6** | | **4** | |
| | 28 **3** | **1** | **9** | | 29 **6** | **8** | **5** | **9** |

## Head-to-Head

| A1 | 12 |
|---|---|
| A2 | 9 |
| A3 | 120 |
| A4 | 184 |

| C1 | 60 |
|---|---|
| C2 | 66 |
| C3 | 72 |
| C4 | $36\pi$ |

| B1 | 747 |
|---|---|
| B2 | 45 |
| B3 | 18 |
| B4 | $\frac{7}{18}$ |

| D1 | 24 |
|---|---|
| D2 | 12 |
| D3 | 4 |
| D4 | 270 |

210

*Relay Race*

| | | | |
|---|---|---|---|
| A1 | 21 times | B1 | 5:54 |
| A2 | 87 | B2 | 1440 degrees |
| A3 | 2 pounds, 15 shillings and 5 pence | B3 | 36% |
| A4 | 231 | B4 | 40 times |
| A5 | 416 ml | B5 | $\frac{14}{25}$ |
| A6 | 2, 5, 6, 7, 10 | B6 | $\frac{3}{10}$ or 0.3 |
| A7 | £1690 | B7 | 3 pounds, 5 shillings and 9 pence |
| A8 | 4 km/h | B8 | 22 |
| A9 | Thursday | B9 | 26 |
| A10 | $\frac{8}{17}$ | B10 | £2000 |
| A11 | 36 sweets | B11 | 550 cm |
| A12 | 92 ducats | B12 | £2.50 |
| A13 | 75 metres | B13 | *A* 25, *B* 50, *C* 10, *D* 20, *E* 5 |
| A14 | $\frac{6}{13}$ | B14 | 110 years |
| A15 | 12 days | B15 | $\frac{47}{45}$ or $1\frac{2}{45}$ (either) |

## *Solutions from the National Final*

*Group Circus*

1.  two of

| 2 | 1 | 9 |
|---|---|---|
| 4 | 3 | 8 |
| 6 | 5 | 7 |

| 2 | 7 | 3 |
|---|---|---|
| 5 | 4 | 6 |
| 8 | 1 | 9 |

| 3 | 2 | 7 |
|---|---|---|
| 6 | 5 | 4 |
| 9 | 8 | 1 |

2.  Equal totals along each edge, and no matching joins.
3.  A = 1; B = 0; C = 8; D = 9
4.  Side faces total 28
5.  5(five) of Hearts
6.  11 counters
7.  Four small congruent trapezia
8.  22 distinct regions
9.  Demonstrations of
    (i) four congruent squares (ii) five congruent squares
10. Cube correctly coloured (all nine colours on each face)

*Crossnumber*

| ¹1 | 4 | ²6 | 4 | ³1 | | ⁴8 | 4 | ⁵1 |
|---|---|---|---|---|---|---|---|---|
| 0 | | 6 | | ⁶1 | 3 | 1 | | 2 |
| ⁷1 | ⁸9 | 1 | ⁹9 | | | ¹⁰3 | 5 | 3 |
| | 0 | | ¹¹7 | 3 | ¹²8 | 0 | | 2 |
| ¹³6 | 0 | | 2 | | 5 | | ¹⁴9 | 1 |
| 7 | | ¹⁵8 | 0 | 1 | 3 | | 6 | |
| ¹⁶5 | 6 | 7 | | | ¹⁷5 | ¹⁸1 | 2 | ¹⁹1 |
| 4 | | ²⁰3 | 6 | ²¹1 | | 0 | | 9 |
| ²²8 | 6 | 4 | | ²³9 | 8 | 9 | 8 | 9 |

212

*Head-to-Head*

| A1 | 80 |
|----|----|
| A2 | 8 |
| A3 | 6 |
| A4 | 5184 |

| C1 | 17 |
|----|----|
| C2 | 8 |
| C3 | 90 |
| C4 | 174 |

| B1 | 2 |
|----|----|
| B2 | 200 |
| B3 | 342 |
| B4 | 8892 |

| D1 | 6 |
|----|----|
| D2 | 24 |
| D3 | 22 |
| D4 | 96 |

*Relay Race*

A1  77
A2  134 (kg)
A3  54°
A4  70
A5  240 (ml)
A6  205 (°)
A7  10
A8  12
A9  60
A10  144 (trees)
A11  KMTK
A12  63 (sweets)
A13  2.5 (%)
A14  110 (°)
A15  134520

B1  £4.14
B2  133 (months)
B3  $\frac{18}{35}$
B4  41 (°)
B5  TMMK
B6  20 (min)
B7  1 (cm)
B8  12
B9  $\frac{1}{24}$
B10  2
B11  8 (cm$^2$)
B12  1.8 (%)
B13  220 (cm)
B14  $\frac{7}{24}$
B15  7

# UKMT and Further Maths Support Programme Senior Team Maths Challenge 2010

The Senior Team Maths Challenge has now completed its third year – one as a pilot competition and two as a fully-fledged national event. The 2009-10 competition consisted of over 50 Regional Finals held across the United Kingdom (and one in the Channel Islands). In all, over 900 teams of four competed, the students being chosen from Years 11, 12 and 13 with at most two from Year 13. The culmination of the competition was the National Final in London with the title of National Champions being retained by Westminster School.

This year's Senior Team Challenge followed a similar pattern to the previous competitions with three Rounds: the Group Round consisting of ten questions to be answered by the team in 40 minutes; the Crossnumber where one pair has the Across clues and the other pair has the Down clues; the Mini-Relay which has sets of four linked questions answered by pairs of students. The rules for this last round were amended slightly this year so that teams were told, if they made a mistake, which answer that they had given was incorrect rather than merely being told that one of the four answers they had given was incorrect. This change was made to address that fact that the Mini-Relay had been found to be hard, relative to the other two Rounds in 2008-9.

Exactly the same structure was used for the National Final in February except that in addition a Poster Competition was completed as the first event. Teams had to answer questions on "Fractal Curves and their Dimension". I would like to thank Peter Neumann, Andrew Jobbings, Alan Slomson, John Silvester and Richard Lissaman for their work in preparing the materials and judging the posters produced. The Poster Competition did not count for the overall competition but a poster based on the work of the winning team – King Edward VI High School for Girls, Birmingham – has been turned into a professionally-produced poster that will be sent to all the schools that took part in the competition.

The National Final was a wonderful event with seventy teams competing with huge energy and enthusiasm throughout the day. Where else would you overhear students swapping methods for generating number sequences or trying to improve their 15-second personal best for the Rubik's cube between Rounds?

Westminster School, the eventual winners and National Champions for the second year running, were presented with their prize by Simonyi Professor for the Public Understanding of Science, Marcus du Sautoy.

As with any UKMT competition thanks must be given to all the volunteers who wrote questions, acted as checkers for the materials produced, ran Regional Finals alongside FMSP Managers and who helped on the day at the National Final.

- The writers: Sheldon Fernandes, Becky Lovelock, Tony Cheslett, Dennis Pinshon, Karen Fogden, Alex Crews, Kerry Burnham, Mark Harwood, Holly McLean, David Crawford, Richard Lissaman, James Welham, Peter Hall, Penny Thompson and Sally Anne Huk.
- The checkers: John Silvester, Jenny Ramsden and Martin Perkins.
- The UKMT representatives who ran Regional Finals: Anne Andrews, Ann Ault, Kerry Burnham, Mary Teresa Fyfe, Peter Hall, Terry Heard, Rita Holland, Pam Hunt, Sally Anne Huk, Andrina Inglis, Andy Kemp, Jacqui Lewis, Simon Lewis, Pat Lyden, Matthew Miller, Mike Moon, Martin Perkins, Dennis Pinshon, Stephen Power, Nikki Shepherd, John Slater, Alan Slomson, Anne Strong, Penny Thompson, James Welham, Rosie Wiltshire and Mary Wimbury.
- Those who helped at the National Final: Ann Ault, Colin Campbell, Rachel Greenhalgh, Terry Heard, Rita Holland, Pam Hunt, Jacqui Lewis, Pat Lyden, Martin Perkins, Dennis Pinshon, Jenny Ramsden, John Silvester, John Slater, Alan Slomson and James Welham.

I am very pleased to say that next year Alex Crews will be leading the efforts of UKMT on the Senior Team Maths Challenge. I am sure that in his capable hands the competition will continue to flourish.

Stephen Power

Lead Volunteer Senior Team Maths Challenge

The following pages contain much of the material which was used in both the Regional Finals and the National Final.

*Regional Group Round*

**1**     Given that
$$y = \left(\sqrt{1 + \sqrt{x}} + \sqrt{1 - \sqrt{x}}\right)\left(\sqrt{1 + \sqrt{x}} - \sqrt{1 - \sqrt{x}}\right)$$
find the value of $y$ when $x = 0.25$.

**2**     Calculate the area of the quadrilateral described in the $(x, y)$ plane by the following inequalities.
$$x > 0$$
$$y > 0$$
$$x + y > 3$$
$$x + y < 4$$

**3**     The product
$$\sqrt{6} \times \sqrt{12} \times \sqrt{18} \times \sqrt{24} \times \sqrt{30} \times \sqrt{36} \times \sqrt{42}$$
can be expressed in the form $2^a 3^b 5^c 7^d$.

What is the value of $a + b + c + d$ ?

**4**     The natural numbers are arranged in a rectangular array as shown.

| 1 | 4 | 9 | 16 | 25 | ... |
|----|----|----|----|----|-----|
| 2 | 3 | 8 | 15 | 24 | ... |
| 5 | 6 | 7 | 14 | 23 | ... |
| 10 | 11 | 12 | 13 | 22 | ... |
| 17 | 18 | 19 | 20 | 21 | ... |
| 26 | 27 | ... | | | |
| ... | ... | | | | |

Assuming the pattern continues in this way, what number will be directly to the right of the number 2009?

**5**      *AB* and *DC* are parallel diameters of the circular ends of a solid cylinder.

*ABCD* is a rectangle with $AB = \dfrac{10}{\pi}$ cm and $BC = 12$ cm.

What is the shortest distance from *A* to *C*, measured along the curved surface of the cylinder?

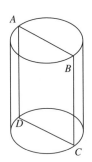

**6**      Valentino wants to create a heart shape from two equal semicircles and an equilateral triangle as shown. He also wants the value of the perimeter of the heart to be *A* cm and the value of the area of the heart to be *A* cm².

What is the exact value of the radius of the semicircles that makes this possible?

**7**      A function, *T*, is defined for positive integers *a* by

$$T(a + 1) = T(a) + a + 1 \text{ and } T(1) = 1.$$

What is the smallest value of *n* such that $T(n) > 2009$?

**8**      A house of cards with three storeys is built using 15 cards.

How many cards are needed to build a house 20 storeys high?

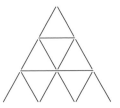

**9**      A French mathematician, Alphonse de Polignac (1817-1890) claimed that every positive odd number could be written as the sum of a power of 2 and a prime number.

He was in fact incorrect, despite checking as far as three million.

What is the smallest 3-digit counterexample to his claim?

**10**     *ABDE* is a square with centre *H*.

The base of the square *DE* is extended so that it meets the straight line *CF* which passes through *H*.

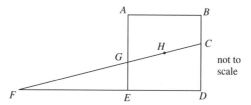

If $BC$ = 3 cm and $CD$ = 4 cm find the area of the triangle *CDF*.

*Regional Final Crossnumber*

218

*Across*

1   Both a square and a cube
6   $\frac{1}{2}p^2(p+1)$ where $p$ is prime
7   Solution to $x^2 - 2009x + 14014 = 0$
8   Cube
9   Prime squared
10  One less than a multiple of eleven
14  Number divisible by two and seven; 19 Across minus 5 Down
16  Fourth power
18  Three times 6 Across
19  One more than a multiple of nine
20  Multiple of either four or nine
23  The mean of 9 Across, 16 Across and 23 Across is 16 Across
25  Sum of two distinct squares
26  4 Down plus twice 11 Down
28  Half the product of two consecutive integers, also a multiple of seven
29  Odd number, four more than a multiple of 25 Across

*Down*

2   Power of two
3   Prime, one less than a multiple of 4 Down
4   Solution to $x^4 - 116x^2 + 1600 = 0$
5   One more than a square, three less than a cube
7   Multiple of seven, its digit sum is prime
11  One more than a multiple of 5 Down, greater than 3 Down
12  Mean of 2 Down, 13 Down and 21 Down
13  One more than three times 3 Down
15  Product of two numbers differing by two
17  24 Down minus a factor of 14 Across
18  Twice a prime squared
19  Remainder when 19 Down is divided by 13 Down is 6 Across
21  Fibonacci number where consecutive digits differ by one
22  Palindrome, twice a prime
24  Twelve times a prime
27  Three times a factor of 18 Across

*Mini-Relay questions*

**A1**   121 is a perfect square.

It has the property that the sum of its digits $(1 + 2 + 1 = 4)$ is also a perfect square.

Find the number of perfect squares $n$, where $0 < n < 400$, such that the digit sum of $n$ is also a perfect square.

**A2**   *T is the number that you will receive.*

The Fibonacci sequence is defined by $F_1 = F_2 = 1$, and $F_{n+1} = F_n + F_{n-1}$ for all $n \geqslant 2$. Let $x$ be the number of values of $n$, $1 \leqslant n \leqslant T$, for which $F_n$ is a triangular number.

Pass on the value of $x$.

**A3**   *T is the number that you will receive.*

Let $T$ be the lowest common multiple of two distinct integers $a$ and $b$.

Pass on the largest possible value of
the highest common factor of $a$ and $b$.

**A4**   *T is the number that you will receive.*

Let the radius of both circles below be $T$.

Calculate the total shaded area.

**B1**   The last non-zero digit of 5! is 2.

$(5! = 1 \times 2 \times 3 \times 4 \times 5 = 1\underline{2}0)$

Pass on the last non-zero digit of 10!

**B2**   *T is the number that you will receive.*

The distance between the points of intersection of the curve $y = x^2 - 6x + 12$ and the line $y = x + \dfrac{T}{4}$ can be expressed as $n\sqrt{2}$.

Pass on the value of $n$.

**B3**   *T is the number that you will receive.*

Solve the equation

$$9^{7T + x} = \left(\frac{1}{3}\right)^{2x + 2 - 20T}$$

Pass on the value of $x$.

**B4**     *T is the number that you will receive.*
The geometric mean of two quantities $P$ and $Q$ is defined to be $\sqrt{PQ}$.
Let the geometric mean of $7T$ and $T + 3$ be $x$.

Find the value of $x$.

**C1**     A train leaves Leeds for Edinburgh at 1:00pm, another train leaves Edinburgh for Leeds at 1:50pm. Both trains travel at the same uniform speed and take 3 hours to complete the journey.
At what time do the trains pass each other?

Your answer should be in the form *a:bc* pm.

Pass on the value of $a + b - c$.

**C2**     *T is the number that you will receive.*
Write $\dfrac{T + 1}{\sqrt{x}} \times \dfrac{T}{\sqrt[3]{x}}$ in the form $ax^{-b}$.

Pass on the value of $ab$.

**C3**     *T is the number that you will receive.*
Express $\dfrac{3 + \sqrt{T}}{\sqrt{T} - 2}$ in the form $a + b\sqrt{T}$.

Pass on the value of $a - b$.

**C4**     *T is the number that you will receive.*
In the diagram below $PS$ is a diameter of the semicircle, $SR = RQ$ and $\angle PSQ = 7T$.

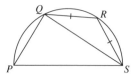

Find the value of $\angle RQS$.

**D1**     Pass on the value of
$$2\sqrt{2}\left(\sqrt{32} - \sqrt{8}\right).$$

**D2**     *T is the number that you will receive.*
A square of side $T$ cm is inscribed in a circle.
Semicircles are constructed on its sides as shown.
Calculate the total shaded area.

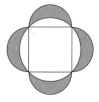

Pass on the cube root of your answer.

**D3**  *T is the number that you will receive.*
Simplify

$$\frac{4x^2 - 22x + 24}{x^2 - T^2} \times \frac{2x + 2T}{2x^2 - 5x + 3} \times \frac{3x^2 - x - 2}{4}.$$

Your answer should be in the form $ax + b$.

Pass on $2ab$.

**D4**  *T is the number that you will receive.*
The angles in an octagon can be arranged in an increasing sequence where the difference between each term and the next is $T°$.

Write down, in degrees, the difference between
the largest and smallest angles.

**E1**  The hot tap on its own fills a bath in 12 minutes. The cold tap on its own fills the bath in 10 minutes. When the plug is removed the full bath is emptied in $7\frac{1}{2}$ minutes. If both taps are turned on and the plug is removed, the bath will fill in $M$ minutes.

Pass on the value of $M$.

**E2**  *T is the number that you will receive.*
Solve the equation

$$y^2 - \left(\frac{1}{2}T - 2\right)y + (T - 4) = 0.$$

Pass on the value of $y^{\frac{1}{2}}$.

**E3**  *T is the number that you will receive.*
A bag contains $T$ red counters and $N$ blue counters. Two counters are withdrawn, without replacement. It is known that the probability of both counters being blue is $\frac{2}{5}$.

Pass on the value of $N$.

**E4**  *T is the number that you will receive.*
$CX$ is a tangent to a circle as shown.
An isosceles triangle $ABC$ is drawn
in the circle so that $AB = BC$ and
$\angle BCX = (24T - 30)°$.

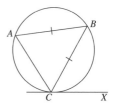

Find the size of angle $\angle ABC$.

**F1**  In the grid below, the middle expression of any row or column is calculated by taking the mean of the two vertically or horizontally adjacent expressions.

| $2x$ | | $6x$ |
|---|---|---|
| | $5x + 4$ | |
| | $2x^2 + 2x + 2$ | $10x + 2$ |

Pass on the positive value of $x$.

**F2**  *T is the number that you will receive.*

The ratio of the volumes of two similar solid cones is 8:1. Calculate the difference in the surface areas.

 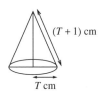

$(T + 1)$ cm

$T$ cm

Your answer should be in the form $a\pi$ cm$^2$.

Pass on one seventh of $a$.

**F3**  *T is the number that you will receive.*

Given that

$$\frac{1}{x} + \frac{1}{y} = T + 3 \text{ and } x + y = T - 11,$$

write down the value of $12xy$.

**F4**  *T is the number that you will receive.*

The function $f$ is defined as

$$f(x) = \begin{cases} x - 12T & \text{if} \quad x > 4 \\ x^2 + T^2 & \text{if} \quad x = 4 \\ x - 6T & \text{if} \quad x < 4 \end{cases}$$

Find the value of $f(5) - f(4) + f(3) - f(2)$.

## Group Round answers

| | | |
|---|---|---|
| 1. | Value of $y$: | 1 |
| 2. | Area of quadrilateral: | 3.5 units$^2$ |
| 3. | $a + b + c + d =$ | 11 |
| 4. | Number to the right of 2009: | 2100 |
| 5. | Distance from $A$ to $C$: | 13 cm |
| 6. | Radius: | $\dfrac{2\pi + 8}{\pi + 4\sqrt{3}}$ cm |
| 7. | Value of $n$: | 63 |
| 8. | Number of cards: | 610 |
| 9. | Three digit number: | 127 |
| 10. | Area of triangle $CDF$: | 56 cm$^2$ |

## Crossnumber: Completed grid

| | | | | | | | | | | |
|---|---|---|---|---|---|---|---|---|---|---|
| ¹7 | ²2 | 9 | █ | | ³2 | | ⁴1 | | ⁵1 | |
| | 0 | | ⁶1 | 9 | 6 | | ⁷2 | 0 | 0 | 2 |
| ⁸6 | 4 | | | | ⁹9 | 6 | 1 | | | 2 |
| | ¹⁰8 | ¹¹8 | 4 | ¹²3 | | | 0 | | ¹³8 | |
| | | 5 | | ¹⁴2 | 6 | ¹⁵6 | 0 | | 0 | |
| ¹⁶6 | ¹⁷2 | 5 | | 0 | | 7 | | ¹⁸5 | 8 | 8 |
| | 8 | | ¹⁹2 | 7 | 8 | 2 | | 7 | | |
| | 3 | | 6 | | ²⁰3 | 1 | 8 | ²¹6 | | |
| ²²8 | | ²³2 | 8 | ²⁴9 | | | | | ²⁵7 | 3 |
| ²⁶1 | 7 | ²⁷2 | 0 | | ²⁸4 | 0 | 6 | | 6 | |
| 8 | | 1 | | 8 | | | ²⁹9 | 5 | 3 | |

## Mini-Relay answers

| | A | B | C | D | E | F |
|---|---|---|---|---|---|---|
| 1 | 12 | 8 | 2 | 8 | 20 | 3 |
| 2 | 5 | 3 | 5 | 4 | 2 | 9 |
| 3 | 1 | 4 | 6 | 12 | 4 | −2 |
| 4 | 2 | 14 | 24(°) | 84(°) | 48(°) | 10 |

*National Final Group Round*

**1**      What is the value of

$$0.1^{-2} + 0.4^{-3} + 0.5^{-6} + 0.1^2 + 0.4^3 + 0.5^6 ?$$

**2**      Calculate the exact area of the region described in the $(x, y)$ plane by the following inequalities:

$$y > x$$

$$y < \sqrt{3}x$$

$$x^2 + y^2 < 8.$$

**3**      Given that $\sqrt[3]{4} \times \sqrt[4]{8} \times \sqrt[5]{16} \times \sqrt[6]{32} = 2^3 \times \sqrt[x]{2}$ calculate the value of $x$.

**4**      A sequence is defined for positive integer values of $n$ by

$$u_{n+3} = u_{n+2} + u_{n+1} - u_n$$
$$u_1 = 0$$
$$u_2 = 1$$
$$u_3 = 1$$

What is the sum of the first 100 terms of the sequence?

**5**      All of the letters in the word

| A | B | R | A | C | A | D | A | B | R | A |

are written on cards and placed in a black bag. Four cards are removed from the black bag and placed in a red bag.

Of the 31 different collections of letters that could be in the red bag, how many do not contain an R ?

**6**      A cuboid is made from $mnp$ unit cubes such that the lengths of the edges of the cuboid are $m$ units, $n$ units and $p$ units. $m$, $n$ and $p$ are prime numbers and $m < n < p$.

An ant is placed at one vertex of the cuboid. It walks along a circuit crossing the four smallest faces of the cuboid, each time travelling along a diagonal of the face.

By the time the ant returns to the starting vertex, on how many of the cubes has it walked?

**7**     The points *A*, *B*, *C*, *D*, *E* and *F* are equally spaced along the diameter of a circle with *A* and *F* at the ends of the diameter.

All of the arcs shown are semi-circles whose diameters have end-points at two of the named points as shown.

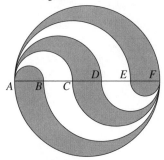

What fraction of the circle with diameter *AF* is shaded?

**8**     The largest possible circle is drawn inside an isosceles triangle with sides of length 100 units, 100 units and 56 units.

If the area of the circle is written as $a\pi$ units$^2$, what is the value of *a*?

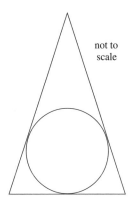

not to scale

**9**     Solve the equations

$$1122x + 3344y = 12276$$

$$3344x + 1122y = 10054$$

**10**    The digits 1, 2, 3, 4, 5, 6, 7, 8 and 9 can be placed in a 3 by 3 grid so that the four three-digit numbers obtained by reading across each of the three rows and also down the diagonal starting in the top left corner, are all squares.

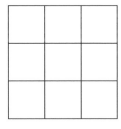

Which digit is in the centre of the grid?

*National Final Crossnumber*

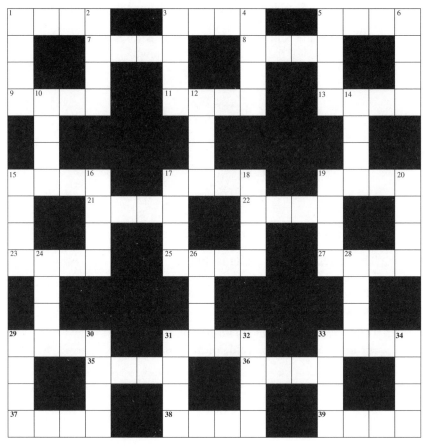

## Across

1 Fifty-three less than a perfect cube.

3 A square number.

5 The product of a prime number and 26 Down.

7 The cube of a prime number.

8 Difference between 34 Down and 33 Down.

9 100 more than the difference between 15 Across and 34 Down.

11 A number that is between 1200 and 1300 and is also two less than the product of a triangle number and a Fibonacci number.

13 The cube of a prime number.

15 A rearrangement of the digits of 34 Down.

17 Value of $y$ in the solution of $3x + 16y = 50801$ and $5y = 4x + 21$.

19   A fourth power.

21   A multiple of 3 Down.

22   Four times a Fibonacci number.

23   Five more than a triangle number.

25   $p^p$, where $p$ is a prime number.

27   A palindromic number.

29   Value of $x$ in the equations in 17 Across.

31   Forty five more than a triangle number, twenty seven less than the following triangle number.

33   33 more than the difference between 34 Down and 25 Across.

35   One less than three times a Fibonacci number.

36   The minimum value of $n^2 + 6n + 2009$.

37   Mean of 33 Across and 34 Down.

38   10 times the highest common factor of 7 Across and 27 Across.

39   A fourth power.

*Down*

1    The product of a prime number and 3 Down.

2    Coefficient of $x$ in expansion of $\left(x^2 + 350x + 13\right)^2$

3    A palindromic number.

4    Sum of 26 Down and 39 Across.

5    Mean of 26 Down, 32 Down and 34 Down.

6    Value of $y$ in the solution of $12x - 6y = 690$ and $11x - 5y = 2084$.

10   Difference between 21 Across and 1 Down.

12   One more than a Fibonacci number.

14   A square number.

15   Sum of 25 Across and 19 Across.

16   32 Down added to the reverse of 18 Down.

17   Three less than a square number.

18   A cube number.

19   The cube of a prime number.

20   Value of $x$ in equations in 6 Down.

24   Two less than twice a Fibonacci number.

26   A fourth power.

28   $\dfrac{4 \times 10^7 \times 5 \times 10^9}{2 \times 10^{19} \times 2 \times 10^{-6}}$.

29   Seven less than nineteen times a triangle number.

30   Thirty less than the sum of the interior angles in a dodecagon.

31  Three hundred less than a fourth power.

32  Twice a Fibonacci number.

33  Larger solution of $x^2 - 1010x + 6024 = 0$.

34  A sixth power.

*Help given to both pairs:*

(a)  The first three triangle numbers over 1000 are 1035, 1081 and 1128.
     The largest four digit triangle number is 9870.

(b)  Here is a list of all the cube numbers with at most four digits:
     1, 8, 27, 64, 125, 216, 343, 512, 729, 1000, 1331, 1728, 2197, 2744, 3375, 4096, 4913, 5832, 6859, 8000 and 9261.

*National Final Mini-Relay*

**A1**  Let $\dfrac{1}{x} + \dfrac{1}{6} + \dfrac{1}{x+8} = \dfrac{1}{2}$ where $x > 0$.

Pass on the value of $x$.

**A2**  *T is the number that you will receive*
A circle has radius $x$ cm and centre $O$.
$A$ and $B$ are points on the circumference
such that $\angle AOB = (10T + 30)°$ as
shown. Find the value of $x$ if the area of
the sector $AOB$ is $28\pi$ cm$^2$.

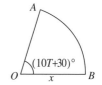

Pass on the value of $x$.

**A3**  *T is the number that you will receive.*
The right-angled triangle shown has
hypotenuse of length $(T + 5)$ cm and
two shorter sides of length $x$ cm and
$(x + 7)$ cm. Find the value of $x$.

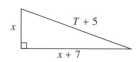

Pass on the value of $x$.

**A4**  *T is the number that you will receive.*
In the diagram shown, $BQ$ and $CQ$
are tangents to the circle and
$\angle CAB = 10T°$.

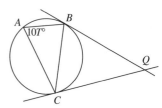

Find, in degrees, the size of $\angle BQC$.

**B1**  Simplify $\sqrt{20} + 2\sqrt{45} - \sqrt{80} - 9\left(\dfrac{8}{27}\right)^{\frac{2}{3}}$.

Write your answer in a form $a\left(\sqrt{b} - c\right)$ where $a$, $b$ and $c$ are integers and $b$ has no square factors.

Pass on the value of $a$.

**B2**  *T is the number that you will receive.*

Line $p$ passes through points $(T - 1, 9)$ and $(2T, 5)$.  Line $q$ is perpendicular to line $p$.

The gradient of $p$ is $A$ and the gradient of $q$ is $B$.

Pass on the value of $20(A + B)$.

**B3**  *T is the number that you will receive*

Simplify $\dfrac{T - 6}{\sqrt[4]{x}} \times Tx^{\frac{2}{3}} \div \left(\dfrac{1}{3}Tx^{\frac{1}{6}}\right)$.

Write your answer in the form $ax^b$.

Pass on the value of $4ab$.

**B4**  *T is the number that you will receive.*

Two similar parallelepipeds, with four rectangular faces each, have volumes in the ratio 1:64.

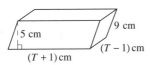 

Find the total surface area of the larger parallelepiped.

**C1**  How many distinct four-digit numbers can be formed by different arrangements of the digits 2, 3, 3, and 5?

Pass on the number of arrangements.

**C2**  *T is the number that you will receive*

The mean of the grouped data shown below in the frequency table is $a$.

| $x$ cm | Frequency |
|:---:|:---:|
| 2 | 6 |
| 4 | $T - 6$ |
| 6 | $T - 2$ |
| $T - 3$ | 12 |

Pass on the value of $a$.

230

**C3**   *T is the number that you will receive.*

A sphere of radius $T$ cm has the same volume as a cylinder of radius 4 cm and height $h$ cm.

Pass on the value of $h$.

**C4**   *T is the number that you will receive.*

A bag contains $\frac{1}{3}T$ red counters and $(T - 11)$ blue counters. Two counters are withdrawn without replacement. Find the probability that both counters are red. Put your answer in the form $\frac{a}{b}$, where $a$ and $b$ have no common factor greater than 1.

Write down the value of $b - a$.

**D1**   Simplify the following:

$$\frac{7x^2 + 14x - 21}{3x^2 + 2x - 5} \times \frac{3x^2 - 7x - 20}{x^2 - x - 12}$$

Pass on your answer.

**D2**   *T is the number that you will receive.*

Pass on the solution to the equation $729^{T-3} = 3^{5x-1}$.

**D3**   *T is the number that you will receive.*

Write $\dfrac{T - 3}{3 - \sqrt{7}}$ in the form $\sqrt{a} + b$.

Pass on the value of $3b - a$.

**D4**   *T is the number that you will receive.*

In the diagram, the diameter of the larger semicircle and the radius of the quadrant are both $T$ cm.

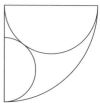

Find the radius, in cm, of the smaller semicircle.

**E1**   Consider the five expressions: $\sqrt{x}, x^2, \dfrac{1}{\sqrt{x}}, x^3, 2x$.

Given that $1 < x < 2$, arrange these expressions in ascending order of magnitude, identify the middle term, and put it in the form $ax^b$.

Pass on the value of $3b$.

**E2**  *T is the number that you will receive.*

Find the mean of the following: $\dfrac{T-5}{3}, \dfrac{1}{2}, \dfrac{1}{6}, \dfrac{1}{4}.$

Your answer should be in the form $\dfrac{a}{b}$, where $a$ and $b$ have no common factor greater than 1.

Pass on the value of $\dfrac{a+b}{7}$.

**E3**  *T is the number that you will receive.*

Consider the following triangle:

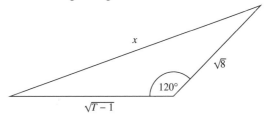

Pass on the value of $x^2 - 2$.

**E4**  *T is the number that you will receive.*

The area of a given shape is calculated by one of the following formulae. The area of the shape is $T^2$, with $x$ and $y$ positive integers and $x > y$.

$$A = \dfrac{7x^2y^2}{x+y} \qquad\qquad A = \dfrac{x^2}{2} + 2\pi y$$

$$A = 3xy^2 + 3x^2y \qquad\qquad A = x(y-x) + y(x-y) - 2xy$$

Find the value of $x$.

**F1**  Solve the equation $\left(\dfrac{1}{4}\right)^{x-3} = 8^{x-8}.$

Pass on the value of $x$.

**F2**  *T is the number that you will receive.*

Liz is buying tins of dog food for her pet corgis. She knows that if each tin lasts for $(T-3)$ days, her supply will last for $(x+3T)$ days whereas if each tin lasts for $(T-4)$ days, her supply will last for $2x-4$ days.

Pass on the value of $x$.

232

**F3**   *T is the number that you will receive.*

The equation $2x^2 + (1 - 2T)x - T = 0$ has two solutions, $x = a$ and $x = b$, with $a > b$.

Pass on the value of $a - 4b$.

**F4**   *T is the number that you will receive.*

In the diagram below, triangles *ABE* and *ACD* are similar. Write down the ratio of the area of trapezium *BCDE* to the area of triangle *ABE* in the form $p : q$ where $p$ and $q$ have no common factor greater than 1.

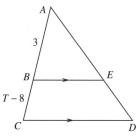

Write down the value of $p + q$.

*Group Round answers*

| | | |
|---|---|---|
| 1. | Value of expression: | 179.714625 |
| 2. | Area of region: | $\frac{\pi}{3}$ units² |
| 3. | Value of $x$: | 20 |
| 4. | Sum of the first 100 terms: | 2500 |
| 5. | Number of collections of letters: | 12 |
| 6. | Number of unit cubes: | $4m + 2n + 2p - 8$ |
| 7. | Fraction of the circle that is shaded: | $\frac{3}{5}$ |
| 8. | Value of $a$: | 441 |
| 9. | $x = 2$ | $y = 3$ |
| 10. | Centre digit: | 2 |

*Crossnumber: Completed grid*

| ¹5 | 7 | 7 | ²9 | | ³1 | 2 | 2 | ⁴5 | | ⁵2 | 5 | 9 | ⁶2 |
|---|---|---|---|---|---|---|---|---|---|---|---|---|---|
| 5 | | ⁷1 | 3 | 3 | 1 | | ⁸3 | 0 | 9 | 2 | | | 9 |
| 5 | | 0 | | | 1 | | 9 | | | 0 | | | 0 |
| ⁹5 | ¹⁰4 | 1 | 0 | | ¹¹1 | ¹²2 | 2 | 2 | | ¹³4 | ¹⁴9 | 1 | 3 |
| | 4 | | | | | 5 | | | | | 0 | | |
| | 4 | | | | | 8 | | | | | 2 | | |
| ¹⁵9 | 4 | 0 | ¹⁶6 | | ¹⁷2 | 5 | 7 | ¹⁸3 | | ¹⁹6 | 5 | 6 | ²⁰1 |
| 6 | | ²¹9 | 9 | 9 | 9 | | ²²3 | 9 | 4 | 8 | | | 5 |
| 8 | | 5 | | | 1 | | 7 | | | 5 | | | 0 |
| ²³6 | ²⁴3 | 3 | 3 | | ²⁵3 | ²⁶1 | 2 | 5 | | ²⁷9 | ²⁸5 | 5 | 9 |
| | 1 | | | | | 2 | | | | | 0 | | |
| | 9 | | | | | 9 | | | | | 0 | | |
| ²⁹3 | 2 | 1 | ³⁰1 | | ³¹2 | 6 | 0 | ³²1 | | ³³1 | 0 | 0 | ³⁴4 |
| 2 | | ³⁵7 | 7 | 5 | 1 | | ³⁶2 | 0 | 0 | 0 | | | 0 |
| 4 | | 7 | | | 0 | | 2 | | | 0 | | | 9 |
| ³⁷2 | 5 | 5 | 0 | | ³⁸1 | 2 | 1 | 0 | | ³⁹4 | 0 | 9 | 6 |

*Mini-Relay answers*

| | A | B | C | D | E | F |
|---|---|---|---|---|---|---|
| 1 | 4 | 4 | 12 | 7 | 6 | 6 |
| 2 | 12 | 9 | 6 | 5 | 3 | 12 |
| 3 | 8 | 9 | 18 | 2 | 12 | 14 |
| 4 | 20 | 6464 | 21 | $\frac{2}{3}$ | 4 | 9 |

# Other aspects of the UKMT and other similar bodies overseas

As well as the Maths Challenges, the UKMT is involved in other events and activities.

## Enriching Mathematical Thinking
## UKMT Teacher Meetings 2010

Six meetings were held this year; in Cambridge (University of Cambridge), Edinburgh (University of Edinburgh), Coventry (University of Warwick), London (University of Greenwich), Manchester (University of Manchester), and Newcastle (University of Newcastle).

In total, over 450 teachers attended the one-day meetings. Each meeting featured three plenary sessions with lunch and refreshment breaks, and delegates received a resource pack to take back to the classroom.

NRICH (www.nrich.maths.org.uk) gave sessions at all six meetings and we are grateful to Charlie Gilderdale, Steve Hewson, Alison Kiddle and Lynne McLure for the quality of these sessions and the accompanying resources.

Rob Eastaway, author, and Director of Maths Inspiration gave a fun inspiring talk at three of the venues. Vinay Kathotia (The Nuffield Foundation), Liz Meenan (University of Leeds and freelance education consultant) and Sara Santos (Royal Institution) gave extremely lively and popular talks, between them covering the remaining three venues.

The UKMT fielded one of its volunteers at each event demonstrating the mathematical thinking behind the questions used in the UK Maths Challenges and the Team Maths Challenge, and how they can be used to stimulate classroom interest. The speakers were Dean Bunnell, Dusty De Sainte Croix, Peter Hall, Mary Wimbury and Alan Slomson.

The delegate fee was kept at £40, which included refreshments, lunch and the resource pack. Feedback was once again overwhelmingly positive.

## Website – www.ukmt.org.uk

Visit the UKMT's website for information about all the UKMT's activities, including the Maths Challenges, latest UKMT news, contact details, the national team competition and how to buy past papers. There's an online quiz featuring past questions from the Challenges, and links to sponsors, supporters and other mathematical organisations providing resources for young mathematicians.

# Overseas bodies

The UKMT has links of varying degrees of formality with several similar organisations in other countries. It is also a member of the World Federation of National Mathematics Competitions (WFNMC). What follows is a brief description of some of these other organisations. Some of the information is taken from the organisations' web sites but a UK slant has been applied.

**"Kangourou des Mathématiques"**

The European Kangaroo Competition

http://www.math-ksf.org/

The obvious question is: why Kangaroo? The name was given in tribute to the pioneering efforts of the Australian Mathematics Trust. The Kangaroo contest is run by local organisers in each country under the auspices of the 'Association Kangourou sans Frontières', which was founded by a small group of countries in 1991. There are now 46 countries involved and more than five million participants throughout Europe and beyond, from the UK to Mongolia and from Norway to Cyprus.

In the UK in 2010, around 7000 children in the years equivalent to English Years 9, 10 and 11 took part in the 'Cadet' and 'Junior' levels of the Kangaroo competition, as a follow-up to the Intermediate Maths Challenge. Four representatives of the UK Mathematics Trust, Andrew Jobbings, Paul Murray and Mary Read, attended the meeting in Berlin, at which the 2010 Kangaroo papers were constructed.

The main objective of the Kangaroo, like all the competitions described in this section, is to stimulate and motivate large numbers of pupils, as well as to contribute to the development of a mathematical culture which will be accessible to, and enjoyed by, many children and young people. The Association also encourages cross-cultural activities; in some countries, for example, prize-winners are invited to attend a mathematics 'camp' with similar participants from other nations.

236

# The Australian Mathematics Trust

www.amt.canberra.edu.au

For over twenty-five years, the Australian Mathematics Competition has been one of the major events on the Australian Education Calendar, with about one in three Australian secondary students entering each year to test their skills. That's over half a million participants a year.

The Competition commenced in 1978 under the leadership of the late Professor Peter O'Halloran, of the University of Canberra, after a successful pilot scheme had run in Canberra for two years.

The questions are multiple-choice and students have 75 minutes in which to answer 30 questions. There are follow-up rounds for high scorers.

In common with the other organisations described here, the AMC also extends its mathematical enrichment activities by publishing high quality material which can be used in the classroom.

Whilst the AMC provides students all over Australia with an opportunity to solve the same problems on the same day, it is also an international event, with most of the countries of the Pacific and South-East Asia participating, as well as a few schools from further afield. New Zealand and Singapore each enter a further 30,000 students to help give the Competition an international flavour.

# World Federation of National Mathematics Competitions – WFNMC

www.amt.canberra.edu.au/wfnmc.html

The Federation was created in 1984 during the Fifth International Congress for Mathematical Education.

The Federation aims to provide a focal point for those interested in, and concerned with, conducting national mathematics competitions for the purpose of stimulating the learning of mathematics. Its objectives include:

- Serving as a resource for the exchange of information and ideas on mathematics competitions through publications and conferences.

- Assisting with the development and improvement of mathematics competitions.
- Increasing public awareness of the role of mathematics competitions in the education of all students and ensuring that the importance of that role is properly recognised in academic circles.
- Creating and enhancing professional links between mathematicians involved in competitions around the world.

The World Federation of National Mathematics Competitions is an organisation of national mathematics competitions affiliated as a Special Interest Group of the International Commission for Mathematical Instruction (ICMI).

It administers a number of activities, including

- The Journal *Mathematics Competitions*
- An international conference every four years. Previous conferences were held in Waterloo, Canada (1990), Pravets, Bulgaria (1994), Zhong Shan, China (1998). In 2002, the WFNMC met in Melbourne, Australia. In 2006, the conference was in the UK.
- David Hilbert and Paul Erdős Awards for mathematicians prominent on an international or national scale in mathematical enrichment activities.

The UKMT sent two delegates, Tony Gardiner and Bill Richardson, to the WFNMC conference in Zhong Shan in 1998 and provided support for several delegates who attended ICME 9 in Tokyo in August 2000, at which the WFNMC provided a strand.

In August 2002, the WFNMC held another conference, similar to the one in 1998. The venue for this was Melbourne, Victoria. On this occasion, the UKMT provided support for two delegates: Howard Groves and Bill Richardson.

In July 2006, WFNMC 5 was held in the UK at Robinson College, Cambridge. This event was a tremendous success with around 100 delegates from many parts of the world.

In July 2007, WFNMC had a strand at ICME 11 in Mexico. UKMT was represented by Bill Richardson.

In July 2010, WFNMC 6 was held in Riga. The UKMT was represented by Howard Groves, Dean Bunnell, David Crawford and James Welham.

# Lists of volunteers involved in the UKMT's activities

*UKMT officer bearers*

               *Chair*:     Professor Bernard Silverman

*Secretary*:     Dr Alan Slomson     *Treasurer*:     Prof. Adam McBride

*The Council*

Professor Bernard Silverman (Chair to March 2010)
Professor Frances Kirwan (Chair from March 2010)

| | |
|---|---|
| Mr Richard Atkins | Professor John Brindley (from April 2009) |
| Professor Chris Budd | Dr Colin Campbell |
| Dr James Cranch | Dr Katie Chicot (from April 2009) |
| Dr Ceri Fiddes | Professor Adam McBride |
| Mr Tony Mann | Mr Steve Mulligan (Vice-Chair) |
| Miss Jenny Ramsden | Mr Bill Richardson (Vice-Chair) |
| Dr Sara Santos | Dr John Silvester |
| Dr Geoff Smith | Mr Alex Voice |
| Mr James Welham | |

*Members of the Trust who are not on the Council or members of a Subtrust*

| | | |
|---|---|---|
| The Mathematical Association | The Royal Institution | Mr Dennis Archer |
| Mr Christopher Bradley | Dr Roger Bray | Mr Dean Bunnell |
| Mrs Mary Teresa Fyfe | Dr Tony Gardiner | Mr Howard Groves |
| Mr Terry Heard | Dr Andrew Jobbings | Mrs Margaret Jackson |
| Miss Susie Jameson | Mrs Patricia King | Professor Tom Körner |
| Dr Vinay Kathotia | Dr Gerry Leversha | Mr Nick Lord |
| Mr Dennis Orton | Mr Peter Ransom | Dr Adrian Sanders |
| Mr Robert Smart | Dr Brian Stewart | Mr Peter Thomas. |

## The Subtrusts

*British Mathematical Olympiad Subtrust*

| | |
|---|---|
| Dr Geoff Smith (Chair) | Dr Don Collins (Treasurer) |
| Mr Richard Atkins | Dr James Cranch |
| Dr Ceri Fiddes | Dr Vesna Kadelberg (Secretary) |
| Professor Imre Leader | |

*Team Maths Challenge Subtrust*

| | |
|---|---|
| Mr Steve Mulligan (Chair) | Mr Dusty de Sainte Croix |
| Miss Pam Hunt (Statistician) | Ms Jacqui Lewis |
| Mr Martin Perkins (Treasurer) | Mr Stephen Power |
| Dr Peter Neumann (Secretary) | Mr James Welham |

*Challenges Subtrust*

| | |
|---|---|
| Mr Bill Richardson (Chair) | Ms Anne Baker |
| Professor John Brindley | Mr David Crawford |
| Mr Colin Dixon | Mrs Karen Fogden |
| Mr Howard Groves | Dr Calum Kilgour |
| Professor Adam McBride | Mr Paul Murray |
| Mr Stephen Power | Miss Jenny Ramsden (Secretary) |
| Professor Chris Robson | Mrs Mary Read |
| Dr Alan Slomson | Mr Alex Voice (Treasurer) |

**Other Committees**

*Finance and General Purposes Committee*

| | |
|---|---|
| Mr Richard Atkins | Professor Adam McBride |
| Mr Stephen Mulligan | Mr Bill Richardson |
| Professor Bernard Silverman | Dr Alan Slomson |
| Ms Mary Wimbury (UKMT Director) | |

*Nominations Committee*

| | |
|---|---|
| Mr Tony Mann (Chair) | Professor Adam McBride |
| Mr Bill Richardson | Mr James Welham |

*Outreach Committee*

| | |
|---|---|
| Mr James Welham (Chair) | Professor John Brindley (Chair) |
| Mrs Mary Teresa Fyfe | Miss Pam Hunt |
| Dr Vinay Kathotia | Mr Nick Lord |
| Mr Tony Mann | Miss Jenny Ramsden |
| Ms Mary Wimbury | |

*Publications Committee*

| | |
|---|---|
| Dr Gerry Leversha (Chair) | Dr Christopher Bradley |
| Mr James Gazet | Mr Nick Lord |
| Mr Mark Strutt | |

*Members of the BMOS Extended Committee*

| | |
|---|---|
| Philip Coggins (Bedford School) | Ben Green (Trinity College, Cambridge) |
| Andrew Jobbings (Shipley) | Jeremy King (Tonbridge School) |
| Patricia King (ex Benenden School, Kent) | Gerry Leversha (St Paul's School) |
| Adam McBride (Uni. of Strathclyde) | David Monk (ex Edinburgh University) |
| Peter Neumann (Queen's Coll., Oxford) | Alan Pears (ex King's College, London) |
| Adrian Sanders (ex Trinity College, Camb.) | Zhivko Stoyanov (University of Bath) |
| Alan West (ex Leeds University) | Brian Wilson (Royal Holloway, London) |

*BMOS Markers*

Jeremy King (Tonbridge School, Leader)

| | |
|---|---|
| Robin Bhattacharrya (Derby) | Philip Coggins (ex Bedford School) |
| James Cranch (Uni. of Leicester) | Tim Cross (KES, Birmingham) |
| Paul Fannon (Sevenoaks School) | Ceri Fiddes (Millfield School) |
| David Forster (Oratory School) | James Gazet (Eton College) |
| John Haslegrave (Trinity College) | Karl Hayward-Bradley (Warwick School) |
| Ina Hughes (University of Leeds) | Paul Jeffreys (ex Trinity College) |
| Andrew Jobbings (Shipley) | Vesna Kadelburg (MPW, Cambridge) |
| Nathan Kettle (Trinity College) | Gerry Leversha (St Paul's School) |
| Tom Lovering (Trinity College) | Heather Macbeth (Trinity College) |
| Sam Maltby (Touch Vision) | Joseph Myers (Codesourcery Inc.) |
| Vicky Neale (Murray Edwards College) | Peter Neumann (Queen's College, Oxford) |
| Sylvia Neumann (Oxford) | Martin Orr (Trinity College) |
| Jenny Owladi (ex Trinity College) | Paul Russell (Churchill College) |
| Geoff Smith (University of Bath) | Jerome Watson (Bedford School) |
| Ben Woolley (Perse School for Girls) | Dominic Yeo (Trinity College) |

*Markers for IMOK and JMO*

| | | |
|---|---|---|
| Anne Andrews | (Buckingham) | IMOK |
| Dean Bunnell | (Queen Elizabeth GS, Wakefield) | IMOK / JMO |
| Philip Coggins | (Bedford School) | IMOK |
| James Cranch | (University of Leicester) | IMOK |
| David Crawford | (Leicester Grammar School) | IMOK / JMO |
| Tim Cross | (KES, Birmingham) | IMOK |
| David Forster | (Oratory School) | IMOK |
| Mary Teresa Fyfe | (Hutchesons' Grammar School, Glasgow) | JMO |
| Carol Gainlall | (Park House School, Newbury) | IMOK |
| Gwyn Gardiner | (KES, Birmingham) | JMO |
| Tony Gardiner | (University of Birmingham) | IMOK / JMO |
| Howard Groves | (RGSAO, Worcester) | JMO |
| Jo Harbour | (ex Trinity College) | IMOK |
| Rita Holland | (ex Wisbech Grammar School) | IMOK / JMO |
| Ina Hughes | (University of Leeds) | IMOK |
| Carl James | (Leicester Grammar School) | IMOK / JMO |
| Andrew Jobbings | (Arbelos, Shipley) | IMOK / JMO |
| Calum Kilgour | (St Aloysius College, Glasgow) | IMOK |
| Gerry Leversha | (St Paul's School) | IMOK |
| Nick Lord | (Tonbridge School) | IMOK |
| Sam Maltby | (Touch Vision) | IMOK |

| | | |
|---|---|---|
| Linda Moon | (Glasgow Academy) | IMOK |
| Michael Moon | (ex The Mount School, York) | IMOK |
| Philip Moon | (The High School of Glasgow) | IMOK |
| Peter Neumann | (The Queen's College, Oxford) | IMOK / JMO |
| Sylvia Neumann | (Oxford) | IMOK / JMO |
| Andrew Parkinson | (Beckfoot School, Bingley) | JMO |
| Steven Power | (St Swithuns School, Winchester) | IMOK / JMO |
| Jenny Ramsden | (High Wycombe) | IMOK / JMO |
| Mary Read | (Haberdashers' Aske's Hatcham College) | IMOK |
| Lionel Richard | (Hutchesons' GS) | IMOK |
| Bill Richardson | (Elgin) | JMO |
| Paul Russell | (Churchill College, Cambridge) | IMOK / JMO |
| John Slater | (Market Rasen) | JMO |
| Alan Slomson | (University of Leeds) | IMOK |
| Jon Stone | (St Paul's School, London) | IMOK |
| Alex Voice | (Westminster Abbey Choir School, London) | IMOK / JMO |
| Christopher Walker | (Summer Fields School, Oxford) | IMOK |
| Jerome Watson | (Bedford School) | IMOK |
| James Welham | (Wycliffe College) | IMOK |
| David Webber | (University of Glasgow) | IMOK / JMO |
| Alan West | (ex University of Leeds) | IMOK |
| Brian Wilson | (Royal Holloway, London) | IMOK |

*Problems Groups*

There are currently five groups. The first being the BMO Setting Committee.

The BMO Setting Committee

| | |
|---|---|
| Jeremy King | (Chair) (Tonbridge School) |
| Paul Jefferys | (ex Trinity College, Cambridge) |
| Gerry Leversha | (St Paul's School) |
| Jenny Owladi | (ex Trinity College) |
| Jack Shotton | (Trinity College, Cambridge) |
| Geoff Smith | (University of Bath) |

The other four groups have overlapping membership. There is one group for each and the chair is shown in []: the Senior Mathematical Challenge (S) [Dean Bunnell]; the Junior and Intermediate Mathematical Challenges (I&J) [Howard Groves]; the Junior Mathematical Olympiad (JMO) [Alex Voice]; the IMOK olympiad papers [Andrew Jobbings]. Those involved are listed below.

| | | |
|---|---|---|
| Steve Barge | (Sacred Heart Catholic College) | S |
| Dean Bunnell | (Queen Elizabeth GS, Wakefield) | S / IMOK / JMO |

| Kerry Burnham | (Torquay Boys' Grammar School) | I&J |
| James Cranch | (University of Sheffield) | IMOK |
| Karen Fogden | (Henry Box School, Witney) | I&J / JMO |
| Mary Teresa Fyfe | (Hutchesons' GS, Glasgow) | S / IMOK / JMO |
| Carol Gainlall | (Park House School, Newbury) | I&J |
| Tony Gardiner | (University of Birmingham) | I&J / IMOK / JMO |
| Michael Griffiths | (Warrington) | S |
| Howard Groves | (RGSAO, Worcester) | S / I&J / IMOK / JMO |
| Andrew Jobbings | (Shipley) | S / I&J / IMOK / JMO |
| Gerry Leversha | (St Paul's School) | IMOK |
| Paul Murray | (Lord Williams School, Thame) | I&J / JMO |
| Andy Parkinson | (Beckfoot School, Bingley) | IMOK |
| Stephen Power | (St. Swithun's Schol, Winchester) | I&J |
| Mary Read | (Haberdashers' Aske's Hatcham C.) | I&J / IMOK |
| Lionel Richard | (Hutchesons' GS) | S |
| Alan Slomson | (University of Leeds) | S / I&J |
| Alex Voice | (Westminster Abbey Choir School) | I&J / JMO |

It is appropriate at this stage to acknowledge and thank those who helped at various stages with the moderation and checking of these papers: Adam McBride, Peter Neumann, Chris Robson and Stephen Power.

### *TMC coordinators and regional helpers*

| | | |
|---|---|---|
| Patricia Andrews | Anne Andrews | Ann Ault |
| Martin Bailey | Anne Baker | Bridget Ballantyne |
| Andrew Bell | Kerry Burnham | Keith Cadman |
| James Cranch | Alex Crews | Dusty de Sainte Croix |
| Geoffrey Dolamore | Sally-Jane Fell | Sheldon Fernandes |
| Jackie Fox | Roy Fraser | Mary Teresa Fyfe |
| Helen Gauld | Peter Hall | Mark Harwood |
| Karl Hayward-Bradley | Terry Heard | Rita Holland |
| Sue Hughes | Sally Anne Huk | Pam Hunt |
| Andrina Inglis | Andrew Jobbings | Nathan Keeling |
| Jacqui Lewis | Tricia Lunel | Pat Lyden |
| Holly McLean | Matthew Miller | Hilary Monaghan |
| Mike Moon | Steve Mulligan | Helen Mumby |
| Paul Murray | Peter Neumann | Pauline Noble |
| Martin Perkins | Dennis Pinshon | Vivian Pinto |
| Stephen Power | Jenny Ramsden | Mary Read |

| Nikki Shepherd | John Slater | Alan Slomson |
| Anne Strong | Penny Thompson | Alex Voice |
| James Welham | Rosie Wiltshire | |

*Additional local helpers and contacts at TMC host venues*

| Morag Anderson | Dorothy Ball | Ralph Barlow |
| Catherine Beater | Helena Benzinski | Anna Bigland |
| James Blowey | Nigel Brookes | James Burley |
| Nicky Burns | Jane Chadwick | Amanda Clayton |
| Nicki Cologne-Brookes | Kath Conway | Andy Crabtree |
| Alan Darlington | Colin Dixon | Selena Dumble |
| Elin Dupasquier | Nadia El-Taha | Michael Evans |
| Ceri Fiddes | Paul Harper | Val Heward |
| Lizzy Howes | Simon Lewis | Claire Maher |
| Helen Martin | Rebecca Martin | Lauren Marx |
| Joanne McCloskey | Lin McIntosh | Marijike Molenaar |
| Heather Morgan | Julie Mundy | Damian Murphy |
| Paul Pearce | Colin Reid | Lois Rollings |
| Paul Stevens | Ally Strachan | Paul Thomas |
| Sam Twinam | Dan Wilson | Lynsay Yeoman |

*BMOS Mentoring Schemes*
Richard Atkins (Director)

*Junior Scheme Coordinator*: John Slater (assisted by Julian Gilbey)

*Intermediate Scheme Coordinator*: Richard Atkins

*Intermediate external mentors:*

| Anne Andrews | Neill Cooper | Yi Feng |
| Vesna Kadelburg | Vicky Neale | Ian Slater |
| Pavel Stroev | | |

*Senior Scheme Coordinators*: Andre Rzym (assisted by James Cranch)

*Senior external mentors:*

| Anne Andrews | Teresa Barata | Chris Bryant |
| Neill Cooper | Owen Cotton-Barratt | James Cranch |
| Janet Dangerfield | Ben Fairbairn | Ildar Gaisin |
| Julian Gilbey | Victoria Gregson | Michael Griffiths |
| Tim Hennock | James Holloway | Vicky Hoskins |
| Ina Hughes | Michael Illing | Vinay Kathotia |

| Kate Land | Robert Lasenby | James Lawrence |
| Jonathan Lee | Kelvin Lee | Charles Leedham-Green |
| Michael Lipton | Freddie Manners | Gerry Netto |
| Peter Neumann | Jerome Ripp | Julia Robson |
| André Rzym | Dirk Schlueter | Peter Scott |
| Jack Shotton | Paul Smith | Balazs Szendroi |
| Stephen Tate | Oliver Thomas | Alan Thompson |
| James Welham | Weijun Xu | Dominic Yeo |
| Rong Zhou | Alison Zhu | |

*Advanced Scheme Coordinator: Tom Lovering*

*Advanced external mentors:*

| Robin Bhattacharyya | Yimin Ge | Paul Jefferys |
| Nathan Kettle | Henry Liu | Tom Lovering |
| Max Menzies | Joseph Myers | |

## NEW FROM UKMT

### Testbase UKMT Challenge Questions, 1997- 2008

This CD ROM allows teachers to access the wealth of past materials from our Junior, Intermediate and Senior Challenges, in indexed format, making it ideal for use in the classroom.

The database of over 800 questions can be searched by topic, difficulty and Challenge level, and allows you to create your own question sheets from them.

See the UKMT website at

www.publications.ukmt.org.uk

for further details and to order.

# UKMT Maths Challenges 2010–11

We hope you have enjoyed the 2009–10 Yearbook.

The dates for the 2010–11 Maths Challenges are:

| | |
|---|---|
| Senior Maths Challenge | Thursday 4 November 2010 |
| Intermediate Maths Challenge | Thursday 3 February 2011 |
| Junior Maths Challenge | Friday 6 May 2011 |

*Follow-on Rounds*

| | |
|---|---|
| British Mathematical Olympiad Round 1 | Thursday 2 December 2010 |
| British Mathematical Olympiad Round 2 | Thursday 27 January 2011 |
| Intermediate Mathematical Olympiad and Kangaroo | Thursday 17 March 2011 |
| Junior Mathematical Olympiad | Tuesday 14 June 2011 |

*Senior Team Maths Challenge* regional events will be running throughout the UK during November 2010. The final will be held on Wednesday 2 February 2011.

*The Team Maths Challenge* regional events will be running throughout the UK from February to April 2011. The final will be held on Monday 20 June.

Please see our website at www.ukmt.org.uk for entry details, or contact us at:

UKMT Maths Challenges Office,
School of Mathematics Satellite,
University of Leeds,
Leeds LS2 9JT

Tel: 0113 343 2339; Fax: 0113 343 5500;
Email: enquiry@ukmt.org.uk;
Website at www.ukmt.org.uk;
Twitter: @UKMathsTrust

# UKMT Publications

The books published by the UK Mathematics Trust are grouped into series.

The *YEARBOOKS* series documents all the UKMT activities, including details of all the challenge papers and solutions, lists of high scorers, accounts of the IMO and Olympiad training camps, and other information about the Trust's work during each year.

1.  *2009-2010 Yearbook*

    This is our twelth Yearbook, having published one a year since 1998-1999. Edited by Bill Richardson, the Yearbook documents all the UKMT activities from that particular year. They include all the challenge papers and solutions at every level; list of high scorers; tales from the IMO and Olympiad training camps; details of the UKMT's other activities; and a round-up of global maths associations.

    Previous Yearbooks are available for purchase. Please contact the UKMT for further details.

## PAST PAPERS

1.  *Ten Years of Mathematical Challenges 1997 to 2006*

    Edited by Bill Richardson, this book was published to celebrate the tenth anniversary of the founding of UKMT. This 188-page book contains question papers and solutions for nine Senior Challenges, ten Intermediate Challenges, and ten Junior Challenges.

2.  *Past Paper Booklets – Junior, Intermediate and Senior Challenges*

    We sell booklets containing the Mathematics Challenge question papers, solutions, and a summary chart of all the answers.

    The Junior and Intermediate booklets contain material for five years, and the Senior Challenge booklet for four years.

3.  *Past Paper Booklets – Follow-on Rounds*

    The JMO booklet contains four years' papers and solutions for the Junior Mathematical Olympiad, the follow up to the JMC.

    The 2010 IMOK booklet contains the papers and solutions for the suite of Intermediate follow-on rounds – the Kangaroo Grey, the Kangaroo Pink, Cayley, Hamilton and Maclaurin. We also have IMOK booklets currently available from 2009 and 2008.

    The two BMO booklets contain material for the British Mathematical Olympiad Round 1. One contains papers and solutions for 2001-2004, and the other for 1997-2000.

The *HANDBOOK* series is aimed particularly at students at secondary school who are interested in acquiring the knowledge and skills which are useful for tackling challenging problems, such as those posed in the competitions administered by the UKMT.

1. *Plane Euclidean Geometry: Theory and Problems*, AD Gardiner and CJ Bradley

   An excellent book for students aged 15-18 and teachers who want to learn how to solve problems in elementary Euclidean geometry. The book follows the development of Euclid; contents include Pythagoras, trigonometry, circle theorems, and Ceva and Menelaus. The book contains hundreds of problems, many with hints and solutions.

2. *Introduction to Inequalities*, CJ Bradley

   Introduction to Inequalities is a thoroughly revised and extended edition of a book which was initially published as part of the composite volume *Introductions to Number Theory and Inequalities*. This accessible text aims to show students how to select and apply the correct sort of inequality to solve a given problem.

3. *A Mathematical Olympiad Primer*, Geoff C Smith

   This UKMT publication provides an excellent guide for young mathematicians preparing for competitions such as the British Mathematical Olympiad. The book contains theory including algebra, combinatorics and geometry, and BMO1 problems and solutions from 1996 onwards.

4. *Introduction to Number Theory*, CJ Bradley

   This book for students aged 15 upwards aims to show how to tackle the sort of problems on number theory which are set in mathematics competitions. Topics include primes and divisibility, congruence arithmetic and the representation of real numbers by decimals.

The *EXCURSIONS IN MATHEMATICS* series consists of monographs which focus on a particular topic of interest and investigate it in some detail, using a wide range of ideas and techniques. They are aimed at high school students, undergraduates, and others who are prepared to pursue a subject in some depth, but do not require specialised knowledge.

1. *The Backbone of Pascal's Triangle*, Martin Griffiths

   Everything covered in this book is connected to the sequence of numbers: 2, 6, 20, 70, 252, 924, 3432,…Some readers might recognize this list straight away, while others will not have seen it before. Either way, students and teachers alike may well be astounded at both the variety and the depth of mathematical ideas that it can lead to.

248

The *PATHWAYS* series aims to provide classroom teaching material for use in secondary school. Each title develops a subject in more depth and detail than is normally required by public examinations or national curricula.

1. *Crossing the Bridge*, Gerry Leversha

   This book provides a course on geometry for use in the classroom, re-emphasising some traditional features of geometrical education. The bulk of the text is devoted to carefully constructed exercises for classroom discussion or individual study. It is suitable for students aged 13 and upwards.

The *PROBLEMS* series consists of collections of high-quality and original problems of Olympiad standard.

1. *New Problems in Euclidean Geometry*, David Monk

   This book should appeal to anyone aged 16+ who enjoys solving the kind of challenging and attractive geometry problems that have virtually vanished from the school curriculum, but which still play a central role in national and international mathematics competitions. It is a treasure trove of wonderful geometrical problesm , with hints for their solutions.

To find out more about these publications and to order copies, please go to website at www.publications.ukmt.org.uk . Alternatively please copy and complete the form on the next page.

In addition to the books above, UKMT continues to publish its termly Newsletter, giving the latest news from the Trust, mathematical articles, examples from Challenge papers and occasional posters for the classroom wall. This is sent free to all schools participating in the Maths Challenges.

# Order Form for UKMT Publications

Please photocopy this form and send a cheque payable to 'UKMT(Leeds)' to:
*UKMT (Publications), School of Mathematics Satellite, University of Leeds, Leeds LS2 9JT*

| | | Quantity | Price | Subtotal |
|---|---|---|---|---|
| Yearbooks | 2009-2010 | | £10 | |
| | 2008-2009 | | £10 | |
| | 2007-2008 | | £8 | |
| Past Paper Booklets | Junior Challenge | | £2.50 | |
| | Intermediate Challenge | | £2.50 | |
| | Senior Challenge | | £2.50 | |
| | Set of all three | | £6 | |
| Follow-on Rounds | JMO | | £2.50 | |
| | IMOK 2010 | | £2.50 | |
| | BMO1 (2001-2004) | | £2.50 | |
| | BMO1 (1997-2000) | | £2.50 | |

We have limited stock of Yearbooks from before 2007. Please contact the Maths Challenges Office for availability and prices.

| | Quantity | Price | Subtotal |
|---|---|---|---|
| Ten Years of Mathematical Challenges | | £10 + p&p* | |
| Plane Euclidean Geometry: Theory and Problems | | £10 + p&p* | |
| Introduction to Inequalities | | £10 + p&p* | |
| A Mathematical Olympiad Primer | | £10 + p&p* | |
| Introduction to Number Theory | | £10 + p&p* | |
| The Backbone of Pascal's Triangle | | £12 + p&p* | |
| Crossing the Bridge | | £10 + p&p* | |
| New Problems in Euclidean Geometry | | £10 + p&p* | |

*p&p: £1 per book on all UK orders less than 5 copies; £5 per book on all overseas orders; p&p is free on all UK orders of 5 copies or more.

**Total:** I enclose a cheque for £            payable to 'UKMT(Leeds)'.

**Your details:**

Name . . . . . . . . . . . . . . . . . . . . . . . . . . . . . . . . . . . . . . . . . . . . . . . . . . .

Address . . . . . . . . . . . . . . . . . . . . . . . . . . . . . . . . . . . . . . . . . . . . . . . . . .

. . . . . . . . . . . . . . . . . . . . . . . . . . . . . . . . . . . . . . . . . . . . . . . . . . . . . . . .

Postcode . . . . . . . . . . . . . . . . . . . . . . . . . . . . .

Telephone . . . . . . . . . . . . . . . . . . . . . . . . . . . .    Email . . . . . . . . . . . . . . . . .

# Memory Lane

We think that you might like to see these again.

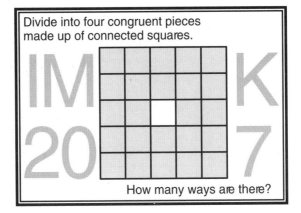

Divide into four congruent pieces made up of connected squares.

How many ways are there?

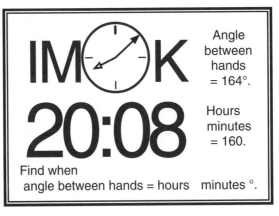

Angle between hands = 164°.

Hours minutes = 160.

Find when angle between hands = hours minutes °.

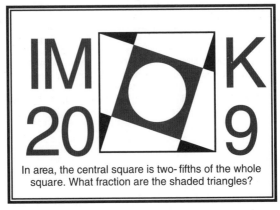

In area, the central square is two-fifths of the whole square. What fraction are the shaded triangles?